303.483
T139
1997

T2-CSE-514

Taking SIDES

Clashing Views on
Controversial Issues in
Science,
Technology, and
Society

Second Edition

Taking
SIDES

Clashing Views on
Controversial Issues in
Science,
Technology, and
Society

Second Edition

Edited, Selected, and with Introductions by

Thomas A. Easton
Thomas College

Dushkin Publishing Group/Brown & Benchmark Publishers
A Times Mirror Higher Education Group Company

Photo Acknowledgments

Part 1   IBM Microelectronics/Tom Way
Part 2   UN Photo 150178/Sean Sprague
Part 3   NASA
Part 4   WHO/Photo by E. Rice
Part 5   WHO/Photo by J. Mohr

Cover Art Acknowledgment

Charles Vitelli

Copyright © 1997 by Dushkin Publishing Group/Brown & Benchmark Publishers,
A Times Mirror Higher Education Group Company,
Guilford, Connecticut 06437

Copyright law prohibits the reproduction, storage, or transmission in any form by
any means of any portion of this publication without the express written permission
of Dushkin Publishing Group/Brown & Benchmark Publishers and of the copyright
holder (if different) of the part of the publication to be reproduced. The Guidelines
for Classroom Copying endorsed by Congress explicitly state that unauthorized
copying may not be used to create, to replace, or to substitute for anthologies,
compilations, or collective works.

Taking Sides ® is a registered trademark of Dushkin Publishing Group/
Brown & Benchmark Publishers, A Times Mirror Higher Education Group Company

Manufactured in the United States of America

Second Edition

10   9   8   7   6   5   4   3   2   1

Library of Congress Cataloging-in-Publication Data

Main entry under title:
    Taking sides: clashing views on controversial issues in science, technology, and society/edited
selected, and with introductions by Thomas A. Easton.—2nd ed.
    Includes bibliographical references and index.
    1. Science—Social aspects. 2. Technology—Social aspects. I. Easton, Thomas A., *comp.*

    0-697-36007-5

    306.45
    96-85833

Printed on Recycled Paper

PREFACE

Those who must deal with scientific and technological issues—scientists, politicians, sociologists, business managers, and anyone who is concerned about a neighborhood dump or power plant, government intrusiveness, expensive space programs, or the morality of medical research, among many other issues—must be able to consider, evaluate, and choose among alternatives. Making choices is an essential aspect of the scientific method. It is also an inescapable feature of every public debate over a scientific or technological issue, for there can be no debate if there are no alternatives.

The ability to evaluate and to select among alternatives—as well as to know when the data do not permit selection—is called critical thinking. It is essential not only in science and technology but in every other aspect of life as well. *Taking Sides: Clashing Views on Controversial Issues in Science, Technology, and Society* is designed to stimulate and cultivate this ability by holding up for consideration 17 issues that have provoked substantial debate. Each of these issues has at least two sides, usually more. However, each issue is expressed in terms of a single question in order to draw the lines of debate more clearly. The ideas and answers that emerge from the clash of opposing points of view should be more complex than those offered by the students before the reading assignment.

The issues in this book were chosen because they are currently of particular concern to both science and society. They touch on the nature of science and research, the relationship between science and society, the uses of technology, and the potential threats that technological advances can pose to human survival. And they come from a variety of fields, including computer and space science, biology, environmentalism, law enforcement, and public health.

Organization of the book   For each issue, I have provided an *issue introduction,* which provides some historical background and discusses why the issue is important. I then present two selections, one pro and one con, in which the authors make their cases. Each issue concludes with a *postscript* that brings the issue up to date and adds other voices and viewpoints. For many issues, I have provided Internet site addresses (URLs) that should prove useful as starting points for further research.

Which answer to the issue question—yes or no—is the correct answer? Perhaps neither. Perhaps both. Students should read, think about, and discuss the readings and then come to their own conclusions without letting my or their instructor's opinions (which perhaps show at least some of the time!) dictate theirs. The additional readings mentioned in both the introductions and the postscripts should prove helpful. It is worth stressing that the issues covered in this book are all *live* issues; that is, the debates they represent are active and ongoing.

The list of contributors at the back of this volume provides information about the authors of the 34 selections reprinted in this book.

Changes to this edition   This second edition represents a considerable revision. There are 6 completely new issues: *Should the Federal Government Point the Way for Science?* (Issue 1); *Should There Be Standards for Science Education?* (Issue 2); *Is Science Hazardous to Human Values?* (Issue 3); *Will the Information Revolution Benefit Society?* (Issue 4); *Can Human Population Stabilize Before Disaster Strikes?* (Issue 5); and *Should Genetic Engineering Be Banned?* (Issue 13).

In addition, either the YES or NO selections have been replaced in 5 issues to bring the debates up to date: *Can the Sun and Wind Supply Our Energy Needs?* (Issue 6); *Should Society Be Concerned About Global Warming?* (Issue 7); *Should the Goals of the U.S. Space Program Include Manned Exploration of Space?* (Issue 9); *Are Electromagnetic Fields Dangerous to Your Health?* (Issue 14); and *Is the Use of Animals in Research Justified?* (Issue 15).

For one of the issues retained from the previous edition, Issue 16 (*Is It Ethical to Use Humans as "Experimental Animals"?*), both selections have been replaced, so the issue should be considered new. In all, there are 18 new selections. The issue introductions and postscripts for the retained issues have been revised and updated where necessary.

A word to the instructor   An *Instructor's Manual With Test Questions* (multiple-choice and essay) is available through the publisher for the instructor using *Taking Sides* in the classroom. It includes suggestions for stimulating in-class discussion for each issue. A general guidebook, *Using Taking Sides in the Classroom,* which discusses methods and techniques for integrating the pro-con approach into any classroom setting, is also available.

Acknowledgments   A special thanks goes to those professors who responded to the questionnaire with specific suggestions for the second edition: John Bumpus, University of Northern Iowa; Joanne English Daly, State University of New York at Stony Brook; and Jack D. Foster, Broome Community College.

Special thanks are due to John Quigg of Thomas College.

Thomas A. Easton
Thomas College

CONTENTS IN BRIEF

CONTENTS

Assistant professor of public policy David H. Guston and professor of human
development Kenneth Keniston argue that science can no longer set its own
path and that public participation must be increased at all levels of decision
making about science. The National Academy of Sciences, a private, nonprofit
society of scholars engaged in scientific and engineering research, asserts that
although the relationship between government or society and science needs
changes, only scientists should decide what research is to be done.

The National Research Council, the principal operating agency of the National Academy of Sciences, asserts that scientific and technological literacy
is becoming increasingly important for all people. To this end, it has developed standards for science education throughout the United States, which
are described. Professor of education and art Elliot W. Eisner views the general idea of standards in education skeptically, insisting that such standards
ignore the fact that children develop at different rates and in different ways.

Bioethicist Daniel Callahan argues that science's domination of the cultural landscape unreasonably excludes other ways of understanding nature and the world and sets it above any need to accept moral, social, and intellectual judgment from political, religious, and even traditional values. Daniel C. Dennett, director of the Center for Cognitive Studies at Tufts University, argues that "the only meaning of life worth caring about is one that can withstand our best efforts to examine it," meaning that evolution—and the scientific approach—are to be valued above all.

John S. Mayo, president emeritus of Lucent Technologies Bell Laboratories, formerly AT&T Bell Laboratories, argues that the information revolution will benefit society by slowing migrations from rural to urban areas, aiding economic development, and improving access to education, health care, and other social services. Political scientist James H. Snider argues that because the information superhighway will make it possible for more people to leave the city for rural areas, human impact on the environment will become more pervasive and more difficult to control.

Geoscientist Stephen L. Gillett argues that because human beings adapt their behavior to circumstances very readily, human population will probably stabilize before it exceeds the capacity of the environment to support it. Biologist Thomas A. Easton argues that humanity is now on the verge of a catastrophic mismatch between population and the food supply, largely because people do not adapt their behavior to circumstances readily enough.

Christopher Flavin, vice president for research at the Worldwatch Institute, argues that the world is on the verge of a massive shift to renewable energy sources, with hydrogen filling the need for a portable fuel. Chauncey Starr, Milton F. Searl, and Sy Alpert, researchers at the Electric Power Research Institute, argue that renewable (solar) energy is limited particularly by its intermittency and lack of portability; thus, the hydrogen solution is of no practical interest.

Journalist Ross Gelbspan argues that the evidence for global warming is incontrovertible, despite the disinformation campaign being waged by the fossil fuels industry, and that the effects on human society will be extreme. Action is therefore needed now. Economists Wilfred Beckerman and Jesse Malkin argue that global warming, if it even occurs, will not be catastrophic and warrants no immediate action; there are other worldwide concerns that are far more pressing.

Mary H. Cooper, a staff writer for *CQ Researcher*, asserts that scientific findings in recent years indicate that the ozone layer is being depleted, exposing Earth's living organisms to increasing levels of harmful ultraviolet radiation from the sun. James P. Hogan, a science fiction writer, maintains that reports of the ozone being destroyed by chlorofluorocarbons are unsupported by any valid scientific evidence.

Associate professor of physics Doug Beason argues that a U.S. government program oriented to the manned space exploration of Mars would provide an invigorating, economy-stimulating focus for the nation. John Merchant, a retired staff engineer at Loral Infrared and Imaging Systems, argues that it will be much cheaper to develop electronic senses and remotely operated machines that humans can use to explore other worlds.

Professor of astronomy Frank Drake and science writer Dava Sobel argue that scientists must continue to search for extraterrestrial civilizations because contact will eventually occur. Professor of astronomy Richard G. Teske doubts that there are any beings outside of Earth with the technological capability to send signals that scientists can receive.

Research scientist Hans Moravec asserts that computers that match and even exceed human intelligence will eventually be developed. Professor of philosophy John R. Searle argues that artificial (machine) intelligence and human intelligence are so different that it is impossible to create a computer that can think.

Robert Costanza, a professor of environmental studies, and policy analyst Laura Cornwell argue that when uncertainty about potential future damage to health or the environment is high, compensation based on a worst-case scenario should be set aside by those who are potentially responsible. Wendy Cleland-Hamnett, the acting deputy assistant administrator for policy, planning, and evaluation at the U.S. Environmental Protection Agency, insists that worst-case scenarios are far too unlikely to be used as the basis for policy.

Andrew Kimbrell, policy director of the Foundation on Economic Trends in Washington, D.C., argues that the development of genetic engineering is so marked by scandal, ambition, and moral blindness that society should be deeply suspicious of its purported benefits. James Hughes, assistant director of research at the MacLean Center for Clinical Medical Ethics in the Department of Medicine at the University of Chicago, argues that the potential benefits of genetic engineering greatly outweigh the potential risks.

Writer Paul Brodeur argues that there is an increased risk of developing cancer from being exposed to electromagnetic fields given off by electric power lines and that the risk is significant enough to warrant immediate measures to reduce exposures to the fields. Jon Palfreman, senior producer at WGBH, the public television station in Boston, Massachusetts, argues that there is no convincing evidence that electromagnetic fields pose any risk to human health.

Elizabeth Baldwin, research ethics officer of the American Psychological Association's Science Directorate, argues that animals do not have the same moral rights as humans do, that their use in scientific research is justified by the resulting benefits to both humans and animals, and that their welfare is protected by law. Research attorney Steven Zak argues that current animal protection laws do not adequately protect animals used in medical and other research and that, for society to be virtuous, it must recognize the rights of animals not to be sacrificed for human needs.

Science writer Charles Petit interviews an AIDS patient who underwent a highly experimental treatment and considers those who resist human experimentation to be far too cautious. Danielle Gordon, assistant editor of *The Bulletin of the Atomic Scientists*, reports the results of a national ethics commission's investigation into experiments that exposed many people to radiation and concludes that experiments on seriously ill patients are ethically troubling.

The American Medical Association's Council on Scientific Affairs and Council
on Ethical and Judicial Affairs argue that using fetal tissue to treat adult
illnesses is ethical, provided appropriate precautions are taken. Theologian
James Tunstead Burtchaell asserts that research with aborted fetal tissue is
unethical because informed consent cannot be obtained from a fetus.

INTRODUCTION

Analyzing Issues in Science and Technology

Thomas A. Easton

INTRODUCTION

As civilization approaches the dawn of the twenty-first century, it cannot escape science and technology. Their fruits—the clothes we wear, the foods we eat, the tools we use—surround us. Science and technology evoke in people both hope and dread for the future, for although new discoveries can lead to cures for diseases and other problems, new insights into the wonders of nature, and new toys (among other things), the past has shown that technological developments can also have unforeseen and terrible consequences.

Those consequences do *not* belong to science, for science is nothing more than a systematic approach to gaining knowledge about the world. Technology is the application of knowledge to accomplish things that otherwise could not be accomplished. Technological developments do not just lead to devices such as hammers, computers, and jet aircraft, but also to management systems, institutions, and even political philosophies. And it is, of course, such *uses* of knowledge that affect people's lives for good and ill.

It cannot be said that the use of technology affects people "for good *or* ill." As Emmanuel Mesthene said in 1969, technology is neither an unalloyed blessing nor an unmitigated curse.[1] Every new technology offers both new benefits and new problems, and the two sorts of consequences cannot be separated from each other. Automobiles, for example, provide rapid, convenient personal transportation, but precisely because of that benefit, they also cause suburban development, urban sprawl, crowded highways, and air pollution.

OPTIMISTS VS. PESSIMISTS

The inescapable pairing of good and bad consequences helps to account for why so many issues of science and technology stir debate in our society. Optimists tend to focus on the benefits of technology and to be confident that society will be able to cope with any problems that arise. Pessimists tend to fear the problems and to believe that the costs of technology will outweigh any possible benefits.

Sometimes the costs of new technologies are immediate and tangible. When new devices fail or new drugs prove to have unforeseen side effects, people can die. Sometimes the costs are less obvious. John McDermott, one of Mesthene's opponents, expressed confidence that technology led to the centralization of power in the hands of an educated elite; to his mind, technology was therefore antidemocratic.[2]

The proponents of technology answer that a machine's failure is a sign that it needs to be fixed, not banned. If a drug has side effects, it may need to be refined, or its list of permitted recipients may have to be better defined (the banned tranquilizer thalidomide, for example, is notorious for causing birth defects when taken early in pregnancy; it is apparently quite safe for men and nonpregnant women). And although several technologies that were developed in the 1960s seemed quite undemocratic at the time, one of them —computers—developed in a very different direction. Early on, computers were huge, expensive machines operated by an elite, but it was not long before they became so small, relatively inexpensive, and "user-friendly" that the general public gained access to them. Proponents lauded this as a true case of technological "power to the people."

CERTAINTY VS. UNCERTAINTY

Another source of debate over science and technology is uncertainty. Science is, by its very nature, uncertain. Its truths are provisional, open to revision.

Unfortunately, people are often told by politicians, religious leaders, and newspaper columnists that truth is certain. By this view, if someone admits uncertainty, then their position can be considered weak and they need not be heeded. This is, of course, an open invitation for demagogues to prey upon people's fears of disaster or side effects (which are always a possibility with new technology) or upon the wish to be told that greenhouse warming and ozone depletion are mere figments of the scientific imagination (they have yet to be proven beyond a doubt).

NATURAL VS. UNNATURAL

Still another source of controversy is rooted in the tendency of new ideas —in science and technology as well as in politics, history, literary criticism, and so on—to clash with preexisting beliefs or values. These clashes become most public when they pit science against religion and "family values." The battle between evolution and creationism, for example, still stirs passions a century and a half after naturalist Charles Darwin first said that human beings had nonhuman predecessors. It is nearly as provocative to some to suggest that homosexuality is a natural variant of human behavior (rather than a conscious choice); or that there might be a genetic component to intelligence or aggressiveness; or that the traditional mode of human reproduction might be supplemented with in vitro fertilization, embryo cloning, surrogate mother arrangements, and even genetic engineering.

Many new developments are rejected as "unnatural." For many people, "natural" means any device or procedure to which they have become accustomed. Very few realize how "unnatural" such seemingly ordinary things as circumcision, horseshoes, and baseball are.

However, humans do embrace change and are forever creating variations on religions, languages, politics, and tools. Innovation is as natural to a person as building dams is to a beaver.

PUBLIC VS. PRIVATE: WHO PAYS, AND WHY?

Finally, conflict frequently arises over the function of science in society. Traditionally, scientists have seen themselves as engaged solely in the pursuit of knowledge, solving the puzzles set before them by nature with little concern for whether or not the solutions to those puzzles might prove helpful to human enterprises such as war, health care, and commerce. Yet again and again the solutions discovered by scientists have proved useful—they have even founded entire industries.

Not surprisingly, society has come to expect science to be useful. When asked to fund research, society feels that it has the right to target research on issues of social concern, to demand results of immediate value, and to forbid research it deems dangerous or disruptive. And society's control of the purse strings gives its demands a certain undeniable persuasiveness.

PUBLIC POLICY

The question of how to target research is only one way in which science and technology intersect the realm of public policy. Here the question becomes, How should society allocate its resources in general? Toward education or prisons? Health care or welfare? Research or trade? Encouraging new technologies or cleaning up after old ones? The problem is that money is limited—there is not enough to finance every researcher who proposes to solve some social problem. Faced with competing worthy goals, society must make choices. Society must also run the risk that the choices made will turn out to be foolish.

THE PURPOSE OF THIS BOOK

Is there any prospect that the debates over the proper function of science, the acceptability of new technologies, or the truth of forecasts of disaster will soon fall quiet? Surely not, for some issues will likely never die, and there will always be new issues to debate afresh. (For example, think of the population debate, which has been argued ever since Thomas Malthus's 1789 "Essay on the Principle of Population," and then consider the debate over the manned exploration of space and whether or not it is worthwhile for society to spend resources in this way.)

Since almost all technological controversies will affect the conditions of our daily lives, learning about some of the current controversies and beginning to think critically about them is of great importance if we are to be informed and involved citizens.

Individuals may be able to affect the terms of the inevitable debates by first examining the nature of science and a few of the current controversies over issues of science and technology. After all, if one does not know what science, the scientific mode of thought, and their strengths and limitations are, one cannot think critically and constructively about any issue with a scientific or technological component. Nor can one hope to make informed choices among competing scientific or technological priorities.

WOMEN AND MINORITIES IN SCIENCE

There are some issues in the area of science, technology, and society that, even though they are of vital importance, you will not find directly debated in this volume. An example of such an issue might be, "Should there be more women and minority members in science?" However, this is not a debate because no one seriously responds to this question in the negative. Although minorities compose 12 percent of college freshmen, they receive only 6 percent of the bachelor's degrees, 4 percent of the master's degrees, and 3.5 percent of the doctorates. The numbers have improved over recent decades, with one group—Asian Americans—gaining much more rapidly than African Americans, Hispanics, and American Indians. But whites still dominate science and engineering, holding 90 percent of the jobs, even more than they do the general workforce, where they hold 80 percent of the jobs.

Women earn more than half the bachelor's and master's degrees, but only a third of the doctorates and 16 percent of the science and engineering jobs, mostly in biology, psychology, and health. Although income disparities between men and women have diminished, they still remain. Women computer scientists and analysts, registered nurses, laboratory technicians and technologists, and health aides all make about 90 percent of what men in these occupations earn.

You should keep such considerations in mind as you read the issues in this book. And you should consider how the problems of discrimination and prejudice (based on race or class or gender) are played out in some of these debates; the debate over the use of humans as "experimental animals" is a prominent example.

Each year the American Association for the Advancement of Science (AAAS) publishes several issues of its journal *Science* that deal with careers in science and that pay frequent attention to women, minority, and foreign-born scientists. These issues contain a wealth of statistical information, interviews, and analyses invaluable to anyone who is considering a career in science. There are also, of course, vast amounts of other material available, such as *Women's Work: Choice, Chance or Socialization? Insights from Psychologists and Other Researchers* by Nancy Johnson Smith and Sylva K. Leduc (Detselig Enterprises, 1992).

People with Internet access can visit the AAAS and *Science* at http://
sci.aaas.org. In particular, watch for this Web page's "Next Wave" section at http://sci.aaas.org.nextwave.

THE SOUL OF SCIENCE

The standard picture of science—a world of observations, hypotheses, experiments, theories, sterile white coats, laboratories, and cold, unfeeling logic—
is a myth. This image has more to do with the way science is presented by
both scientists and the media than with the way scientists actually perform
their work. In practice, scientists are often less orderly, less logical, and more
prone to very human conflicts of personality than most people suspect.

The myth remains because it helps to organize science. It provides labels
and a framework for what a scientist does; it may thus be especially valuable
to student scientists who are still learning the ropes. In addition, the image
embodies certain important ideals of scientific thought. These ideals make
the scientific approach the most powerful and reliable guide to truth about
the world that human beings have yet devised.

THE IDEALS OF SCIENCE: SKEPTICISM,
COMMUNICATION, AND REPRODUCIBILITY

The soul of science is a very simple idea: *Check it out.* Years ago, scholars
believed that speaking the truth simply required prefacing a statement with
"According to" and some ancient authority, such as Aristotle, or a holy text,
such as the Bible. If someone with a suitably illustrious reputation had once
said something was so, it was so.

This attitude is the opposite of everything that modern science stands for.
As Carl Sagan says in *The Demon-Haunted World: Science as a Candle in the
Dark* (Random House, 1995), "One of the great commandments of science is,
'Mistrust arguments from authority.'" Scientific knowledge is based not on
authority but on reality. Scientists take nothing on faith; they are *skeptical*.
When a scientist wants to know something, he or she does not look it up
in the library or take another's word for it. Scientists go into the laboratory,
or the forest, or the desert—wherever they can find the phenomena they
wish to know about—and they "ask" those phenomena directly. They look
for answers in nature. And if they think they know the answer already, it is
not of books that they ask, "Are we right?" but of nature. This is the point
of scientific experiments—they are how scientists ask nature whether or not
their ideas check out.

The concept of "check it out" is, however, an ideal. No one can possibly check everything out for himself or herself. Even scientists, in practice,
look up information in books and rely on authorities. But the authorities
they rely on are other scientists who have studied nature and reported what
they learned. And, in principle, everything those authorities report can be

checked. Experiments performed in the lab or in the field can be repeated. New theoretical or computer models can be designed. Information that is in the books can be confirmed.

In fact, a good part of the "scientific method" is designed to make it possible for any scientist's findings or conclusions to be confirmed. For example, scientists do not say, "Vitamin D is essential for strong bones. Believe me. I know." They say, "I know that vitamin D is essential for proper bone formation because I raised rats without vitamin D in their diet, and their bones became soft and crooked. When I gave them vitamin D, their bones hardened and straightened. Here is the kind of rat I used, the kind of food I fed them, the amount of vitamin D I gave them. Go and do likewise, and you will see what I saw."

Communication is therefore an essential part of modern science. That is, in order to function as a scientist, you must not keep secrets. You must tell others not just what you have learned but how you learned it. You must spell out your methods in enough detail to let others repeat your work.

Scientific knowledge is thus *reproducible* knowledge. Strictly speaking, if a person says, "I can see it, but you cannot," that person is not a scientist. Scientific knowledge exists for everyone. Anyone who takes the time to learn the proper techniques can confirm any scientific finding.

THE STANDARD MODEL OF THE SCIENTIFIC METHOD

As it is usually presented, the scientific method has five major components: *observation, generalization* (identifying a pattern), stating a *hypothesis* (a tentative extension of the pattern or explanation for why the pattern exists), *experimentation* (testing that explanation), and *communication* of the test results to other members of the scientific community, usually by publishing the findings. How each of these components contributes to the scientific method is discussed below.

Observation
The basic units of science—and the only real facts that the scientist knows —are the individual *observations*. Using them, scientists look for patterns, suggest explanations, and devise tests for their ideas. Observations can be casual or they may be more deliberate.

Generalization
After making observations, a scientist tries to discern a pattern among them. A statement of such a pattern is a *generalization*. Cautious experimenters do not jump to conclusions. When they think they see a pattern, they often make a few more observations just to be sure the pattern holds up. This practice of strengthening or confirming findings by replicating them is a very important part of the scientific process.

The Hypothesis

A tentative explanation suggesting why a particular pattern exists is called a *hypothesis*. The mark of a good hypothesis is that it is *testable*. But there is no way to test a guess about past events and patterns and to be sure of absolute truth in the results, so a simple, direct hypothesis is needed. The scientist says, in effect, "I have an idea that X is true. I cannot test X easily or reliably. But if X *is* true, then so is Y. And I can test Y." Unfortunately, tests can fail even when the hypothesis is perfectly correct.

Many philosophers of science insist on *falsification* as a crucial aspect of the scientific method. That is, when a test of a hypothesis shows the hypothesis to be false, the hypothesis must be rejected and replaced with another. This is not to be confused with the falsification, or misrepresentation, of research data and results, which is a form of scientific misconduct.

In terms of the X and Y hypotheses mentioned above, if it has been found that Y is not true, can we say that X is false too? Perhaps, but bear in mind that X was not tested. Y was tested, and Y is the hypothesis that the idea of falsification says must be replaced, perhaps with hypothesis Z.

The Experiment

The *experiment* is the most formal part of the scientific process. The concept, however, is very simple: an experiment is a test of a hypothesis. It is what a scientist does to check an idea out. It may involve giving a new drug to a sick patient or testing a new process to preserve apples, tomatoes, and lettuce.

If the experiment does not falsify the hypothesis, that does not mean that the hypothesis is true. It simply means that the scientist has not yet come up with a test that falsifies the hypothesis. As the number of times and the number of different tests that fail to falsify a hypothesis increase, the likelihood that the hypothesis is true also increases. However, because it is impossible to conceive of and perform all the possible tests of a hypothesis, the scientist can never *prove* that it is true.

Consider the hypothesis that all cats are black. If you see a black cat, you do not really know anything at all about the color of all cats. But if you see a white cat, you certainly know that not all cats are black. You would have to look at every cat on Earth to prove the hypothesis, but only one (of a color other than black) to disprove it. This is why philosophers of science often say that *science is the art of disproving*, not proving. If a hypothesis withstands many attempts to disprove it, then it may be a good explanation of the phenomenon in question. If it fails just one test, though, it is clearly wrong and must be replaced with a new hypothesis.

Researchers who study what scientists actually do point out that most scientists do not act in accord with this reasoning. Almost all scientists, when they come up with what strikes them as a good explanation of a phenomenon or pattern, do *not* try to disprove the hypothesis. Instead, they design experiments to *confirm* it. If an experiment fails to confirm the hypothesis, then the researchers try another experiment, not another hypothesis.

The logical weakness in this approach is obvious, but it does not keep researchers from holding onto their ideas for as long as possible. Sometimes they hold on so long, even without confirming the hypothesis, that they wind up looking ridiculous. Other times the confirmations add up over the years, and any attempts to disprove the hypothesis fail to do so. The hypothesis may then be elevated to the rank of a theory, principle, or law. *Theories* are explanations of how things work (the theory of evolution *by means of* natural selection, for example). *Principles* and *laws* tend to be statements of things that invariably happen, such as the law of gravity (masses attract each other, or what goes up must come down) or the gas law (if you increase the pressure on an enclosed gas, the volume will decrease and the temperature will increase).

Communication

Each scientist is obligated to share her or his hypotheses, methods, and findings with the rest of the scientific community. This sharing serves two purposes. First, it supports the basic ideal of skepticism by making it possible for others to say, "Oh, yeah? Let me check that." It tells the skeptics where to look to see what the scientist saw and what techniques and tools to use.

Second, communication allows others to use in their work what has already been discovered. This is essential because science is a cooperative endeavor. People who work thousands of miles apart build with and upon each other's discoveries—some of the most exciting discoveries have involved bringing together information from very different fields.

Scientific cooperation stretches across time as well. Every generation of scientists both uses and adds to what previous generations have discovered. As Sir Isaac Newton said in 1675, in a letter to fellow scientist Robert Hooke, "If I have seen further than [other men], it is by standing upon the shoulders of Giants."

The communication of science begins with a process called "peer review," which typically has three stages. The first stage occurs when a scientist seeks funding—from government agencies, foundations, or other sources—to carry out a research program. He or she must prepare a report describing the intended work, laying out the background, hypotheses, planned experiments, expected results, and even the broader impacts on other fields. Committees of other scientists then go over the report to determine whether or not the applicant knows his or her area, has the necessary abilities, and is realistic in his or her plans.

Once the scientist has acquired funding, has done the work, and has written a report of the results, that report will be submitted to a scientific journal, which begins the second stage. Before publishing the report, the journal's editors will show it to other workers in the same or related fields and ask them whether or not the work was done adequately, the conclusions are justified, and the report should be published.

The third stage of peer review happens after publication, when the broader scientific community can judge the work.

It is certainly possible for these standard peer review mechanisms to fail. By their nature, these mechanisms are more likely to approve ideas that do not contradict what the reviewers think they already know. Yet, unconventional ideas are not necessarily wrong, as German geophysicist Alfred Wegener proved when he tried to gain acceptance for his idea of continental drift in the early twentieth century. At the time, geologists believed that the crust of the Earth—which is solid rock, after all—did not behave like liquid. Yet, Wegener was proposing that the continents floated about like icebergs in the sea, bumping into each other, tearing apart (to produce matching profiles like those of South America and Africa), and bumping again. It was not until the 1960s that most geologists accepted his ideas as genuine insights instead of harebrained delusions.

THE NEED FOR CONTROLS

Many years ago, I read a description of a "wish machine." It consisted of an ordinary stereo amplifier with two unusual attachments. The wires that would normally be connected to a microphone were connected instead to a pair of copper plates. The wires that would normally be connected to a speaker were connected instead to a whip antenna of the sort usually seen on cars.

To use this device, one put a picture of some desired item between the copper plates. It could be, for instance, a photo of a person with whom one wanted a date, a lottery ticket, or a college that one wished to attend. One test case used a photo of a pest-infested cornfield. The user then wished fervently for the date, the winning lottery ticket, a college acceptance, or whatever else one craved. In the test case, the testers wished that all the pests in the cornfield would drop dead.

Supposedly, the wish would be picked up by the copper plates, amplified by the stereo amplifier, and then sent via the whip antenna to wherever wish orders go. Whoever or whatever fills those orders would get the message and grant the wish. Well, in the test case, when the testers checked the cornfield after using the machine, there was no longer any sign of pests. What's more, the process seemed to work equally well whether the amplifier was plugged in or not.

You are probably now feeling very much like a scientist—skeptical. The true, dedicated scientist, however, does not stop with saying, "Oh, yeah? Tell me another one!" Instead, he or she says, "Let's check this out."[3]

Where must the scientist begin? The standard model of the scientific method says that the first step is observation. Here, our observations (as well as our necessary generalization) are simply the description of the wish machine and the claims for its effectiveness. Perhaps we even have the device itself.

What is our hypothesis? We have two choices, one consistent with the claims for the device and one denying those claims: the wish machine always works, or the wish machine never works. Both are equally testable and equally falsifiable.

How do we test the hypothesis? Set up the wish machine, and perform the experiment of making a wish. If the wish comes true, the device works. If the wish does not come true, the device does not work.

Can it really be that simple? In essence, yes. But in fact, no.

Even if you do not believe that wishing can make something happen, sometimes wishes do come true by sheer coincidence. Therefore, even if the wish machine is as nonsensical as most people think it is, sometimes it will *seem* to work. We therefore need a way to shield against the misleading effects of coincidence.

Coincidence is not, of course, the only source of error we need to watch out for. For instance, there is a very human tendency to interpret events in such a way as to agree with our preexisting beliefs, or our prejudices. If we believe in wishes, we therefore need a way to guard against our willingness to interpret near misses as not quite misses at all. There is also a human tendency not to look for mistakes when the results agree with our prejudices. The cornfield, for instance, might not have been as badly infested as the testers said it was, or a farmer might have sprayed it with pesticide between checks, or the testers may have accidentally checked the wrong field. The point is that correlation does not necessarily reflect cause. In other words, although an event seems to occur as the result of another, there may be other factors at work that negate the relationship.

We also need to check whether or not the wish machine does indeed work equally well when the amplifier is unplugged as when it is plugged in, and then we must guard against the tendency to wish harder when we know that it is plugged in. Furthermore, we would like to know whether or not placing a photo between the copper plates makes any difference, and then we must guard against the tendency to wish harder when we know that the wish matches the photo.

Coincidence is easy to protect against. All that is necessary is to repeat the experiment enough times to be sure that we are not seeing flukes. This is one major purpose of replication. Our willingness to shade the results in our favor can be defeated by having another scientist judge the results of our wishing experiments. And our eagerness to overlook errors that produce favorable results can be defeated by taking great care to avoid any errors at all; peer reviewers also help by pointing out such problems.

Other sources of error are harder to avoid, but scientists have developed a number of helpful *control* techniques. One technique is called "blinding." In essence, blinding requires setting up the experiment in such a way that the critical aspects are hidden from either the test subjects, the scientist who is physically performing the experiment, or both. This helps to prevent individuals' expectations from influencing the outcome of the experiment.

In the pharmaceutical industry, blinding is used whenever a new drug is tested. The basic process goes like this: A number of patients with the affliction that the drug is supposed to affect are selected. Half of them—chosen randomly to avoid any unconscious bias that might put sicker patients in one group[4]—are given the drug. The others are given a dummy pill, or a sugar pill, also known as a *placebo*. In all other respects, the two groups are treated exactly the same.

Although, placebos are not supposed to have any effect on patients, they can sometimes have real medical effects, apparently because people tend to believe their doctors when they say that a pill will cure them. That is, when we put faith in our doctors, our minds do their best to bring our bodies into line with whatever the doctors tell us. This mind-over-body effect is called the "placebo effect." To guard against the placebo effect, experimenters employ either single-blind or double-blind techniques.

Single-Blind With this approach, the researchers do not tell the patients what pill they are getting. The patients are therefore "blinded" to what is going on. Both placebo and drug then gain equal advantage from the placebo effect. If the drug seems to work better or worse than the placebo, then the researchers can be sure of a real difference between the two.

Double-Blind If the researchers know what pill they are handing out, they can give subtle, unconscious cues that let the patients know whether they are receiving the drug or the placebo. The researchers may also interpret any changes in the symptoms of the patients who receive the drug as being caused by the drug. It is therefore best to keep the researchers in the dark too; and when both researchers and patients are blind to the truth, the experiment is said to be "double-blind." Drug trials often use pills that differ only in color or in the number on the bottle, and the code is not broken until all the test results are in. This way nobody knows who gets what until the knowledge can no longer make a difference.

Obviously, the double-blind approach can work only when there are human beings on both sides of the experiment, as experimenter and as experimental subject. When the object of the experiment is an inanimate object (such as the wish machine), only the single-blind approach is possible.

With suitable precautions against coincidence, self-delusion, wishful thinking, bias, and other sources of error, the wish machine could be convincingly tested. Yet, it cannot be perfectly tested, for perhaps it only works sometimes, such as when the aurora glows green over Copenhagen, in months without an *r*, or when certain people use it. It is impossible to rule out all the possibilities, although we can rule out enough to be pretty confident that the gadget is pure nonsense.

Similar precautions are essential in every scientific field, for the same sources of error lie in wait wherever experiments are done, and they serve very much the same function. However, no controls and no peer review system, no matter how elaborate, can completely protect a scientist—or science—from error. Here, as well as in the logical impossibility of proof (remember, experiments only fail to disprove) and science's dependence on the progressive growth of knowledge, lies the uncertainty that is the hallmark of science. Yet, it is also a hallmark of science that its methods guarantee that uncertainty will be reduced (not eliminated). Frauds and errors will be detected and corrected. Limited understandings of truth will be extended.

Those who bear this in mind will be better equipped to deal with issues of certainty and risk.

NOTES

1. Mesthene's essay, "The Role of Technology in Society," *Technology and Culture* (vol. 10, no. 4, 1969), is reprinted in A. H. Teich, ed., *Technology and the Future*, 6th ed. (St. Martin's Press, 1993).

2. McDermott's essay, "Technology: The Opiate of the Intellectuals," *The New York Review of Books* (July 31, 1969), is reprinted in A. H. Teich, ed., *Technology and the Future*, 6th ed. (St. Martin's Press, 1993).

3. Must we, really? After all, we can be quite sure that the wish machine does not work because, if it did, it would likely be on the market. Casinos would then be unable to make a profit for their backers, deadly diseases would be eradicated, and so on.

4. Or patients that are taller, shorter, male, female, homosexual, heterosexual, black, white—there is no telling what differences might affect the test results. Drug (and other) researchers therefore take great pains to be sure groups of experimental subjects are alike in every way but the one way being tested.

PART 1

The Place of Science and Technology in Society

The partnership between human society and science and technology is an uneasy one. Science and technology undoubtedly offer benefits, in both the short term and the long, but they also challenge accepted beliefs and present society with new worries.

The issues in this section deal with the best ways to ensure that society benefits from science and technology, how to ensure that citizens understand the science and technology that pervade their lives, the conflict between science and traditional elements of society, and the accessibility of advancing technology.

- Should the Federal Government Point the Way for Science?

- Should There Be Standards for Science Education?

- Is Science Hazardous to Human Values?

- Will the Information Revolution Benefit Society?

ISSUE 1

Should the Federal Government Point the Way for Science?

YES: David H. Guston and Kenneth Keniston, from "Updating the Social Contract for Science," *Technology Review* (November/December 1994)

NO: National Academy of Sciences, from *Allocating Federal Funds for Science and Technology* (National Academy Press, 1995)

ISSUE SUMMARY

YES: Assistant professor of public policy David H. Guston and professor of human development Kenneth Keniston argue that science can no longer set its own path and that public participation must be increased at all levels of decision making about science.

NO: The National Academy of Sciences, a private, nonprofit society of scholars engaged in scientific and engineering research, asserts that although the relationship between government or society and science needs changes, only scientists should decide what research is to be done.

What scientists do as they apply their methods is called *research*. Scientists who perform *basic* or *fundamental research* seek no specific result. Basic research is motivated essentially by curiosity. It is the study of some intriguing aspect of nature for its own sake. Basic researchers have revealed vast amounts of detail about the chemistry and function of genes, explored the behavior of electrons in semiconductors, revealed the structure of the atom, and discovered radioactivity. They have opened our minds to the immensity of both time and the space of the universe in which we live, and they have produced photos of the surface of Mars.

Applied or *strategic research* is more mission-oriented. Applied scientists turn basic discoveries into devices and processes, such as transistors, integrated circuits, and computers; genetic engineering; cures for diseases; and nuclear weapons and power plants. They have also used their basic understanding of the atmosphere to improve weather forecasting. And space research has yielded communications, weather, and earth-resource-survey satellites. There are thousands of such examples, all of which are answers to specific problems or needs, and many of which were quite surprising to the basic researchers who first gained the raw knowledge that led to these developments.

The unexpected fruits, or "spinoffs," of basic research have been used to justify steady growth in funding for this side of science ever since Vannevar

Bush's 1945 report *Science, the Endless Frontier* (reprint, National Science Foundation, 1990). However, the search for justification is an everlasting struggle. In 1953 Warren Weaver, in "Fundamental Questions in Science," *Scientific American* (September 1953), expressed concern that the successes of applied science meant the neglect of basic science. Today there is a movement to focus on "national goals" and "science in the national interest" and to emphasize applied research over basic research.

It is easy to see what drives this movement. Society has a host of problems that cry out for immediate solutions. Yet there is also a need for research that is not tied to explicit need because such research undeniably supplies a great many of the ideas, facts, and techniques that problem-solving researchers use in solving society's problems. Basic researchers, of course, use the same ideas, facts, and techniques as they continue their probings into the way nature works.

There is also increasing pressure for public participation in deciding what scientists work on. Science, say some, must be removed from control by social, political, and intellectual elites, and scientists must be held accountable if they expect society to fund their work. Politicians expect a guarantee of results; the public demands guarantees of safety and of benefit to all society, not just the elite. David H. Guston and Kenneth Keniston recognize that such expectations are fed by the past successes of science and technology, the vast expense of the scientific enterprise, and a few spectacular technological failures. Yet, in the following selection, they say that in a democracy, the public should not be "excluded from decision making about science." That is, decisions should not be left to the experts alone. For many years, of course, the experts *have* made the decisions. And the National Academy of Sciences believes that they should continue doing so. "Panels of the nation's leading experts," says the academy, should advise science policymakers, and working scientists—the peers in the peer review system—should decide what specific projects get funded.

YES

David H. Guston and
Kenneth Keniston

UPDATING THE SOCIAL
CONTRACT FOR SCIENCE

In the years following World War II, the United States established a scientific enterprise that became the envy of the world. This enterprise rested on a vision of science as an "endless frontier" that would replace the American West as the font of economic growth, rising standards of living, and social change. The institutions that supported this frontier were a distinctively American blend of public and private enterprises, eventually including an array of national laboratories, mission agencies, and even a National Science Foundation. The practices that supported it entailed what Harvard political scientist Don K. Price called a new type of federalism: the provision of financial support to scientists at public and private research universities without co-opting their independence.

Research universities were the intellectual centerpiece of this enterprise, since it was there that most of the basic research was performed. At the heart of federal support for universities was the practice of competitive, peer-reviewed grants. The bargain that was struck between the federal government and university science—what is often called the "social contract for science" —can be stated concisely. On one hand, government promised to fund the basic science that peer reviewers found most worthy of support. Scientists, on the other hand, promised to ensure that the research was performed well and honestly, and to provide a steady stream of scientific discoveries that would be translated into new products, medicines, or weapons.

After five decades, the social contract for science shows signs of extreme duress. Scientists and politicians have serious complaints about each other. The issues are, by now, familiar: scientific fraud and dishonesty, the adequacy of science funding, indirect costs of research, administrative burdens in science, scientific priorities, big science, pork-barrel science, and so on. Reports by the congressional Office of Technology Assessment, the National Academy of Sciences, and the Carnegie Commission on Science, Technology, and Government have analyzed what some perceive as a "crisis" in science policy.

From David H. Guston and Kenneth Keniston, "Updating the Social Contract for Science," *Technology Review*, vol. 97, no. 8 (November/December 1994). Copyright © 1994 by *Technology Review*. Reprinted by permission.

Despite this scrutiny, the underlying causes of today's conflicts in science policy remain obscure. We do not believe that the antagonism between science and politics signals either a new or a terminal crisis. But today's struggles do indicate that the old contract between science and government needs updating; they also point to enduring and irreducible tensions between the principles of science and those of democratic government.

CHANGED GOVERNMENT

Although scientists sometimes lament the passing of a golden age of government support for science, the history of postwar science policy fails to reveal a truly privileged past. Throughout the last 50 years, controversies between the political and the scientific communities have always been present—over the loyalty of scientists and the merits of military research, over financial accounting for grants, over applied versus basic research, over payment for the indirect costs of research, and above all, over how much money Washington should dedicate to scientific research.

The pattern of federal funding for research and development [R&D] also belies any image of a lost golden age. Those who pine for the good old days usually recall the mid-1060s, when federal R&D spending reached an all-time high, whether measured as a percentage of the gross national product (in which case 1964 was the maximum) or as a share of total federal spending (in which case the peak came in 1965). But measured in constant dollars, the situation is less clear. By the Office of Management and Budget's method of discounting for inflation, the peak of real federal spending was 1966 or 1967. By the

National Science Foundation's method, R&D spending in 1990 was about 30 percent *higher* than the supposed 1966 peak.

In any event, the mid-60s spending levels are a problematic reference point, because federal spending for science and technology in those years was inflated by competition with the Soviets and by the Apollo program. From 1963 to 1972, defense R&D accounted for almost 54 percent of federal expenditures in science and technology. The Reagan defense buildup raised average defense R&D spending between 1983 and 1992 to about 56 percent of total federal R&D. But the average defense share has since fallen to less than 53 percent, and President Clinton has promised to reduce the defense share to 50 percent. Furthermore, space-related R&D, which accounted for 27 percent of federal expenditures between 1963 and 1972, accounted for only 7 percent between 1983 and 1992.

Another way to look at R&D spending is to compare it with the rest of the federal budget. Over the last decade the share of R&D in the domestic discretionary budget has risen, while almost all other items have fallen. That is, through the 1980s, R&D consumed a growing share of the shrinking pie of nondefense, nonentitlement spending. For this reason, calls for greatly increased science budgets are ill-starred from the beginning. The sufferings of scientists may be real, but in the words of Rep. George Brown (D-Calif.), one of the strongest patrons of science, they are not unique.

It nevertheless remains true that irreversible changes have occurred in the last five decades. Indeed, perhaps the simplest explanation for the heightening of tensions between government and science is that the original contract was made between a kind of government that no longer exists and a kind of scientific community that has long since disappeared.

In the postwar years, both the executive and legislative branches have changed in ways that affect the support of science. At the executive level, the "imperial presidency" has extended the chief executive's prerogatives far beyond their prewar limits, and the "management presidency," centered in the Office of Management and Budget, has emphasized control of the sprawling bureaucracy. The White House has added analytical capabilities: the special assistant to the president for science and technology, and the president's Science Advisory Committee. More recently, scientific advisory committees have proliferated in other departments and agencies. The executive branch increasingly tries to coordinate federal R&D in the various agencies, the most recent mechanism being the National Science and Technology Council, composed of Cabinet chiefs and the heads of independent agencies and chaired by the president.

In Congress, the power of committee chairs has declined through the postwar years and has been replaced by a radically decentralized organization, with participation from subcommittees as well as action outside of committees. There has been a resurgence of congressional oversight directed at maintaining accountability over burgeoning programs and agencies. In the early 1970s, Congress augmented its analytical capabilities by creating the Office of Technology Assessment and the Congressional Budget Office, expanding the Congressional Research Service, and increasing control over the General Accounting Office.

Committee and personal staffs have increased in size and professional competence. Congress has also created an Office of Inspector General in each major department and agency to monitor the implementation of policy.

Such changes—even if not intentionally related to science—have given both the executive and the legislative branch greater motivation and competence to evaluate and oversee the scientific community.

CHANGED SCIENCE

If government has been transformed in the last five decades, so has science. The scientific enterprise has grown vastly in workforce, complexity, and size of projects, and it has therefore grown more expensive to fund. For example, the scientific workforce nearly doubled between 1965 and 1988, from 495,000 to about 950,000. And the proportion of the nation's workforce who are scientists and engineers engaged in R&D rose from its previous high of 67.9 per 10,000 in 1968 to 75.9 per 10,000 in 1987.

Federal funding of research has always sought to turn out more PhDs so as to provide the nation with a highly trained scientific workforce. But however commendable this goal, it has a bizarre consequence: the more successful the program is, the greater will be the future demand for research financing. It is rather as if a welfare program created a half-dozen new welfare applicants for every one who is given federal assistance. This steady increase in the number of scientists means that despite real growth in R&D funding, a smaller percentage of applications for grants can be funded each year. The scarcity of research funds felt by the scientific community is quite genuine on a per capita basis.

The size and complexity of scientific projects have also increased greatly. The Manhattan Project and other wartime endeavors inaugurated a trend toward "megascience." Research projects today involve more people and require more expensive equipment than ever before. Science has become a vastly more complex aggregate of new technologies and advanced education. As a result, the price of research has gone up much faster than inflation. For this reason, too, scarcity is felt even in the midst of generous funding.

Meanwhile, popular support for science has waned. The almost unqualified public enthusiasm that characterized the immediate postwar period has given way to a far more nuanced view of science and technology. Attitudes have been negatively influenced by conspicuous technological failures—Chernobyl, Bhopal, *Challenger*—which raise concerns about science by the reverse application of the logic that predicts technological benefits from scientific triumphs. It was President Eisenhower who appointed the first special assistant to the president for science and technology. But it was also Eisenhower who warned the American public in his farewell address that "public policy could itself become the captive of a scientific-technological elite." The apprehension of such an elite found expression through many voices: social critics like Theodore Roszak, environmental activists like Rachel Carson, and antimilitary movements that blossomed on the campuses of research universities.

Of all the changes since the postwar negotiation of the social contract for science, the end of the Cold War is probably the most consequential. Ever since 1945, the promise of military applications and the specter of Soviet competition has driven federal R&D expenditures in both military and civilian agencies. The expected usefulness of science and technology to the conduct of the Cold War—both in material terms of building effective weapons and in symbolic terms of conquering the new frontiers of space, the atom, and the cell—meant that governments and publics (in the former Soviet Union and the United States alike) viewed science in a favorable light. But today, without an implacable communist foe, the instrumental value of science and technology has lost some of its urgency.

The result, especially for the physical sciences, is that a new rationale for public support is needed. Previously, the goal upon which almost everyone agreed was countering the Soviet threat. Today, other goals for science are alleged—or, more precisely, revived. For the founders of the American system of science funding, the military rationale was only one among many, including human betterment through fuller employment, a rising standard of living, and better health. The health claim has never lost its persuasiveness, but the rationales of employment and living standards are now being resurrected and redefined.

This redefinition sometimes involves a claim that science-based innovation is the elixir that will stimulate the nation's economy and improve its international economic competitiveness. According to this argument, such innovation has produced entire new industries—consider the transistor and genetic engineering—and will give the United States a technological advantage in competing with other nations for markets and high-wage jobs. In its simplest form, the argument posits a direct causal link between the advances of science, success in the international marketplace, and a rising standard of living.

In this simple version, the argument is open to an obvious criticism: the United States is unquestionably the world's leading scientific power, but it lags by international standards in health, has fallen behind in productivity gains, and is being overtaken in standard of living and international trade. More sophisticated versions of the theory therefore argue that good science is a necessary but not sufficient condition for productivity. A primary point of this more subtle formulation maintains that the postwar research system, even though highly successful so far, has become less effective in today's environment because it was geared toward a different set of military, political, technological, and economic challenges.

Even this cursory analysis of changes in the last five decades suggests that the current strains in government-science relations were inevitable and necessary. Government has increased in size, complexity, competence, and capacity both to support and to oversee science. Science, too, has grown and now faces the consequences of its maturity. The old military rationale for public support has lost much of its cogency, and science faces a more critical public than it did 50 years ago. The old contract was written in simpler days. It has become more fragile today partly because the two parties that agreed to it have changed.

The contract clearly must be updated. But it must also confront the basic tensions between science and democracy.

SCIENCE VERSUS DEMOCRACY

Imagine members of Congress commissioning a National Academy of Sciences report on the organization of science-funding agencies, then gathering testimony from scientists on priorities in science funding, the role of different sectors and institutions in the scientific enterprise, the tension between centralization and pluralism in research, the merits of large-scale versus small-scale projects, and the financial accountability of researchers. Is this Rep. Brown's recent Task Force on the Health of Research? Rep. John Dingell's Subcommittee on Oversight and Investigations? Rep. Don Fuqua's Science Policy Task Force of the mid-1980s? The Fountain Committee, the Elliot Committee, or the Daddario Subcommittee of the 1960s?

Actually, it is the Allison Commission of the 1880s, a select congressional committee that examined all these questions with regard to the federal scientific establishment. Like some dysfunctional family, the science policy community in the United States seems to confront the same problems, never finally resolving them even over many years. Why do the same problems constantly arise? Why is it that no institutional arrangements seem capable of eliminating the tensions between government and science?

One can find only a partial answer in the complaints that scientists and politicians make about each other. Politicians are charged with a lack of knowledge and appreciation of the scientific enterprise; scientists, with arrogance, elitism, and political naïveté. But the dysfunction exists not simply because politicians can be ignorant or scientists arrogant. The deeper reason lies in fundamental and ineradicable differences between the organizing principles of a democratic polity and the organizing principles of a democratic polity and the organizing principles of the scientific community.

There are three fundamental tensions that make for an uneasy relation between government and science. The first is simply that popular tastes and preferences are different from, and sometimes antagonistic toward, those of the scientific community. One might call this the populist tension, and it can result in popular pressure for a more equitable geographic distribution of research funds, for more applied research, for a particular focus of programmatic research such as women's health, or for a greater emphasis on teaching and patenting than on research itself.

Scientists rightly ask whether public opinion should matter in science, because popular pressures could seriously reduce the long-term viability of the scientific enterprise, and at times can reflect "antiscientific" attitudes. But in a democratic society, citizens must be allowed to choose between the viability of science and the viability of other valued enterprises. Even though science is the pursuit of the truth, it is still only one pursuit among many that citizens value. What the populist tension really does is force the advocates of scientific research to articulate a publicly compelling rationale for their activities and then, like any beneficiary of public funds, to be accountable for the outcomes.

The second tension derives from the fact that the economic organization necessary for science to flourish may be at odds with the economic organization necessary for democracy to flourish. One might call it the plutocratic tension, because of the importance of wealth in determining the distribution of scientific resources. This tension is obvious in political concerns about the concentration of R&D funding at a small number of major research universities, as well as worries about the real growth of the R&D budget when most other domestic programs are contracting. It is also evident in concern over the growing fuzziness between public and private interests, as public employees and private firms benefit financially from the fruits of publicly funded research. Another expression of this tension is the fear that the benefits of science-based technology—from the profits yielded by new drugs to the conveniences of consumer technologies—more often accrue to the haves of society than to the have-nots. The basic question behind the plutocratic tension is whether science, because it is relatively rich and privileged, will become richer and more privileged still, and will mostly benefit the non-scientists who are already rich and privileged.

The third tension between democratic politics and scientific practice arises from the fact that democratic processes and goals are largely incompatible with scientific processes and goals. One might call this the exclusionary tension, because the requirements for membership in decision making within science are more exclusive—that is, being a scientist or an expert—than for membership in democratic decision making in general. Democratic decision making constantly seeks to encourage and expand participation; scientific decision making limits it. There is a risk that science may oppose democratic decisions that deviate from or deny some scientifically defined truth. But as political theorist Robert Dahl has written about the idea of allowing experts to guard democracy against incorrect decisions, scientific guardianship, if carried to an extreme, is simply a prettier name for dictatorship.

The tensions between democracy and science boil down to conflicting values: democratic politics cherishes participation and the pursuit of justice; science cherishes inquiry and the pursuit of truth. Because the gap between participation and truth can never be closed, the tensions will always exist.

Any two parties with different goals and structures require a carefully wrought contractual relation if they are to collaborate productively. It therefore follows that something like a social contract for science continues to be necessary. It follows, too, that this contract should give explicit attention to the details of the interaction between government and science, or, more precisely, between the public and scientists. An attempt to run science on democratic principles would destroy science; but that does not mean that the existing institutions and processes of science are democratic enough. An attempt to run government on scientific principles would destroy democracy; but similarly, that does not mean that our current politics is sufficiently informed by scientific knowledge. Only by deliberately designing institutions and processes that confront the inevitable tensions between democratic government and scientific practice can these tensions be minimized.

The old contract between government and science was fragile because it denied these tensions, attempting to keep politics and science as separate as possible. Such a contract has indeed outlived its usefulness. The new contract as it evolves must take into account the blurred boundaries between politics and science, all the while recognizing that the differences between them are intrinsic.

THE FUTURE OF THE CONTRACT

Scientists and politicians must be willing to concede to the other some role in each other's enterprise. The scientific community, in particular, must confront directly the fact that it is in competition for federal funding with other meritorious projects. Like it or not, if science expects public support, it moves into an arena where it must be political—in the best sense, and possibly the worst—in order to justify its claim to public support.

By being political, we do not simply mean joining the horde of lobbyists competing on behalf of clients for public boons—although in the United States, lobbying is a time-honored and appropriate activity. More than that, we mean recognizing and responding to the ways in which science and its support are embedded in public attitudes and public policy.

The scientific community and the research universities in which this community is rooted must undertake an educational role with a dual purpose: first, to make clear the nature and workings of science; and second, to bring to the greater community those scientific insights, findings, theories, outlooks, and facts that can indeed contribute to the public good.

In both regards, university science has only begun to explore its role. Academic scientists need to participate more actively in broadly educational activities such as training science and technology journalists, along with focused pedagogic activities like collaborating with educators in primary and secondary schools to improve scientific literacy.

Given the American science must compete with other good purposes and institutions for the favorable opinion and support of a democratic government, and given that the Cold War has ended, the future relationship between science and government depends heavily on the capacity of the scientific community to articulate a plausible rationale for public support and to demonstrate that rationale at every turn. As military preparedness yields to international economic competitiveness and domestic well-being on the list of national priorities, support for science will depend on the scientific community's willingness and capacity to help resolve economic and domestic problems.

What this requires is a program of vigorous outreach to the public, to public administrators, to leaders of the private sector, and to lawmakers. If academic science indeed has a contribution to make, it is no longer enough—if it ever was—for scientists to wait in their laboratories for the telephone to ring. More enterprising and collaborative projects are necessary. This change will be difficult for scientists whose talents lie in the laboratory rather than in public speaking. But there are others who are gifted teachers and interlocutors, and whose enthusiasm for science impels them to share its beauty and its relevance with others. The scientific community must treasure such individuals or risk undercutting public support for science.

At out own institution, we think of the Leaders in Manufacturing Program, an alliance of MIT [Massachusetts Institute of Technology] faculty with several major U.S. corporations, aimed at training a cohort of corporate leaders versed in the latest manufacturing technologies and management strategies. In the same vein is the creation of workshops for congressional staff members on science and technology. At a more general level, MIT's Knight Science Journalism Fellowship Program has expanded the knowledge of more than 100 leading science and technology journalists and media experts over the last 10 years.

The scientific community must initiate more activities like these: projects that move beyond lobbying to outreach and education, activities that constitute a series of "mini-contracts" between the needs of particular constituencies and the capacities of the scientific community to respond to those needs. It is not enough for the scientific community simply to claim that it is useful; the relevance of scientific knowledge and perspectives to the public interest must be demonstrated again and again in concrete projects.

Government, too, will require new strategies and perhaps new institutions if the contract with science is to be successfully renegotiated. One urgent and oft-noted need is for a more rational way to determine the level of overall federal spending for R&D and the priorities within those expenditures. Too often, public financing of science and technology is based on the political power of a particular disease lobby, the eagerness of members of Congress to earmark scientific and technological projects for their home districts, or intensive lobbying by a group of scientists for their own specialty. Needed instead is an orderly, open, and publicly accessible process. In this regard, the recently established White House National Science and Technology Council (NSTC) promises to be instrumental in drafting an overall R&D budget and in setting priorities within the budget. This body continues to rely on the tried-and-true process of peer review for evaluating individual projects.

What the NSTC needs is a reasonable and articulate strategy for choosing among projects and disciplines. Such a strategy might include giving priority to important disciplines in which the United States compares unfavorably with other nations (as a recent report of the National Academy of Sciences suggests) and inviting consumers of research in industry, education, health, and other fields to assess the output of federal research funding.

At the same time, however, the combination of political priority setting and scientific peer review must not shut out public input. Precisely because research is difficult and performing it can require many years of training, the temptation to confuse the performance of scientific research with the making of science policy is great. The making of science policy by the federal government, or for that matter by state and local governments, needs to be open and democratic. We have urged scientists to reach out to the public to explain what they do and to help ensure that their work is put to good use. This outreach goes for naught if the public is excluded from decision making about science. In this regard, public input, and not just expert advice, is essential at all levels of science policymaking. A "national forum" on science and technology priorities, such as that recently proposed by the Carnegie Commission on Science, Technology, and Government, could help provide such public input if properly constituted. Millions of Americans, not themselves scientists, have strong and legitimate opinions about the value to them and to the nation of space travel, local technology-development centers, and cancer research, among other scientific and technological projects. Their participation should be welcomed and respected.

A third major obligation of government is to preserve R&D as an example of the sturdy American principle of federalism—that decisions should be made and actions taken at the most local level possible. In science policy, this means resisting the temptation to micromanage scientific work, and the researchers and institutions that conduct it, from the distance of Washington. To be sure, government needs to establish standards: it may rightly impose exacting ethical and financial requirements upon researchers who receive public monies. But the only way to implement such requirements consistent with the federalism that inspired the social contract for science is to insist that universities and their researchers maintain primary responsibility. For example, an incentive system for dealing with indirect costs—in which the government sets the overall rate and universities can pocket the remainder if they come in under that rate—may be preferable on grounds of both principle and efficiency to either the preexisting system of making a separate agreement with each university, or any more invasive system in which government accountants would formulate budgets for overhead.

In science policy, as in other areas of governance, a primary responsibility of public officials is to preserve as many independent centers of initiative and locally governed activities as is consistent with the broad rules of accountability and fairness. In the long run, science and technology flourish when multiple independent centers of activity are encouraged; they fail to thrive under the heavy hand of centralized control and unified direction. This is just as it should be in a federal republic like the United States.

These amendments in the social contract for science will never resolve some of the tensions inherent between science and government. But in recognizing the tensions, the changes can make for a more robust and productive relationship. The American system of science and technology has been outstanding in the last half-century in good part because public policy was designed to foster a plurality of centers of scientific and technical excellence with the maximum possible autonomy and responsibility delegated to each local center. No better principle than federalism can be imagined for the new social contract for science.

NO   National Academy of Sciences

ALLOCATING FEDERAL FUNDS FOR SCIENCE AND TECHNOLOGY

PREFACE

In a report accompanying funding for the National Institutes of Health [NIH] for Fiscal Year 1995, the Senate Appropriations Committee requested a study from the National Academy of Sciences, the National Academy of Engineering, and the Institute of Medicine. The study was to address "the criteria that should be used to judging the appropriate allocation of funds to research and development activities, the appropriate balance among different types of institutions that conduct such research, and the means of assuring continued objectivity in the allocation process." The study originated from the Appropriations Committee's concern "that at a time when there is much opportunity to understand and cure disease, funding for health research supported by NIH in the next fiscal year is held to below the inflation rate for medical research due to budget constraints. Similarly, other Federal research agencies are confronted with constrained resources resulting from the virtual freeze in discretionary outlays."

The charge was daunting when it was requested by the Appropriations Committee and is even more so now. With a year's passage, the concern with a "virtual freeze in discretionary outlays" seems an understatement. The efforts by both the Administration and the Congress to reduce the federal deficit have prompted proposals to cut programs, consolidate or abolish agencies, and even do away with whole departments. The federal research and development enterprise has not been exempt from examination, nor should it be. Since the end of World War II, this enterprise has become vast and complex, and it accounts for a significant part of the discretionary outlays of the federal government. It is thus important that the nature and structure of federal support for research and development, as well as the benefits it brings, be understood to assure that as budgets are reduced, the strengths of U.S. science and technology are maintained, while the anachronistic or weak

From National Academy of Sciences, *Allocating Federal Funds for Science and Technology* (National Academy Press, 1995). Copyright © 1995 by The National Academy of Sciences. Reprinted by permission of National Academy Press, Washington, DC. Notes omitted.

aspects are pruned.... The theme of the committee's report is continuance in the face of change.

Continuance builds on the spectacularly successful results of postwar federal investments in research and development. By any measure, these investments have been recouped many times over in contributing to a strong and globally competitive U.S. economy, hastening the end of the Cold War, providing continuing national security against new enemies, advancing the fight against disease, improving our environment, and producing revelations about ourselves, our world, and our cosmos.

Change comes in acknowledging that the federal research and development enterprise must adapt to a new world. The Cold War is over. Global competition is both economic and military, involving many more nations than did the past bipolar confrontation of nuclear superpowers. These problems create opportunities. Indeed, science and technology will be even more important in the future than they are today. Change is also reflected in the very doing of science, as computers and high-speed communication networks expand access to databases and facilities throughout the world and enable daily collaboration among scientists and engineers separated by great distances.

Over time, institutions and programs have been created that no longer serve us well. Even good programs and institutions must give way to successors that are better and are more closely linked to new national needs. These are painful messages. Some of the committee's members have built their professional lives through programs and institutions that may not survive application of the principles the committee proposes for judging

future expenditures. At the same time, the committee believes strongly that failure to make these choices will prove costly, serving neither the nation nor the scientific community. That said, the committee appreciates that its principles for judging programs and institutions are, by necessity, general and must be given more specificity when applied to particular programs and institutions. As a practical matter, the committee did not offer specific details for implementing the judgments that must be made. The committee believes that those who must make the decisions and execute them should be given the latitude to apply these principles sensibly....

Some will think it politically unwise that we recommend a process and guidelines for identifying activities that can be reduced or eliminated and for reallocating the savings to ones more essential to preserving U.S. leadership in science and technology. We have been told that our advice will be only partially followed—that the cuts will be made but that the savings will not be reallocated to federal science and technology. Perhaps. But we see no alternative. We can only hope that the case we have made is convincing, and trust that our recommendations to maintain U.S. strength in science and technology will be accepted. The committee believes that the political wisdom that created the remarkably successful U.S. research and development enterprise will endure, driven by the U.S. public's strong and abiding support for federal science and technology....

— Frank Press
Chair
Committee on Criteria for Federal
Support of Research and Development

DETERMINING PRINCIPLES FOR ALLOCATING FEDERAL FUNDS

The federal government has played a pivotal role in developing the world's most successful system of research and development. Over the past 5 decades the U.S. scientific and technical enterprise has expanded dramatically, and the federal investments in it have produced enormous benefits for the nation's economy, national defense, health, and social well-being. Science and technology will be at least as important for our nation's future as they have been for our past, but further expansion of federal funding for research and development is unrealistic in the next several years. Both the current administration's 10-year budget plan and the 7-year plans passed by the House and Senate propose significant reductions in federal discretionary spending. Maintaining the vigor of research and development is important—indeed essential—to the nation's future and will require the ability to increase funding for new opportunities selectively, even while reducing the overall budget.

The Committee on Criteria for Federal Support of Research and Development believes that it will be possible to sustain this country's scientific and technological preeminence and the strong federal role within the current fiscal constraints if the recommendations in this report are adopted. Ensuring the nation's future health, however, may well require augmented investments later—after the current period of reorganization and consolidation has helped control costs and sharpen focus.

As we consider how to restructure federally funded research and development to meet today's budget realities, it is important to recognize the con-siderable strengths of the current system. Those strengths should not be lost. "Top-down" mission-oriented management and "bottom-up" investigator-initiated research projects have combined to create a powerful research and development engine that is the envy of the world. Computer science, surface science, molecular biology, and other fields have emerged in response to new opportunities, and widely disparate fields have been combined to create entirely new applications. Competitively funded research and development projects subject to national merit review and conducted in every state of our nation have proven particularly effective. Federally funded university science and engineering, in addition to yielding new discoveries, has produced new generations of scientists and engineers who serve in academia, industry, and government and also fill critical management positions there. Investments in science have dramatically expanded our knowledge of ourselves and our universe, and new technologies have improved our daily lives. The fruits of federally funded research and development have been applied effectively by U.S. industry. Drawing on the support provided by many sponsoring agencies and the results from a wide range of performing institutions, the American entrepreneurial spirit has tapped federally funded research and development to form entirely new industries in areas such as microelectronics, biotechnology, and communications and information technology, among others....

The extraordinary success of U.S. research and development can be continued within current budget constraints. However, ensuring continuing success will require rigorous discipline and a coherent and comprehensive approach for deciding how resources are used. This report proposes a new process for allocating and monitoring federal spending for science and technology across disciplines and government agencies. With an integrated view and a coherent federal science and technology budget, it will be possible to make selective reductions in some areas, so as to free badly needed resources for more productive investments and new opportunities that arise. . . .

The United States Should Strive to Continue as the World Leader in Science and Technology

RECOMMENDATION. The President and Congress should ensure that the FS&T [Federal Science and Technology] budget is sufficient to allow the United States to achieve preeminence in a select number of fields and to perform at a world-class level in the other major fields.

The pool of approximately $35 billion to $40 billion in annual public support for FS&T is large and diverse. The committee believes that it is possible within that budget to reduce some programs, eliminate others, increase support of high-opportunity fields, and restrain federal spending—all while maintaining our nation's tradition of excellence in science and technology. To continue as a world leader, the United States should strive for clear leadership in the most promising areas of science and technology and those deemed most important to our national goals. In other major fields, the United States should perform on a par with other nations so that it is "poised to pounce" if future discoveries increase the importance of one of these fields. If the nation sets priorities in this way (see bulleted items below) and uses them in conjunction with the FS&T budget process, the result will be better decisions about reallocating and restructuring the U.S. research and development enterprise, preserving its core strengths, and positioning it well for strong future performance.

The international comparisons needed to assess U.S. achievement of its goals for leadership in research and development should be conducted by panels of the nation's leading experts under White House auspices. Reallocation decisions should be made with the advice and guidance of these expert panels, capable of determining the appropriate scope of the fields to assess and to judge the international stature of U.S. efforts in each field. These panels would recommend to the President, his advisors, and Congress:

- Which fields must attain or maintain preeminence, based on goals such as economic importance, national security, unusual opportunity for significant discoveries, global resource or environmental issues, control of disease, mitigation of natural disasters, food production, a presidential initiative (such as human space-flight), or an unanticipated crisis;
- Which fields require increases in funding, changes in direction, restructuring, or other actions to achieve these goals; and
- Which fields have excess capacity (e.g., are producing too many new investigators, have more laboratories or facilities than needed) relative to national needs and international benchmarks.

The committee believes that designing the budget process so as to secure an FS&T budget sufficient to ensure preeminence in select fields and world status in others will allow the United States to maintain continued world leadership. The FS&T budget process must be coupled to systematic review of investments by the nation's best scientific and technical experts, reporting to the highest reaches of government, to produce an appropriately balanced mix of activities. The committee emphasizes that wise federal investments will lead to the creation of new wealth in the future to an even greater extent than they have in the past. As a result, these investments will help reduce the federal deficit in the long run. After a period of budget constraints, reconfiguration, and adjustment, national needs may justify increased investments in FS&T....

Maintaining U.S. Leadership in Science and Technology Despite Budget Constraints Will Require Discipline in the Allocation of Resources for Federal Investments....

RECOMMENDATION. The federal government should encourage, but not directly fund, private-sector commercial technology development, with two limited exceptions:

- *Development in pursuit of government missions, such as weapons development and spaceflight; or*
- *Development of new enabling, or broadly applicable, technologies for which government is the only funder available.*

The federal government has long sponsored research and education as a means of developing technologies for its own use and has also encouraged the development of state-of-the-art technologies in its capacity as a customer. The histories of the development of airframes and aircraft engines, missiles and satellites, advanced materials, semiconductors, and computers are replete with examples of federal procurement and research support that have contributed to the creation of com-

mercially important technology. Indeed, the government was the first purchaser of key pieces of equipment used to build the components of what has become the Internet. Both FS&T funding and federal procurement will continue to be important in these and other emerging growth sectors linked to federal missions such as health and environmental cleanup. In the future, however, funding for the nation's science and technology base may contribute more to stimulating new sectors of economic growth than will federal procurement and the "demand pull" on an emerging technology.

Even before the end of the Cold War, high-technology spin-offs from federally funded R&D [research and development] in defense and space had diminished. Efforts have been under way for some time to foster the development of dual-use technologies or to use off-the-shelf commercial technologies in federal programs that develop products for government use. In many cases, civilian applications have now surpassed military ones.

As the Academies' Committee on Science, Engineering, and Public Policy pointed out in its 1993 report, U.S. leadership in high-technology markets cannot be achieved or maintained primarily through federal actions. Commercial technology development will occur largely in the private sector. Firms motivated by market forces and judged by their performance in satisfying demand have a better record than governments of investing in new technologies with large commercial payoffs. As the presumptive owner of the results, the private sector should be the funder of such commercial technology development projects.

The federal government's main role in encouraging commercial technology development and ensuring economic success is to maintain an environment conducive to private-sector development and adoption of new technologies. Such an environment depends on a range of federal policies that influence taxation, macroeconomic stability, national savings, and the volume of international trade. Economic success also is determined by legislation concerned with unfair monopolies, patent protection, product liability, and environmental and consumer protection. Although examination of these critical issues is beyond the scope of this report, the committee believes that government policies, such as those related to taxation, regulation, intellectual property rights protection, social mandates, and others, are usually more important to commercial outcomes than is direct government funding to industry.

The government should not subsidize specific private firms for projects that they would undertake anyway. In a suitable economic context, a firm engaged in product or process innovation will capture or "appropriate" a large fraction of the benefits that it creates. If so, market incentives will guide firms to undertake the right kinds of innovations without any central planning or guidance.

In many cases, however, no one firm can capture the full benefits of its investment. This is generally the case for investment in basic research and can also apply in development related to emerging technologies. One approach to addressing this problem is represented by Sematech, an industry consortium created to improve semiconductor manufacturing, and for which the federal government provided some initial funding. Federal funding may help to establish such consortia in limited and highly specific areas and can be appropriate to support research in consortia formed by industry.

In addition, the government may still have a role in fostering new enabling technologies. Many people believe that nanotechnology (i.e., at scales of one-billionth of a meter) and micromanufacturing, for example, offer exciting commercial opportunities. Government should support training and research that will establish the general scientific and technical principles that firms will ultimately exploit to develop new commercial products and processes. Such investments are appropriate for the federal government because they can generate large benefits that accrue to the nation but would not be captured by any one firm. For example, federal support for research as a component in the education of individuals entering careers in electrical engineering and computer science has helped to produce the skilled people who have developed our modern information technology industries. Support for the work at universities has resulted in the development of the protocols used to exchange information over computer networks, a crucial piece of intellectual capital that all firms have been able to exploit as they enter this new field. Transfer to industry of state-of-the-art technical knowledge produced at science and engineering schools occurs most effectively when faculty, graduate students, and postdoctoral fellows move to the private sector.

Federal funding that improves graduate and undergraduate education is an example of another way to encourage commercial development indirectly, while also supporting R&D in the national interest. In addition to helping stimulate the development and transfer of new enabling technologies into the private sector, the engineering research centers funded by NSF [National Science Foundation], for instance, have helped change the nature of graduate engineering education. By working in close collaboration with their counterparts in industry, graduate students and faculty have become more aware of the specific technology needs and practices of industry. As a consequence, engineering research programs are more focused and students are better prepared to work in industrial research and development laboratories.

The government also sponsors research and development with potential commercial applications in its own laboratories, in FFRDCs, including the national laboratories, and in independent medical research institutes and other nonprofit organizations (almost half of FS&T funding goes to those organizations, the rest to universities and industrial laboratories). Education is not a central mission of those organizations —an important consideration given that movement of people is one of the most effective ways to transfer new ideas and technologies into the private sector. Several recent reports have noted other reasons that federal laboratories, whether operated by the government or contractors, generally have been less successful than they could be at transferring new enabling technologies to potential users in the private sector. New mechanisms such as cooperative research and development agreements (CRADAs) between firms and the government laboratories were introduced to address this problem. Many successful collaborations have been forged between federal laboratories and industry. Several recent reports argue, however, that CRADAs may be less effective than alternatives, that they are difficult to evaluate because of inadequate data, that ownership of intellectual property is often uncertain, and that they create few jobs. Under some

CRADAs, the government may be performing research that the partner firm would have done on its own in the absence of a cooperative research agreement. The committee believes that in many cases the government resources that support CRADA research could be better spent on other, more productive items in the FS&T budget.

In addition to providing funds for research and graduate education at universities and government laboratories, the federal government also supports a variety of other programs that promote the development of commercial technologies in the private sector. They include the Advanced Technology Program [ATP], the Technology Reinvestment Program [TRP], the Manufacturing Extension Partnerships program [MEP], Small Business Innovation Research grants and other small business set-asides, and direct government subsidy to private firms. Those programs have different goals and structures but share in their intention to cultivate industrial innovation. The ATP and the TRP involve funding of private-sector projects; the MEP program is modeled after the agricultural extension service program and primarily helps small businesses to incorporate new technologies. Most of these programs are too new to be carefully evaluated, and, because of inherent features in program design and prospects of unstable funding, we may never be able to tell whether some of them achieved their goals.

At this time, the very concept of a government role in subsidizing the development of private-sector product and process development is controversial. Some difficult questions arise with subsidized partnership programs such as the ATP— will they succeed in fostering new, commercially relevant technologies that otherwise would not develop as quickly, and are they the most efficient uses of increasingly scarce federal R&D dollars? The committee is skeptical that the answer to these questions is yes. It therefore believes that these subsidized industrial partnership programs should be continued only if the case is convincingly made that the government is the funder of last resort for an important enabling technology, and they should be pursued only on an experimental basis, with careful attention to their goals, the distribution of proprietary rights, and how they will be evaluated. Where a new technology is needed to address a specific mission such as a military need, however, federal leadership is better justified....

Within the General Constraints Determined by National Priorities, the Selection of Individual Projects Must Reflect the Standards of the Scientific and Technical Community

RECOMMENDATION. Because competition for funding is vital to maintain the high quality of FS&T programs, competitive merit review, especially that involving external reviewers, should be the preferred way to make awards.

The highest-quality projects and people should be supported with FS&T funds. The best-known mechanism to accomplish that is some form of open competition involving evaluation of merit by peers. Competitive merit review involves the use of criteria that include technical quality, the qualifications of the proposer, relevance and educational impacts of the proposed project, and other factors pertaining to research goals rather than to political or other nonresearch considerations. Open competition means that, at some level within the framework of

an agency's mission, researchers propose their best ideas and anyone may apply and be funded regardless of institution or geographic location. However, in the case of highly targeted missions, quality can also be maintained by knowledgeable program managers who have established external scientific and technical advisory groups to help assess quality and to help monitor whether agency needs are met.

The committee believes that the principle of merit review—which emphasizes competition among ideas, diversity of funders and performers of research and development, and organizational flexibility—has been largely responsible for the remarkable quality, productivity, and originality of U.S. science and technology in the past. Competitive merit review should be the method of choice for making future decisions about FS&T funding.

Many federal research and development agencies have developed some form of competitive merit review process to use in making extramural awards for research, training, and facilities. They have also worked to develop equivalent systems of review for allocating intramural funding, but merit review of in-house research is much more difficult because federal research scientists and engineers are in the civil service and still retain salary and benefits even if they are not productive or their area has lower priority or has become obsolete. That problem is a perennial one in the periodic reviews of federal laboratories. The FFRDCs, including the national laboratories, also have procedures for allocating research funding competitively based on performance. Some do it well, but overall the results have been uneven.

There are other approaches to promoting high quality in federally supported research and development. Some programs try to identify top researchers and give them long-term support rather than require them to submit specific proposals to compete every few years. Some funding for agricultural research is allocated to state agricultural experiment stations and land-grant colleges on a formula basis, and the supported institutions choose the researchers and their projects. Evaluations of that system of formula-grant allocation have not given high marks to its responsiveness or the quality of the resulting research. Other federal funding is awarded competitively to research centers, which in turn distribute the funding among individual researchers and groups.

There is benefit to having a variety of approaches to supporting FS&T, especially because mission agencies have specialized assignments to fulfill. However, the committee believes that fiscal constraint makes it important to level the playing field. Competitive merit review should therefore be increased relative to other mechanisms for awarding FS&T funds. Merit review is best exemplified by the processes used at the NSF and NIH, that is, the use of external peer review to identify and select the best proposals for individual research projects as part of a review process based on competition and expert evaluation of merit criteria. That approach enables those two agencies to choose the best performers. Accordingly, use of competitive merit review to allocate federal funding should be the default presumption, supplemented with other mechanisms for inherently governmental functions that cannot be accomplished through competitive merit review....

LOOKING TO THE FUTURE

A robust national system of innovation lies at the heart of our economy, our health, and our national security. That system of innovation depends on federal investments. The committee believes that its recommendations address a crucial need: maintaining the strength and vigor of U.S. research and development despite the prospect of declining federal discretionary spending over the next several years. Seeing the science and technology enterprise through the lens of a unified FS&T budget can help leaders in government and the American public to gauge its fiscal health. A carefully constructed comprehensive budget offers a unitary view, not artificially balkanized into agency budgets, but sensitive to the complexities and relationships among government programs vital to maintaining the United States at the forefront of world-class science and technology. The corollary proposals provide the basis for continuing excellence—emphasizing programs and people rather than institutions, subjecting all federal science and technology activities to competitive merit review, linking science and engineering research to education, and maintaining a pluralistic system of research and development tied to public missions. The committee's recommendations are designed to help root out obsolete or noncompetitive activities, allowing good programs to be replaced by even better ones.

Science and technology have utterly transformed our world over the past 50 years, touching almost every aspect of our daily lives—from communication to transportation to health. They will be at least as important over the next half century. Preeminence in science and technology has become a national asset, at once a point of pride and an immensely practical investment. Prudent stewardship of science and technology, as much as any other area of federal policy, will dictate how our children and our grandchildren live.

POSTSCRIPT

Should the Federal Government Point the Way for Science?

The debate about the extent to which the government should be involved in scientific research is not new. Before the publication of Vannevar Bush's report *Science, the Endless Frontier* in 1945, Senator Harley M. Kilgore (D-West Virginia) said that he wanted "federal research activities to be planned in accordance with liberal social purposes" (see Daniel J. Kevles, "The Changed Partnership," *The Wilson Quarterly*, Summer 1995). Bush's report was in large part an effort to head off any attempt to put science under the explicit control of society, saying that it would surely pay off more handsomely if left to itself, though with generous public funding. On the record, Bush was quite right: Science and technology had helped the United States to win World War II, antibiotics were the miracle drugs of the time, television was just around the corner, and computers were just being built. Science and technology wore a definite shine.

As Kevles notes, much of the shine wore off over the next few decades. Because so much of their funding came from the Defense Department and was aimed at winning wars, science and technology soon began to smell of death, not life. In the 1960s, when thousands of young people were rejecting established authority (particularly the government) for various reasons, government funding stripped science of legitimacy in many people's eyes. Technological disasters such as the Three Mile Island nuclear power plant failure did not help. And then science and technology proved helpless in the face of increasing poverty (psychiatric medications were even held responsible, in part, for the rise in numbers of the homeless) and new diseases such as AIDS.

J. Michael Bishop, in "Enemies of Promise," *The Wilson Quarterly* (Summer 1995), states that a good part of the problem lies in the public's sense of betrayal when science fails to solve problems, due largely to the public's failure to understand just what science can and cannot do. He also says that ignorance is surprisingly widespread in academia, where specialization can mean that a physicist does not know what a gene is and " 'post-modernists' [believe that] the supposedly objective truths of science are in reality all 'socially constructed fictions,' no more than 'useful myths,' and science itself is 'politics by other means.' "

Do Bishop's assertions indicate that the National Academy of Sciences is correct that experts should make the decisions regarding scientific research? Such a "social contract," however, cannot be one-sided. Radford Byerly, Jr., and Roger A. Pielke, Jr., in "The Changing Ecology of United States Science,"

Science (September 15, 1995), argue that when the parties to such a contract change their interpretations, it must be revised. "To be sustainable," they say, "science must meet two related conditions: (i) democratic accountability, including accountability to societal goals, and (ii) sustained political support." If science fails to meet these conditions, it will lose public funding.

On the other hand, renowned physicist Burton Richter, in "The Role of Science in Our Society," *Physics Today* (September 1995), says, "Of course we hope for practical benefits, and that hope has been amply fulfilled. We should not, however, focus too narrowly on the practical, for to do that is to deny the needs of the spirit." Richter seems to have more faith than most politicians that it is worth society's while to fund research that does not have obvious short-term payoffs.

ISSUE 2

Should There Be Standards for Science Education?

YES: National Research Council, from *National Science Education Standards* (December 1995)

NO: Elliot W. Eisner, from "Standards for American Schools: Help or Hindrance?" *Phi Delta Kappan* (June 1995)

ISSUE SUMMARY

YES: The National Research Council, the principal operating agency of the National Academy of Sciences, asserts that scientific and technological literacy is becoming increasingly important for all people. To this end, it has developed standards for science education throughout the United States, which are described.

NO: Professor of education and art Elliot W. Eisner views the general idea of standards in education skeptically, insisting that such standards ignore the fact that children develop at different rates and in different ways.

How much science should people know? This question has been of considerable interest to educators and to government agencies for many years. It gained considerable importance in 1957, when the Soviet Union beat the United States into space with the first artificial satellite, Sputnik. The U.S. government decided that science education had been inadequate and mounted a major effort to improve it. That effort seemed to pay off in that the United States beat the Soviet Union to the moon. But then Japan, Germany, and other countries began to outdo the United States in a number of commercial technologies, and comparisons of how much math and science various countries' students knew repeatedly showed that students in the United States fell toward the back of the pack. Among the reasons put forward for the differences were that many other nations have more ambitious, more precisely specified, and more unified curricula than the United States, where "each of our states and 16,000 school districts is more or less doing its own thing" (Albert Shanker, "Where We Stand," 1992, quoted by *CQ Researcher*, March 11, 1994, p. 233).

In the late 1980s the American Association for the Advancement of Science's "Project 2061" attempted to define what scientific knowledge a typical high school graduate should have. In 1991 science educators asked the National Academy of Sciences to develop standards for students from kindergarten through grade 12. The standards were seen as covering not only the facts that children (all children, regardless of race, gender, family income, religion, disability, or ambition) should learn but also broader concepts, teaching methods and resources, and more. The aim was to produce a citizenry that could understand the many scientific and technological issues that arise in modern life, make appropriate decisions, and adapt to the changing needs of the workplace.

The development process was not easy, for controversies arose at every turn. However, a broad consensus was eventually achieved, and the final report was published late in 1995.

Is the controversy over? Surely not. The Maine legislature, for example, is considering a bill to set new learning standards in the state's schools, while opponents of standards are out in full force. In Maine, as in other states, some of the opposition is aimed explicitly at the science component of the standards; many home-schooling parents and religious conservatives do not want their children exposed to ideas—evolution, sex education, human diversity, and even critical thinking, among others—that threaten their values. Others object that standards in any area will be expensive to implement, will give government too much control over local matters, or "will mire schools more deeply in mediocrity [because] the effect will be to intensify all the elements of the current system that do not work" (Dennis Gray, "National Standards: A Contrary View," *Basic Education*, January 1994). Those in favor of standards speak of the need for a competent workforce, scientific literacy, and accountability.

On the national level, proponents of standards say that scientific literacy is essential for international competitiveness. Another contention is that, as America as a society is shamed by high school graduates who cannot read, society should similarly be shamed by graduates who do not know what a gene is or that there is such a thing as verifiable, objective knowledge. Yet there remain those who believe that science is irrelevant to what really matters or that it is inimical to their beliefs and values.

The proponents' case is concisely made in the following selection from the National Research Council's own overview of its *National Science Education Standards* report. The overview also contains descriptions of the standards themselves. The opposition is represented by Elliot W. Eisner, who says that the standards are superficial attempts to solve a genuine problem with much more profound roots. He argues that we need to pay more attention to the differences among children and less attention to creating a standardized educational product. We should value variations in learning and achievement.

YES

National Research Council

NATIONAL SCIENCE EDUCATION STANDARDS

NATIONAL SCIENCE EDUCATION STANDARDS: AN OVERVIEW

In a world filled with the products of scientific inquiry, scientific literacy has become a necessity for everyone. Everyone needs to use scientific information to make choices that arise every day. Everyone needs to be able to engage intelligently in public discourse and debate about important issues that involve science and technology. And everyone deserves to share in the excitement and personal fulfillment that can come from understanding and learning about the natural world.

Scientific literacy also is of increasing importance in the workplace. More and more jobs demand advanced skills, requiring that people be able to learn, reason, think creatively, make decisions, and solve problems. An understanding of science and the processes of science contributes in an essential way to these skills. Other countries are investing heavily to create scientifically and technically literate work forces. To keep pace in global markets, the United States needs to have an equally capable citizenry.

The National Science Education Standards present a vision of a scientifically literate populace. They outline what students need to know, understand, and be able to do to be scientifically literate at different grade levels. They describe an educational system in which all students demonstrate high levels of performance, in which teachers are empowered to make the decisions essential for effective learning, in which interlocking communities of teachers and students are focused on learning science, and in which supportive educational programs and systems nurture achievement. The Standards point toward a future that is challenging but attainable—which is why they are written in the present tense.

The intent of the Standards can be expressed in a single phrase: Science standards for all students. The phrase embodies both excellence and equity.

From National Research Council, *National Science Education Standards* (National Academy Press, 1996). Copyright © 1996 by The National Academy of Sciences. Reprinted by permission of National Academy Press, Washington, DC.

The Standards apply to all students, regardless of age, gender, cultural or ethnic background, disabilities, aspirations, or interest and motivation in science. Different students will achieve understanding in different ways, and different students will achieve different degrees of depth and breadth of understanding depending on interest, ability, and context. But all students can develop the knowledge and skills described in the Standards, even as some students go well beyond these levels.

By emphasizing both excellence and equity, the Standards also highlight the need to give students the opportunity to learn science. Students cannot achieve high levels of performance without access to skilled professional teachers, adequate classroom time, a rich array of learning materials, accommodating work spaces, and the resources of the communities surrounding their schools. Responsibility for providing this support falls on all those involved with the science education system.

Implementing the Standards will require major changes in much of this country's science education. The Standards rest on the premise that science is an active process. Learning science is something that students do, not something that is done to them. "Hands-on" activities, while essential, are not enough. Students must have "minds-on" experiences as well.

The Standards call for more than "science as process," in which students learn such skills as observing, inferring, and experimenting. Inquiry is central to science learning. When engaging in inquiry, students describe objects and events, ask questions, construct explanations, test those explanations against current scientific knowledge, and communicate their ideas to others. They identify their assumptions, use critical and logical thinking, and consider alternative explanations. In this way, students actively develop their understanding of science by combining scientific knowledge with reasoning and thinking skills.

The importance of inquiry does not imply that all teachers should pursue a single approach to teaching science. Just as inquiry has many different facets, so teachers need to use many different strategies to develop the understandings and abilities described in the Standards.

Nor should the Standards be seen as requiring a specific curriculum. A curriculum is the way content is organized and presented in the classroom. The content embodied in the Standards can be organized and presented with many different emphases and perspectives in many different curricula.

Instead, the Standards provide criteria that people at the local, state, and national levels can use to judge whether particular actions will serve the vision of a scientifically literate society. They bring coordination, consistency, and coherence to the improvement of science education. If people take risks in the name of improving science education, they know they will be supported by policies and procedures throughout the system. By moving the practices of extraordinary teachers and administrators to the forefront of science education, the Standards take science education beyond the constraints of the present and toward a shared vision of the future.

Hundreds of people cooperated in developing the Standards, including teachers, school administrators, parents, curriculum developers, college faculty and administrators, scientists, engineers, and government officials. These individuals drew heavily upon earlier reform efforts, research into teaching and learning, accounts of exemplary practice, and their own personal experience and insights. In turn, thousands of people reviewed various drafts of the standards. That open, iterative process produced a broad consensus about the elements of science education needed to permit all students to achieve excellence.

Continuing dialogues between those who set and implement standards at the national, state, and local levels will ensure that the Standards evolve to meet the needs of students, educators, and society at large. The National Science Education Standards should be seen as a dynamic understanding that is always open to review and revision.

ORGANIZATION OF THE STANDARDS

... [T]he National Science Education Standards are presented in six [categories]:

- Standards for science teaching.
- Standards for professional development for teachers of science.
- Standards for assessment in science education.
- Standards for science content.
- Standards for science education programs.
- Standards for science education systems.

For the vision of science education described in the Standards to be attained, the standards contained in all six [categories] need to be implemented....

SCIENCE TEACHING STANDARDS

The science teaching standards describe what teachers of science at all grade levels should know and be able to do. They are divided into six areas:

- The planning of inquiry-based science programs.
- The actions taken to guide and facilitate student learning.
- The assessments made of teaching and student learning.
- The development of environments that enable students to learn science.
- The creation of communities of science learners.
- The planning and development of the school science program.

Effective teaching is at the heart of science education, which is why the science teaching standards are presented first. Good teachers of science create environments in which they and their students work together as active learners. They have continually expanding theoretical and practical knowledge about science, learning, and science teaching. They use assessments of students and of their own teaching to plan and conduct their teaching. They build strong, sustained relationships with students that are grounded in their knowledge of students' similarities and differences. And they are active as members of science-learning communities.

In each of these areas, teachers need support from the rest of the educational system if they are to achieve the objectives embodied in the Standards. Schools, districts, local communities, and states need to provide teachers with the necessary resources—including time, appropriate numbers of students per teacher, materials, and schedules. For teachers to design and implement new ways of teaching and learning science, the practices, policies, and overall culture of most schools must change. Such reforms cannot be accomplished on a piecemeal or ad hoc basis.

Considerations of equity are critical in the science teaching standards. All students are capable of full participation and of making meaningful contributions in science classes. The diversity of students' needs, experiences, and backgrounds requires that teachers and schools support varied, high-quality opportunities for all students to learn science.

PROFESSIONAL DEVELOPMENT STANDARDS

The professional development standards present a vision for the development of professional knowledge and skill among teachers. They focus on four areas:

- The learning of science content through inquiry.
- The integration of knowledge about science with knowledge about learning, pedagogy, and students.
- The development of the understanding and ability for lifelong learning.
- The coherence and integration of professional development programs.

As envisioned by the standards, teachers partake in development experiences appropriate to their status as professionals. Beginning with preservice experiences and continuing as an integral part of teachers' professional practice, teachers have opportunities to work with master educators and reflect on teaching practice. They learn how students with diverse interests, abilities, and expe-

riences make sense of scientific ideas and what a teacher does to support and guide all students. They study and engage in research on science teaching and learning, regularly sharing with colleagues what they have learned. They become students of the discipline of teaching.

Reforming science education requires substantive changes in how science is taught, which requires equally substantive change in professional development practices at all levels. Prospective and practicing teachers need opportunities to become both sources of their own growth and supporters of the growth of others. They should be provided with opportunities to develop theoretical and practical understanding and ability, not just technical proficiencies. Professional development activities need to be clearly and appropriately connected to teachers' work in the context of the school. In this way, teachers gain the knowledge, understanding, and ability to implement the Standards.

ASSESSMENT STANDARDS

The assessment standards provide criteria against which to judge the quality of assessment practices. They cover five areas:

- The consistency of assessments with the decisions they are designed to inform.

- The assessment of both achievement and opportunity to learn science.

- The match between the technical quality of the data collected and the consequences of the actions taken on the basis of those data.

- The fairness of assessment practices.

- The soundness of inferences made from assessments about student achievement and opportunity to learn.

In the vision described by the Standards, assessments are the primary feedback mechanism in the science education system. They provide students with feedback on how well they are meeting expectations, teachers with feedback on how well their students are learning, school districts with feedback on the effectiveness of their teachers and programs, and policy makers with feedback on how well policies are working. This feedback in turn stimulates changes in policy, guides the professional development of teachers, and encourages students to improve their understanding of science.

Ideas about assessments have undergone important changes in recent years. In the new view, assessment and learning are two sides of the same coin. Assessments provide an operational definition of standards, in that they define in measurable terms what teachers should teach and students should learn. When students engage in assessments, they should learn from those assessments.

Furthermore, assessments have become more sophisticated and varied as they have focused on higher-order skills. Rather than simply checking whether students have memorized certain items of information, new assessments probe for students' understanding, reasoning, and use of that knowledge—the skills that are developed through inquiry. A particular challenge to teachers is to communicate to parents and policy makers the advantages of new assessment methods.

Assessments can be done in many different ways. Besides conventional paper and pencil tests, assessments might include performances, portfolios, interviews, investigative reports, or written essays. They need to be developmentally appropriate, set in contexts familiar to students, and as free from bias as possible. At the district, state, and national levels, assessments need to involve teachers in their design and administration, have well-thought-out goals, and reach representative groups to avoid sampling bias.

Assessments also need to measure the opportunity of students to learn science. Such assessments might measure teachers' professional knowledge, the time available to teach science, and the resources available to students. Although difficult, such evaluations are a critical part of the Standards.

SCIENCE CONTENT STANDARDS

The science content standards outline what students should know, understand, and be able to do in the natural sciences over the course of K–12 education. They are divided into eight categories:

- Unifying concepts and processes in science.
- Science as inquiry.
- Physical science.
- Life science.
- Earth and space science.
- Science and technology.
- Science in personal and social perspective.
- History and nature of science.

The first category is presented for all grade levels, because the understandings and abilities associated with these concepts need to be developed throughout a student's educational experiences. The other seven categories are clustered for grade levels K–4, 5–8, and 9–12.

Each content standard states that as a result of activities provided for all students in those grade levels, the content of the standard is to be understood or certain abilities are to be developed. The standards refer to broad areas of content, such as objects in the sky, the interdependence of organisms, or the nature of scientific knowledge. Following each standard is a discussion of how students can learn that material, but these discussions are illustrative, not proscriptive. Similarly, the discussion of each standard concludes with a guide to the fundamental ideas that underlie that standard, but these ideas are designed to be illustrative of the standard, not part of the standard itself.

Because each content standard subsumes the knowledge and skills of other standards, they are designed to be used as a whole. Although material can be added to the content standards, using only a subset of the standards will leave gaps in the scientific literacy expected of students.

SCIENCE EDUCATION PROGRAM STANDARDS

The science education program standards describe the conditions necessary for quality school science programs. They focus on six areas:

- The consistency of the science program with the other standards and across grade levels.

- The inclusion of all content standards in a variety of curricula that are developmentally appropriate, interesting, relevant to student's lives, organized around inquiry, and connected with other school subjects.

- The coordination of the science program with mathematics education.

- The provision of appropriate and sufficient resources to all students.

- The provision of equitable opportunities for all students to learn the standards.

- The development of communities that encourage, support, and sustain teachers.

Program standards deal with issues at the school and district level that relate to opportunities for students to learn and opportunities for teachers to teach science. The first three standards address individuals and groups responsible for the design, development, selection, and adaptation of science programs—including teachers, curriculum directors, administrators, publishers, and school committees. The last three standards describe the conditions necessary if science programs are to provide appropriate opportunities for all students to learn science.

Each school and district must translate the National Science Education Standards into a program that reflects local contexts and policies. The program standards discuss the planning and actions needed to provide comprehensive and coordinated experiences for all students across all grade levels. This can be done in many ways, because the Standards do not dictate the order, organization, or framework for science programs.

SCIENCE EDUCATION SYSTEM STANDARDS

The science education system standards consist of criteria for judging the performance of the overall science education system. They consider seven areas:

- The congruency of policies that influence science education with the teaching, professional development, assessment, content, and program standards.
- The coordination of science education policies within and across agencies, institutions, and organizations.
- The continuity of science education policies over time.
- The provision of resources to support science education policies.
- The equity embodied in science education policies.
- The possible unanticipated effects of policies on science education.
- The responsibility of individuals to achieve the new vision of science education portrayed in the standards.

Schools are part of hierarchical systems that include school districts, state school systems, and the national education system. Schools also are part of communities that contain organizations that influence science education, including colleges and universities, nature centers, parks and museums, businesses, laboratories, community organizations, and various media.

Although the school is the central institution for public education, all parts of the extended system have a responsibility for improving science literacy. For example, functions generally decided at the state (but sometimes at the local) level include the content of the school science curriculum, the characteristics of the science program, the nature of science teaching, and assessment practices. These policies need to be consistent with the vision of science education described in the Standards for the vision as a whole to be realized.

Today, different parts of the education system often work at cross purposes, resulting in waste and conflict. Only when most individuals and organizations share a common vision can we expect true excellence in science education to be achieved.

TOWARD THE FUTURE

Implementing the National Science Education Standards is a large and significant process that will extend over many years. But through the combined and continued support of all Americans, it can be achieved. Change will occur locally, and differences in individuals, schools, and communities will produce different pathways to reform, different rates of progress, and different final emphases. Nevertheless, with the common vision of the Standards, we can expect deliberate movement over time, leading to reform that is pervasive and permanent.

No one group can implement the Standards. The challenge extends to everyone within the education system, including teachers, administrators, science teacher educators, curriculum designers, assessment specialists, local school boards, state departments of education, and the federal government. It also extends to all those outside the system who have an influence on science education, including students, parents, scientists, engineers, businesspeople, taxpayers, legislators, and other public officials. All of these individuals have unique and complementary roles to play in improving the education that we provide to our children.

Efforts to achieve the vision of science education set forth in the Standards will be time-consuming, expensive, and sometimes uncomfortable. They also will be exhilarating and deeply rewarding.

Above all, the great potential benefit to students requires that we act now. There is no more important task before us as a nation.

NO
Elliot W. Eisner

STANDARDS FOR AMERICAN SCHOOLS: HELP OR HINDRANCE?

Efforts to reform American schools are not exactly a novel enterprise. When the Soviet Union sent Sputnik circling the globe in 1957 the U.S. Congress looked to the schools to recover what we had thought we had: leadership in space. The curriculum reform movement of the 1960s was intended, in part, to help us regain our technological superiority in the Cold War. In the 1970s "accountability" became the central concept around which our education reform efforts turned. If only we could identify the expected outcomes of instruction and invent means to describe their presence, school administrators and teachers could be held accountable for the quality of their work.

In April 1983 *A Nation at Risk* was published. In its memorable opening passage the impact of the schools on U.S. society was likened to a foreign invasion. By the late 1980s *A Nation at Risk*, one of the most prominent reform publications of the century, seemed to have faded, and its passing set the stage for America 2000—the reform agenda of the Bush Administration, now signed on to by the Clinton Administration. America 2000 was intended to do what the curriculum reform movement of the 1960s, the accountability movement of the 1970s, and *A Nation at Risk* and the "excellence movement" of the 1980s had been unable to accomplish.

We now have in Goals 2000 (the Clinton version of America 2000) an approach to education reform that uses standards as the linchpin of its efforts. Standards are being formulated for the certification of teachers, for the content of curricula, and for the outcomes of teaching. Virtually every subject-matter field in education has formulated or is in the process of formulating or revising national standards that describe what students should know and be able to do.

If anyone detects a slight echo of the past in today's reform efforts, let me assure you that you are not alone. We seem to latch on to approaches to reform that are replays of past efforts that themselves failed to come to grips with what it is that makes school practices so robust and resistant to change.

Consider, for example, the concept of standards. The term is attractive. Who among us, at first blush at least, would claim that schools—or any other

From Elliot W. Eisner, "Standards for American Schools: Help or Hindrance?" *Phi Delta Kappan*, vol. 76, no. 10 (June 1995). Copyright © 1995 by Elliot W. Eisner. Reprinted by permission of the author and *Phi Delta Kappan*. Notes omitted.

institution for that matter—should be without them? Standards imply high expectations, rigor, things of substance. To be without standards is not to know what to expect or how to determine if expectations have been realized—or so it seems.

Yet once we get past the illusions that the concept invites—once we think hard about the meaning of the term—the picture becomes more complex. To begin with, the meaning of the term is not as self-evident as many seem to believe. A standard meal, for example, is a meal that I think we would agree is nothing to rave about—and the same could be said of a standard hotel room or a standard reply to a question. A standard can also be a banner, something that trumpets one's identity and commitment. A standard can represent a value that people have cared enough about to die for. Standards can also refer to units of measure. The National Bureau of Standards employs standards to measure the quality of manufactured products. Electrical appliances, for example, must achieve a certain standard to get the UL seal of approval.

Which conception of standards do we embrace in the reform movement? Surely we do not mean by standards a typical level of performance, since that is what we already have without an iota of intervention. As for standards that represent beliefs or values, we already have mission statements and position papers in abundance, but they do not have the level of specificity that reformers believe is needed for standards to be useful.

The third conception of standards —as units of measure that make it possible to quantify the performance of students, teachers, and schools—

seems closer to what we have in mind. We live in a culture that admires technology and efficiency and believes in the possibility of objectivity. The idea of measurement provides us with a procedure that is closely associated with such values. Measurement makes it possible to describe quantity in ways that allow as little space as possible for subjectivity. For example, the objectivity of an objective test is not a function of the way in which the test items were selected, but of the way in which the test is scored. Objective tests can be scored by machine, with no need for judgment.

Standards in education, as we now idealize them, are to have such features. They are to be objective and, whenever possible, measurable. Once a technology of assessment is invented that will objectively quantify the relationship of student performance to a measurable ideal, we will be able to determine without ambiguity the discrepancy between the former and the latter, and thus we will have a meaningful standard.

Those who have been working in education for 20 or so years or who know the history of American education will also know that the vision I have just described is a recapitulation of older ideals. I refer to the curriculum reform movement of the 1960s. It was an important event in the history of American education, but it was not the only significant movement of that period. You will also remember that it was in the 1960s that American educators became infatuated with "behavioral objectives." Everyone was to have them. The idea then, like the notion of standards today, was to define our educational goals operationally in terms that were sufficiently specific to determine without ambiguity whether or not the student had achieved them.

The specifics of the procedures, given prominence by Robert Mager's 1962 book, *Preparing Instructional Objectives*, required that student behavior be identified, that the conditions in which it was to be displayed be described, and that a criterion be specified that made it possible to measure the student's behavior in relation to the criterion. For Mager a behavioral objective might be stated as follows: "At the end of the instructional period, when asked to do so, the student will be able to write a 200-word essay with no more than two spelling errors, one error in punctuation, and no errors in grammar."

It all seemed very neat. What people discovered as they tried to implement the idea was that to have behaviorally defined instructional objectives that met the criteria that Mager specified required the construction of *hundreds* of specific objectives. Heaven knows, school districts tried. But it soon became apparent that teachers would be bogged down with such a load. And even so ardent a supporter of behavioral objectives as James Popham eventually realized that teachers would be better off with just a few such objectives. The quest for certainty, which high-level specificity and precision implied, was soon recognized as counterproductive.

Those who know the history of American education will also know that the desire to specify expected outcomes and to prescribe the most efficient means for achieving them was itself the dominant strain of what has come to be called the "efficiency movement" in education. The efficiency movement, which began in 1913 and lasted until the early 1930s, was designed to apply the principles of scientific management to schools. Its progenitor, Frederick Taylor, the inventor of time-and-motion study, was a management consultant hired by industrialists to make their plants more efficient and hence more profitable. By specifying in detail the desired outcomes of a worker's efforts and by eliminating "wasted motion," output would increase, profits would soar, wages would rise, and everyone would benefit.

American school administrators thought that in Taylor's approach to the management of industrial plants they had found a surefire method for producing efficient schools. Moreover, Taylor's approach was based on "science." The prescription of expected outcomes, of the manner of performance, and of the content in which competence is to be displayed is a not-too-distant cousin of the teacher performance standards and curriculum content standards that accompany today's discussions of standards for student performance.

School administrators caught up in the efficiency movement gradually learned that the basic conception and the expectations that flowed from it—namely, that one could mechanize and routinize teaching and learning—did not work. Even if it were possible to give teachers scripts for their performance, it was not possible to give students scripts. There was no "one best method," and there was no way to "teacher-proof" instruction.

My point thus far is that what we are seeing in American education today is a well-intentioned but conceptually shallow effort to improve our schools. My point thus far is to make it plain that the current effort in which we are enmeshed is no novelty; we have been here before. My point thus far is to suggest that successful efforts at school reform will entail a substantially deeper analysis of schools and their relationships to communities and teachers than has thus far been under-taken.

* * *

To try to do justice to the aspirations of the national education reform movement, I will try to make a sympathetic presentation of its arguments. I start with the acknowledgment that there is a sense of sweet reason to the arguments that the reformers have made. After all, with standards we will know where we are headed. We can return rigor to schooling; we can inform students, parents, and teachers of what we expect; we can have a common basis for appraising student performance; and we can, at last, employ a potent lever for education reform. Without standards, we are condemned to an unbroken journey into an abyss of mediocrity; we will remain a nation at risk.

In addition, the task of formulating standards is salutary for teachers and others involved in curriculum planning. By establishing national goals for each subject that schools teach, we will be able to achieve professional consensus that will give us a unified and educationally solid view of what students are expected to learn. By trying to define standards for each field, a single vision of a subject will be created, teachers will have an opportunity to profit from the goals and standards formulated by their peers, and ambiguity will be diminished because teachers will know not only the direction their efforts are to take, but also the specific destinations toward which their students are headed. Furthermore, teachers will have something of a timetable to help determine not only whether, but when, they have arrived.

As if they had just taken a cold shower, a population of sometimes lethargic and burned-out teachers will be reawakened and will become alert. Our nation will, at last, have a national educational agenda, something that it has never possessed. Ultimately, such resources and the approach to education that those resources reflect will help us regain our competitive edge in a global economy. Parents will be satisfied, students will know what is expected of them, and the business community will have the employees it needs for America to become number one by the year 2000, not only in science and in math but in other fields as well. Our students and our schools will go for and get the gold at the educational Olympics in which we are competing. Our schools will become "world class."

An attractive vision? It seems so, yet a number of questions arise. You will recall that the standards about which reformers speak are national standards. The organizations—and there are dozens—that are engaged in formulating standards are doing so for the nation as a whole, not for some specific locality. Put another way, in a nation in which 45 million students in 50 states go to approximately 108,000 schools overseen by some 15,000 school boards and in which 2.5 million teachers teach, there is the presumption that it makes good educational sense for there to be uniform expectations with respect to goals, content, and levels of student achievement. . . .

Uniformity in curriculum content is a virtue *if* one's aim is to be able to compare students in one part of the country with students in others. Uniformity is a virtue when the aspiration is to compare the performance of American students with students in Korea, Japan, and Germany. But why should we wish to make such comparisons? To give up the idea that there needs to be one standard for all students in each field of study is not to give up the aspiration to seek high levels of educational quality in both pedagogical practices and educational outcomes. Together, the desire to compare and the recognition of individuality create one of the dilemmas of a social meritocracy: the richness of a culture rests not only on the prospect of cultivating a set of common commitments, but also on the prospect of cultivating those individual talents through which the culture at large is enriched. . . .

You will remember that I referred to standards as units of measure that make possible the "objective" description of quantitative relationships. But there are qualitative standards as well. To have a *qualitative* standard you must create or select an icon, prototype, or what is sometimes called a benchmark against which the performance or products of students are matched. To have a *quantitative standard* you must specify the number or percentage of correct answers needed to pass a test or the number of allowable errors in a performance or product and to use that specification as the standard.

In each case, there is a fixed and relatively unambiguous unit of measurement. In the qualitative case, the task for both judge and performer is one of matching a performance with a model. This kind of matching is precisely what occurs in the Olympics. Olympic judges know what a particular dive should look like, and they compare a diver's performance to the model. The diver, too, knows what the model looks like and does his or her best to replicate the model.

With respect to the quantitative case, the application of a standard occurs in two different ways. The first has to do with determining the correctness of any individual response. An item response is judged correct if the appropriate bubble is filled in, or if the appropriate selection is made, or if some other indication is given that the student has hit a prespecified mark. The prespecified correct response serves as a standard for each item. Once these item responses are summed, a determination is made as to whether the total number of correct responses meets a second standard, the standard specified as a passing grade by the test-maker or by some policy-making body.

Notice that in both cases innovation in response is not called for. The diver replicates a known model. The test-maker determines whether a student's score is acceptable, not by exercising judgment, but by counting which bubbles have been filled in and comparing the number of correct responses to a fixed predetermined standard.

There are, we must acknowledge, a number of important tasks that students must learn in school in which innovation is not useful. Learning how to spell correctly means knowing how to replicate the known. The same holds true for much of what is taught in early arithmetic and in the language arts. There are many important tasks and skills that students need to learn—i.e., conventions—that are necessary for doing more important work and that educational programs should help them learn. The more important work that I speak of is the work that makes it possible for students to think imaginatively about problems that matter to them, tasks that give them the opportunity to affix their own personal signature to their work, occasions to explore ideas and questions that have no correct answers, and projects in which they can reason and express their own ideas.

Learning to replicate known conventions is an important part of the *tacti-*

cal outcomes of education, but it is not adequate for achieving the *strategic aspirations* that we hold. These strategic aspirations require curricula and assessment policies that invite students to exercise judgment and to create outcomes that are not identical with those of their peers. Again, the cultivation of productive idiosyncrasy ought to be one of the aims that matter in American schools, and, to my way of thinking, we ought to build programs that make the realization of such an outcome possible, even if it means that we will not find it easy to compare students. When we seek to measure such outcomes, we will not be able to use a fixed standard for scoring the work students have produced. We will have to rely on that most exquisite of human capacities—judgment.

. . . The creation of conditions that allow students to display their creative and reasoning abilities in ways that are unique to their temperaments, their experience, and their aims is of fundamental importance in any educational enterprise—in contrast to one concerned with training. And because such features are important, it is criteria that must be salient in our assessment.

* * *

Standards are appropriate for some kinds of tasks, but, as I argued above, those tasks are instrumental to larger and more important educational aims. We really don't need to erect a complex school system to teach the young how to read utility bills, how to do simple computation, or how to spell; they will learn those skills on their own. What we do need to teach them is how to engage in higher-order thinking, how to pose telling questions, how to solve complex problems that have more than one

answer. When the concept of standards becomes salient in our discourse about educational expectations, it colors our view of what education can be and dilutes our conception of education's potential. Language matters, and the language of standards is by and large a limiting rather than a liberating language.

The qualities that define inventive work of any kind are qualities that by definition have both unique and useful features. The particular form those features take and what it is that makes them useful are not necessarily predictable, but sensitive critics—and sensitive teachers—are able to discover such properties in the work. Teachers who know the students they teach recognize the unique qualities in students' comments, in their paintings, in the essays they write, in the ways in which they relate to their peers. The challenge in teaching is to provide the conditions that will foster the growth of those personal characteristics that are socially important and, at the same time, personally satisfying to the student. The aim of education is not to train an army that marches to the same drummer, at the same pace, toward the same destination. Such an aim may be appropriate for totalitarian societies, but it is incompatible with democratic ideals.

If one used only philosophical grounds to raise questions about the appropriateness of uniform national standards for students in American schools, there would still be questions enough to give one pause. But there are developmental grounds as well. The graded American public school system was built on an organizational theory that has little to do with the developmental characteristics of growing children. In the mid-19th century we thought it made very good sense for the school to be organized into grades and for there to be a body of content assigned to each grade. Each grade was to be related to a specific age. The task of the student was to master the content taught at that grade as a precondition for promotion to the next grade. At the end of an eight-or 12-year period, it was assumed that, if the school and the teacher had done their jobs, everyone would come out at roughly the same place.

If you examine the patterns of human development for children from age 5 to age 18, you will find that, as children grow older, their rate of development is increasingly variable. Thus the range of variation among children of the same age increases with time.

For example, for ordinary, nonhomogeneous classes, the average range of reading achievement is roughly equal to the grade level: at the second grade there is, on average, a two-year spread in reading achievement. Some second-graders are reading at the first-grade level, and others are reading at the third-grade level. At the fourth grade the spread is about four years, and at the sixth grade, about six years. In the seventh grade the range is about seven years: some children are reading at the fourth-grade level, and some are reading at the 10th-grade level.

What this means is that children develop at their own distinctive pace. The tidy structure that was invented in the 19th century to rationalize school organization may look wonderful on paper, but it belies what we know about the course of human development. Because we still operate with a developmentally insensitive organizational structure in our schools, the appeal of uniform standards by grade level or by outcome seems reasonable. It is not. Variability, not uniformity, is the hallmark of the human condition.

I do not want to overstate the idea. To be sure, humans are like all other humans, humans are like some other humans, and humans are like no other humans. All three claims are true. But we have become so preoccupied with remedying the perceived weaknesses of American schools that we have underestimated the diversity and hence the complexity that exists.

The varieties of unappreciated complexity are large. Let me suggest only a few. When evaluating students in the context of the classroom, the teacher—the person who has the widest variety of information about any particular student —takes into consideration much more than the specific features of a student's particular product. The age, grade, and developmental level of the student; the amount of progress a student has made; the degree of effort that the student has expended; the amount of experience a student has had in a domain are all educationally relevant considerations that professionally competent teachers take into account in making judgments about a student's progress. Experienced teachers know in their bones that the student's work constitutes only one item in an array of educational values and that these values sometimes compete. There are times when it may be more important educationally for a teacher to publicly acknowledge the quality of a student's work than to criticize it, even when that work is below the class average.

Beyond the details of the classroom, there are more general questions having to do with the bases on which educational standards are formulated. Should educational standards be derived from the average level of performance of students in a school, in a school district, in a state, in a nation, *in the world*? How much talk have we heard of *"world class"* standards?

If national policy dictates that there will be uniform national standards for student performance, will there also be uniform national standards for the resources available to schools? To teachers? To administrators? Will the differences in performance between students living in well-heeled, upper-class suburbs and those living on the cusp of poverty in the nation's inner cities demonstrate the existing inequities in American education? Will they not merely confirm what we already know?

The socioeconomic level of the students and the resources available to them and their teachers in a school or school district do make a difference. If those urging standards on us believe that the use of standards will demonstrate inequities—and hence serve to alleviate them—why haven't these already painfully vivid inequities been effective in creating more equitable schools?

And, one might wonder, what would happen to standards in education if by some magic all students achieved them? Surely the standards would be considered too low. At first blush this doesn't sound like a bad thing. Shouldn't the bar always be higher than we can reach? Sounds reasonable. Yet such a view of the function of standards will ineluctably create groups of winners and losers. Can our education system flourish without losers? Is it possible for us to frame conceptions of education and society that rest on more generous assumptions? And consider the opposite. What will we do with those students who fail to meet the standards? Then what?

Perhaps one of the most important consequences of the preoccupation with national standards in education is that it distracts us from the deeper, seemingly intractable problems that beset our schools. It distracts us from paying attention to the importance of building a culture of schooling that is genuinely intellectual in character, that values questions and ideas at least as much as getting right answers. It distracts us from trying to understand how we can provide teachers the kind of professional opportunities that will afford the best among them opportunities to continue to grow through a lifetime of work. It distracts us from attending to the inevitable array of interactions between teaching, curriculum, evaluation, school organization, and the often deleterious expectations and pressures from universities.

How should these matters be addressed? Can schools and teachers and administrators afford the kind of risk-taking and exploratory activity that genuine inquiry in education requires?

Vitality within any organization is more likely when there are opportunities to pursue fresh possibilities, to exercise imagination, to try things out, and to relinquish the quest for certainty in either pedagogical method or educational outcome. Indeed, one of the important aims of education is to free the mind from the confines of certainty. Satisfaction, our children must learn, can come from the uncertainty of the journey, not just from the clarity of the destination.

I am not sure that American society is willing at this time to embrace so soft a set of values as I have described. We have become a tough-minded lot. We believe that we can solve the problems of crime by reopening the doors to the gas chamber and by building more prisons. But it's never been that simple. Nor is solving the problems of schooling as simple as having national education standards.

And so I believe that we must invite our communities to join us in a conversation that deepens our understanding of the educational process and advances our appreciation of its possibilities. Genuine education reform is not about shallow efforts that inevitably fade into oblivion. It is about vision, conversation, and action designed to create a genuine and evolving educational culture. I hope we can resist the lure of slogans and the glitter of bandwagons and begin to talk seriously about education. That is one conversation in which we must play a leading role.

POSTSCRIPT

Should There Be Standards for Science Education?

There are actually two issues involved in the debate over standards in science education. The first is whether or not children should be obliged to learn about concepts (evolution, safe sex, homosexuality, the legitimacy of other religions or races, etc.) of which their parents do not approve because such learning threatens the parents' values. The second is whether or not standards are a good idea in education at all. Those who say yes have given rise to an "educational standards movement" that has drawn a great deal of attention over the years. For a good summary, see Anne C. Lewis, "An Overview of the Standards Movement," *Phi Delta Kappan* (June 1995).

Science education standards are only one small part of the broader, more philosophical issue. The federal government has striven to establish standards across the board, most notably with the 1994 legislation that established Goals 2000 and the National Educational Standards and Improvement Council (NESIC). However, when the Republicans took control of Congress, they did away with NESIC and left standards to the states. See David Cohen, "What Standards for National Standards?" *Phi Delta Kappan* (June 1995).

Matthew Gandel of the American Federation of Teachers calls for rigorous, "world-class" academic standards in "Not All Standards Are Created Equal," *Educational Leadership* (March 1995). In response, Kenneth R. Howe, in "Wrong Problem, Wrong Solution," *Educational Leadership* (March 1995), says that content standards miss the point of providing more students with adequate opportunity to learn. Arthur L. Costa and Rosemarie Liebmann, in "Process Is as Important as Content," *Educational Leadership* (March 1995), argue that "content-driven curriculum is passé." William G. Spady, in "We Need More Than 'Educentric' Standards," *Educational Leadership* (September 1995), indicates that more stress should be placed on students' abilities to use what they learn.

"Content" seems to be less controversial among science educators. Rodger W. Bybee, in "Achieving Scientific Literacy," *The Science Teacher* (October 1995), says that content is an essential part of scientific literacy, along with some sense of process. Harold Pratt, in "A Look at the Program Standards," *The Science Teacher* (October 1995), points out that the National Science Education Standards call not only for content and direction but also for coordination, commitment, and additional resources.

The National Academy of Science's report on science education standards can be found on the Internet at: http://www.nap.edu/nap/online/nses/overview.html

ISSUE 3

Is Science Hazardous to Human Values?

YES: Daniel Callahan, from "Calling Scientific Ideology to Account," *Society* (May/June 1996)

NO: Daniel C. Dennett, from *Darwin's Dangerous Idea: Evolution and the Meanings of Life* (Simon & Schuster, 1995)

ISSUE SUMMARY

YES: Bioethicist Daniel Callahan argues that science's domination of the cultural landscape unreasonably excludes other ways of understanding nature and the world and sets it above any need to accept moral, social, and intellectual judgment from political, religious, and even traditional values.

NO: Daniel C. Dennett, director of the Center for Cognitive Studies at Tufts University, argues that "the only meaning of life worth caring about is one that can withstand our best efforts to examine it," meaning that evolution—and the scientific approach—are to be valued above all.

Science and technology have come to play a huge role in human culture, largely because they have led to vast improvements in nutrition, health care, comfort, communication, transportation, and mankind's ability to affect the world. Science has also enhanced our understanding of human behavior and of how the universe works, and in this it frequently contradicts what people have long thought they knew. Furthermore, it actively rejects any role of God in scientific explanations. It has long been a dogma of scientific faith that "why" questions are unreasonable to ask. They are teleological; they presume there is an intent or design behind the phenomena we wish to explain. As an answer, "God's will" is out of bounds, largely because accepting it means accepting that it is a waste of time to look for other answers.

Many people therefore reject what science tells us, especially those who see science as denying both the existence of God and the importance of "human values" (meaning those behaviors that are affirmed by traditional religion). This leads to a basic antipathy between science and religion, especially conservative religion, and especially in those areas—such as human origins—where science and Scripture seem to be contradicting each other.

We see this antipathy most plainly in the vigorous conflict between creationists and evolutionists. This has been true ever since Charles Darwin first published *On the Origin of Species by Means of Natural Selection* in 1859, in which he expounds his theory of evolution. However, the antipathy extends back at least to the French Revolution in the late 1700s, which featured the destruction of religion in the name of rationality and science (the worship of God was officially abolished November 10, 1793).

William L. Johnson, associate dean of academic affairs at Ambassador University in Big Sandy, Texas, offered an excellent example of the rejection of science in favor of religion in a 1994 speech that was reprinted in "Evolution: The Past, Present, and Future Implications," *Vital Speeches of the Day* (February 15, 1995). He argued that the triumph of Darwin's theory of evolution by means of natural selection "meant the end of the traditional belief in the world as a purposeful created order.... [A]nd the consequent elimination of God from nature has played a decisive role in the secularization of Western society. Darwinian theory broke man's link with God and set him adrift in a cosmos without purpose or end." Johnson suggested that evolution—and perhaps the entire scientific approach to nature—should be abandoned in favor of a return to religion because of the untold damage that he feels has been done to the human values that underpin society.

Religious people are not the only people who see in science a threat to "human values." Science also contradicts people's preferences, often based less on religion than on tradition and prejudice. For instance, science insists that no race is superior to any other, that homosexuality is natural, not wicked, and that different ways of living deserve respect. It also insists on the value of evidence, rationality, and skepticism over wishes, sentimentality, and the voice of authority.

Many people feel that science neglects a very important side of human existence embodied in the phrase "human values." Daniel Callahan sees this side as the source of moral, political, and intellectual judgment, which science tends to escape through its dominance of our society. He argues in the following selection that science has become a religion or ideology in its own right—as intolerant as any other—and that it sorely needs judgment or criticism to keep it from steamrollering the more human side of life. Daniel C. Dennett finds far more value in science than in religion or tradition. He maintains that Darwin had the single best idea of all time, that in it lies our hope of finding the truest meaning of life, and that religion can be far more damaging to human life and society than anything in science.

YES

Daniel Callahan

CALLING SCIENTIFIC IDEOLOGY
TO ACCOUNT

I come to the subject of science and religion with some complex emotions and a personal history not irrelevant to my own efforts to think about this matter. It seems appropriate for me to lay this history out a bit to set the stage for the argument I want to make. For the first half of my life, from my teens through my mid-thirties, I was a serious religious believer, a church member (Roman Catholic), and someone whose identity as both a person and as an intellectual had a belief in God at its center. During that time I had little contact with the sciences; literature and philosophy caught my imagination. I was a fine example, for that matter, of the gap between the two cultures that C. P. Snow described, caught up as I was in the humanities and generally ignorant about science. I spent most of my time among humanists and religious believers (though believers of a generally liberal kind).

All of that changed in my late thirties. Two events happened simultaneously. The first was a loss of my religious faith, utterly and totally. I ceased to be a theist, became an atheist, and so I remain today. I did not, however, have any revolt against organized religion (as it is sometimes pejoratively called) or the churches; nor did I lose respect for religious believers. They just seem to me wrong in their faith and mistaken in their hope. The second event was my discovery of the field of biomedical ethics, seemingly a fertile area for my philosophical training and an important window into the power of the biomedical sciences to change the way we think about and live our lives. With this new interest I began spending much of my time with physicians and bench scientists and worked hard to understand the universe of science that I was now entering (through the side door of biomedical ethics).

Meanwhile, as I was undergoing my own personal changes, the relationship between science and religion was shifting in the country as well. When I was growing up, there was still considerable debate about religion and science, with some believers arguing that there was a fundamental incompatibility between them and others holding that they were perfectly congenial. Some scientists, for their part, wrote books about religion, saying that they had found God in their science. Others, of a more positivistic bent, thought

From Daniel Callahan, "Calling Scientific Ideology to Account," *Society*, vol. 33, no. 4 (May/June 1996). Copyright © 1996 by Transaction Publishers. Reprinted by permission. All rights reserved.

that science had forever expunged the notion of a God and that science would eventually offer an explanation of everything.

This debate seemed to subside significantly in the 1970s and 1980s. Science came almost totally to win the minds and emotions of educated Americans, and technological innovation was endlessly promoted as the key to both human progress and economic prosperity, a most attractive combination of doing good and doing well. While public opinion polls and church attendance figures, not to mention the gestures of politicians, showed the continuing popularity of religion, it was science that had captured the academy, the corridors of economic power, and high-brow prestige in the media. There remained, to be sure, skirmishes here and there over such issues as the teaching of creationism in the schools, particularly in the Bible Belt, and mutterings about the "religious Right" and its opposition to abortion, embryo and fetal research, and the like. Although there had been some bursts of anti-technology sentiments as part of the fallout of the 1960s culture wars, they had little staying power. The "greening of America" soon ran into a drought.

Science, in short, finally gained the ascendancy, coming to dominate the cultural landscape as much as the economic marketplace. This was the world of science I entered and in which I still remain enmeshed. My reaction to the news in May 1995 that a religious group, with the help of Jeremy Rifkin, was entering a challenge to the patenting of life was one of rueful bemusement: what a quixotic gesture, almost certainly doomed to failure but not, perhaps, before a round of media attention. Such battles make good copy, but that's about it.

The specific issue of the patenting of life deserves discussion, and someone or other would have raised it. Yet it hardly signals a new struggle between science and religion. It is neither that central an issue, nor did it appear even to galvanize a serious follow-up response among most religious groups. Congress, moreover, has given no indication that it will take up the issue in any serious way. In other words, it appears to have sunk as an issue as quickly as it arose.

Yet I confess to a considerable degree of uneasiness here. Science should not have such easy victories. It needs to have a David against its Goliath. This is only to say that scientific modernism—that is, the cultural dominance of science—desperately needs to have a serious and ongoing challenger. By that I mean the challenge of a different way of looking at nature and the world, one capable of shaking scientific self-satisfaction and complacency and resisting its at-present overpowering social force. Science needs, so to speak, a kind of loyal opposition.

This kind of opposition need not and should not entail hostility to the scientific method, to the investment of money in scientific research, or to the hope that scientific knowledge can make life better for us. Not at all. What it does entail is a relentless skepticism toward the view that science is the single and greatest key to human progress, that scientific knowledge is the only valid form of knowledge, and that some combination of science and the market is the way to increased prosperity and well-being for all. When religion can only fight science with the pea-shooters of creationism and antipatenting threats, it has little going for it. That response surely does not represent a thoughtful, developed, and articulate counterbalance to the hold of science on modern societies.

I say all of this because what I discovered upon entering the culture of science—that is, scientism—was something more than a simple commitment to the value and pursuit of scientific knowledge. That is surely present, but it is also accompanied socially by two other ingredients, science as ideology and science as faith.

SCIENCE AS IDEOLOGY

By science as ideology I mean that constellation of values that, for many, constitutes a more or less integrated way of interpreting life and nature, not only providing a sense of meaning but also laying out a path to follow in the living of a life. At the core of that ideology is a commitment to science as the most reliable source of knowledge about the nature of things and to technological innovation as the most promising way to improve human life. Closely related features of that ideology are an openness to untrammeled inquiry, limited by neither church nor state, skepticism toward all but scientifically verifiable claims, and a steady revision of all knowledge. While religion should be tolerated in the name of toleration rather than on grounds of credibility, it should be kept in the private sphere, out of the public space, public institutions, and public education. The ideology of scientism is all-encompassing, a way of knowing, and, culturally embodied, a way of living.

By science as faith I mean the ideology of science when it includes also a kind of non-falsifiable faith in the capacity of science not simply to provide reliable knowledge but also to solve all or most human problems, social, political, and economic. It is non-falsifiable in the sense that it holds that any failure to date of science to find solutions to human problems says nothing at all about its future capacity to do so; such solutions are only a matter of time and more refined knowledge. As for the fact that some of the changes science and technology have wrought are not all good, or have both good and bad features, science as faith holds that there is no reason in principle that better science and new knowledge cannot undo earlier harm and avoid future damage. In a word, no matter what science does, better science can do even better. No religious believer, trying to reconcile the evil in the world with the idea of a good and loving God, can be any more full of hope that greater knowledge will explain all than the scientific believer. And there is no evidence that is allowed to count against such a belief, and surely not religious arguments.

It is at just this point that I, the former religious believer, find it hard to confidently swallow the ideology of science, much less the serene faith of many of its worshippers. I left one church but I was not looking to join another. Nonetheless, when I stepped into the territory of science that appeared to be exactly the demand: If you want to be one of us, have faith. Yet a perspective that aims to supply the kind of certain metaphysical and ethical knowledge once thought limited to religion and to provide the foundations for ways of life seems to me worthy of the same kind of wariness that, ironically, science first taught me to have about religion. If science warns us to be skeptical of traditionalism, of settled but unexamined views, of knowledge claims poorly based on hard evidence, on acts of faith that admit of no falsifiability, why should I not bring that same set of attitudes to science itself? That interesting magazine, *The Skeptical Inquirer*, dedicated to getting the hard facts to debunk superstition, quackery, and weird claims by strange groups, does not run many articles devoted to debunking science or claims made in behalf of the enlightenment it can bring us. (I believe it has yet to publish even one such article, but I may be wrong about that.)

Maybe that is not so surprising. Such rebelliousness seems utterly unacceptable to scientism, utterly at odds with its solemn pieties and liturgical practices. To question the idea of scientific progress, to suggest that there are valid forms of nonscientific knowledge, to think that societies need something more than good science and high technology to flourish is to risk charges of heresy in enlightened educated circles every bit as intimidating as anything that can be encountered in even the most conservative religious groups. The condescension exhibited toward the "religious Right" surely matches that once displayed by Christianity toward "pagans." Even a Republican-dominated, conservative Congress knows it can far better afford politically to drastically cut or eliminate funding for the National Endowments for the Humanities and the Arts than for the National Science Foundation or the National Institutes of Health.

Now I come to the heart of my problem with the ideology and faith of scientism. Like any other human institution and set of practices, science needs to be subject to moral, social, and intellectual judgment; it needs to be called to task from time to time. Ideally that ought to be done by institutions that have the cultural clout to be taken seriously and by means of criteria for judgment that cannot themselves easily be called into question. Religion itself has always had this notion as part of its own self-understanding: It believes that it—churches, theologies, creeds—stands under the higher judgment of God and recognizes that it can itself fall into idolatry, the worship of false gods. One might well complain that the churches have seemed, in fact, exceedingly slow in rendering negative judgment upon themselves. Even so, they have the idea of such judgment and on occasion it has indeed been exercised.

Unfortunately—and a profound misfortune it is—science no longer has seriously competitive ways of thinking or institutions that have a comparable prestige and power. Science no longer has a counterweight with which it must contend, no institution or generally persuasive perspective that can credibly pass judgment on scientific practices and pretensions. No secular force or outlook or ideology exists to provide it. Religion once played that role: Popes, prelates, and preachers could once rain some effective fire and brimstone down on science, often enough mistakenly yet sometimes helpfully. But religion, too concerned to protect its own turf, too unwilling to open its eyes to new possibilities and forms of knowledge, offered mainly condemnation along with, now and then, some lukewarm support. Moreover, the gradual secularizing of the cultures of the developed countries of the world, relegating religion to the domestic sphere, took away religion's platform to speak authoritatively to public life. Scientific modernism was there to fill the gap, and it has been happy to do so. It is not possible to utter prayers in public schools, but there are no limits to the homage that can be lavished upon science and its good works.

The absence of a counterweight to the ideology of science has a number of doleful effects. It helps to substantiate the impression that there is no alternative, much less higher, perspective from which to judge science and its works. If you are the king of the hill, all things go your way and those below you are fearful or hesitant to speak out. It helps as well to legitimate the mistaken belief that all other forms of knowledge are not only inferior but that they are themselves always subject to the superior judgment of science. Accordingly, claims of religious knowledge of a credible kind were long ago dismissed by science. At its best, science is benignly tolerant of religion, patting it on the head like a kindly but wiser grandparent. At its worst, it can be mocking and dismissive. The kinds of knowledge generated by the humanities fare a little better, but not all that much.

From the perspective of my own field, bioethics, it is distressing to see the way that claims for the value or necessity of scientific research are treated with an extraordinary deference, usually going unquestioned. A recent federal panel on embryo research, for instance, set the issue up as a struggle between the moral status of the embryo, on the one hand, and that of the "need" (not just desire on the part of researchers) for embryo research, on the other. In a fine display of nuanced, critical thinking, the panel took apart excessive claims for the rights of embryos, urging "respect" but allowing research. As for the claims of research, they were accepted without any doubts or hesitations at all; they seemed self-evident to the panel, not in need of

justification. Even Henry VIII, the king of his hill, hardly got that kind of deference, even from those luckless wives he had beheaded. In a culture saturated with the ideology of science, there seems hardly any forceful voice to call it to account.

If there was a loyal opposition, it would not let the claims and triumphalism of the scientific establishment go unchallenged. It would treat that establishment with respect, but it would fully understand that it is an *establishment*, intent on promoting its own cause and blowing its own horn, critical of its opponents and naysayers, and of course never satisfied with the funds available to it (funds that, if forthcoming in greater quantity, will someday find a cure for cancer, discover the molecular basis for disease, give us cheap energy generated by cold fusion, etc., etc.). A loyal opposition would bring to science exactly the same cool and self-critical eye that science itself urges in the testing of scientific ideas and hypotheses. One of the great intellectual contributions of science has been its methodological commitment to self-criticism and self-revision; and that is one reason it came to triumph over religion, which has not always shown much enthusiasm for skepticism about its key doctrines.

But if self-criticism and self-revision are at the heart of the scientific method, then a good place to begin employing them is at home, on the scientific ideology that culturally sustains the whole apparatus. A loyal opposition would do this not only to temper exaggerated self-congratulations on the part of science but also to keep science itself scientific.

The insuperable limitation of the scientific method is that it cannot be used to criticize the ideology of science or its methods. To try to do so only begs the question of its validity. In the end, we judge that method more by its fruits and consequences than by its a priori validity. The problem here is that science cannot tell us what consequences we ought to want, what kind of knowledge we need, or what uses are best for the knowledge that science demonstrates. Science, that is, is far more helpful with our means than our ends. Good science cannot tell us how to organize good societies or develop good people (or even tell us how to define "good") or tell us what is worth knowing. There is no scientific calculus to tell us how much a society should invest in scientific research; that is a matter of prudence.

It is here that the other forms of knowledge ought and must come into play: the knowledge developed by the humanities or the "soft" social sciences; the political values and structures created by democratic societies, built upon argument, some consensus, and some compromise. My own domain, that of the humanities, was long ago intimidated by science. It does not complain about the grievous disparity between research resources lavished upon it in comparison with science. Those humanists who dare enter the church of science and mutter to its high priests are given the back of the scientific hand, quickly labeled as cranks or, black mark of black marks, Luddites. The scientific establishment should help to encourage and support other forms of knowing and should be willing to learn from them; that would be to display the openness and creativity it touts as its strength. It does not, however, take the fingers of even one hand to count the number of Nobel laureates in science who have petitioned Congress for stronger support for the humanities.

What is a proper role for religion in a society captured by the ideology of science? Its most important role, the one it has played from time to time with other principalities and powers, would be simply to urge some humility on science and to call it to task for pretentiousness and power grabbing. Science ought to stand under constant moral judgment, and there is an important role for religion to play in formulating some of the criteria for such judgment. It is thus proper for religion to remind science of something religion should always be reminding itself of as well: Neither science nor religion are whole and entire unto themselves. Religion stands under the judgment of God (it tells us), and science stands under the judgment of the collective conscience of humankind (which religion does *not* tell us). Religion can remind the world, and those in science, that the world can be viewed from different perspectives. And it can remind that world, including science, what it means to attempt, as does religion, to make sense of everything in some overall coherent way. There is no need to agree with the way in which religion comprehends reality in order to be reminded of the human thirst for some sense of coherence and meaning in the world.

There has always been an aspect of science that overlaps with supernatural religion. That is the kind of natural piety and awe that many scientists feel in the face of the mysteries and beauty of the natural world. This can be called a kind of natural religion, and some scientists easily make the move from the natural to the supernatural, even if many of their more skeptical colleagues—who also share the sense of natural awe—do not follow them in taking that step.

This natural awe frequently expresses itself in a hesitation to manipulate nature for purely self-interested ends, whether economic or medical. The concern of ecologists for the preservation of biodiversity, the hesitations of population geneticists about germ-line therapy, the worry of environmentalists about the protection of tropical forests or of biologists for the preservation of even rare species, all testify to that kind of natural piety. It is here that there is room for an alliance between science and religion, between that science that sees the mystery and unprobed depths of the natural world and that religion that sees nature as the creation and manifestation of a beneficent god.

It is important, for that matter, that science find allies in its desire to keep its natural piety alive and well. The primary enemies of that piety are the casual indifference of many human beings to nature and the more systematic despoiling of nature carried out in the name of the market, human betterment, or the satisfying of private fantasies and desires. Environmentalism has long been torn by a struggle that pits conservationists against preservationists. Conservationists believe that the natural world can be cultivated for human use and its natural resources protected if care is taken. Preservationists, and particularly the "deep ecologists," are hostile to that kind of optimism, holding that nature as it is needs to be protected, not manipulated or exploited. Conservationism has a serious and sober history and has been by no means oriented toward a crude exploitation of nature. But it is a movement that has often been allowed to shade off into that kind of technological optimism that argues that whatever harm scientific progress and technological innovation cause, it can just as readily be undone and corrected by science.

This is the ideology of science taken to extremes, but a common enough viewpoint among those who see too much awe of nature, too much protectionism, as a threat to economic progress. Religion could well throw its weight behind responsible conservation, and it would not hurt a bit if some theologians and church groups took up the cause of deep ecology. That is an unlikely cause to gain great support in an overcrowded world, and particularly in the poverty-stricken parts of that world. But it is a strong countercurrent worth introducing into the larger stream of efforts to preserve and respect nature. A little roughage in the bowels helps keep things moving.

Perhaps the cultural dominance of science is nowhere so evident as in a feature of our society frequently overlooked: the powerful proclivity to look to numbers and data as the key to good public policy. Charts, tables, and graphs are the standard props of the policy analyst and the legislator. This is partly understandable and justifiable. With issues of debate and contention, hard data is valuable. It can help to determine if there is a real problem, the dimensions of that problem, and the possible consequences of different solutions. But the soft underside of the deification of data is the too frequent failure to recognize that data never tells its own story, that it is always subject to, and requires, interpretation.

There is no data that can carry out that work. On the contrary, at that point we are thrown back upon our values, our way of looking at the world and society, and our different social hopes and commitments. The illusion of the inherent persuasiveness of data is fostered by scientism, which likes to think that there can be a neutral standpoint from which to assess those matters that concern us, that scientific information plays that role, and that the answer to any moral and social battles is simply more and better information.

The dominance of the field of economics in social policy itself tells an interesting story: the need to find a policy discipline that has all the trapping of science in its methods and that can capture its prestige. It is a field that aspires to be a science and that speaks the culturally correct language of modeling, hypothesis testing, and information worship. And it has been amply rewarded for its troubles, recently gaining the blessing of a Nobel prize for its practitioners to signal its status as a science, and for many years capturing the reins of public power and office in a way unmatched by any other academic discipline.

There is a prestigious government Council of Economic Advisors. There is not now, and probably never will be, a Council of Philosophical Advisors, or Historical Advisors, or Humanistic Advisors. But then, that is likely to be the fate of any field that cannot attach itself to the prestige of science. It will lack social standing, just as religion now lacks serious intellectual standing. Note that I say "intellectual standing." There is no doubt that religion can still have a potent political status or that religion can from time to time make trouble for science (or, more accurately, make trouble for the agendas of some scientists, for example, for those who would like to do embryo research). But in the larger and more enduring world of dominant ideas and ideologies, science sits with some serenity, and much public adulation, in an enviable position. It is interesting to note what no one seems to have noticed. In the demise of communism as a political philosophy and a set of political regimes, one of its features has endured nicely: its faith in science. That is the one feature it shared with the Western capitalist democracies that triumphed over it. It is also, let it be noted, a key feature of a market ideology, the engine of innovation, a major source of new products, and—in its purported value neutrality—a congenial companion for a market ideology that just wants to give people the morally neutral gift of freedom of economic choice, not moralisms about human nature and the good society of a kind to be found in the now-dead command economies of the world.

Allow me to end as I began. There was a time when I hoped my own field, bioethics, might serve as the loyal opposition to scientific ideology, at least its biomedical division. In its early days, in the 1960s and 1970s, many of those first drawn to it were alarmed by the apparently unthinking way in which biomedical knowledge and technologies were being taken up and disseminated. It seemed important to examine not only the ethical dilemmas generated by a considerable portion of the scientific advances but also to ask some basic questions about the moral premises of the entire enterprise of unrelenting biomedical progress. That latter aspiration has yet to be fulfilled. Most of those who have come into the field have accepted scientific ideology as much as most scientists, and they have no less been the cultural children of their times, prone to look to medical progress and its expansion of choice as a perfect complement to a set of moral values that puts autonomy at the very top of the moral hierarchy. Nothing seems to so well serve the value of autonomy as the expanded range of human options that science promises to deliver, whether for the control of procreation or the improvement of health or the use of medical means to improve our lives. Not many people in bioethics, moreover, care to be thought of as cranks, and there is no faster way to gain that label than to raise questions about the scientific enterprise as a whole. Bioethicists have, on the whole, become good team players, useful to help out with moral puzzles now and then and trustworthy not to probe basic premises too deeply. Unless one is willing to persistently carry out such probes, the idea of a loyal opposition carries no weight.

Can religion, or bioethics, or some other social group or force in our society call science to account when necessary? Can it do so with credibility and serious credentials? Can it do so in a way that helps science to do its own work better, and not simply to throw sand in the eyes of scientists? I am not sure, but I surely hope so. I can only say, for my part, that I left one church and ended in the pews of another one, this one the Church of Science. In more ways than one—in its self-confidence, its serene faith in its own value, and its ability to intimidate dissenters—it seems uncomfortably like the one I left. How can it be made to see that about itself?

NO

Daniel C. Dennett

DARWIN'S DANGEROUS IDEA: EVOLUTION AND THE MEANINGS OF LIFE

We used to sing a lot when I was a child, around the campfire at summer camp, at school and Sunday school, or gathered around the piano at home. One of my favorite songs was "Tell Me Why." ...

> Tell me why the stars do shine,
> Tell me why the ivy twines,
> Tell me why the sky's so blue.
> Then I will tell you just why I love you.

> Because God made the stars to shine,
> Because God made the ivy twine,
> Because God made the sky so blue.
> Because God made you, that's why I love you.

This straightforward, sentimental declaration still brings a lump to my throat—so sweet, so innocent, so reassuring a vision of life!

And then along comes Darwin and spoils the picnic. Or does he? ... From the moment of the publication of *Origin of Species* in 1859, Charles Darwin's fundamental idea has inspired intense reactions ranging from ferocious condemnation to ecstatic allegiance, sometimes tantamount to religious zeal. Darwin's theory has been abused and misrepresented by friend and foe alike. It has been misappropriated to lend scientific respectability to appalling political and social doctrines. It has been pilloried in caricature by opponents, some of whom would have it compete in our children's schools with "creation science," a pathetic hodgepodge of pious pseudo-science.[1]

Almost no one is indifferent to Darwin, and no one should be. The Darwinian theory is a scientific theory, and a great one, but that is not all it is. The creationists who oppose it so bitterly are right about one thing: Darwin's dangerous idea cuts much deeper into the fabric of our most fundamental beliefs than many of its sophisticated apologists have yet admitted, even to themselves.

From Daniel C. Dennett, *Darwin's Dangerous Idea: Evolution and the Meanings of Life* (Simon & Schuster, 1995). Copyright © 1995 by Daniel C. Dennett. Reprinted by permission of Simon & Schuster. References and some notes omitted.

The sweet, simple vision of the song, taken literally, is one that most of us have outgrown, however fondly we may recall it. The kindly God who lovingly fashioned each and every one of us (all creatures great and small) and sprinkled the sky with shining stars for our delight—*that* God is, like Santa Claus, a myth of childhood, not anything a sane, undeluded adult could literally believe in. *That* God must either be turned into a symbol for something less concrete or abandoned altogether.

Not all scientists and philosophers are atheists, and many who are believers declare that their idea of God can live in peaceful coexistence with, or even find support from, the Darwinian framework of ideas. Theirs is not an anthropomorphic Handicrafter God, but still a God worthy of worship in their eyes, capable of giving consolation and meaning to their lives. Others ground their highest concerns in entirely secular philosophies, views of the meaning of life that stave off despair without the aid of any concept of a Supreme Being— other than the Universe itself. Something *is* sacred to these thinkers, but they do not call it God; they call it, perhaps, Life, or Love, or Goodness, or Intelligence, or Beauty, or Humanity. What both groups share, in spite of the differences in their deepest creeds, is a conviction that life does have meaning, that goodness matters.

But can *any* version of this attitude of wonder and purpose be sustained in the face of Darwinism? From the outset, there have been those who thought they saw Darwin letting the worst possible cat out of the bag: nihilism. They thought that if Darwin was right, the implication would be that nothing could be sacred. To put it bluntly, nothing could have any point.

Is this just an overreaction? What exactly are the implications of Darwin's idea— and, in any case, has it been scientifically proven or is it still "just a theory"?

Perhaps, you may think, we could make a useful division: there are the parts of Darwin's idea that really are established beyond any reasonable doubt, and then there are the speculative extensions of the scientifically irresistible parts. Then —if we were lucky—perhaps the rock-solid scientific facts would have no stunning implications about religion, or human nature, or the meaning of life, while the parts of Darwin's idea that get people all upset could be put into quarantine as highly controversial extensions of, or mere interpretations of, the scientifically irresistible parts. That would be reassuring.

But alas, that is just about backwards. There are vigorous controversies swirling around in evolutionary theory, but those who feel threatened by Darwinism should not take heart from this fact. Most—if not quite all—of the controversies concern issues that are "just science"; no matter which side wins, the outcome will not undo the basic Darwinian idea. That idea, which is about as secure as any in science, really does have far-reaching implications for our vision of what the meaning of life is or could be.

In 1543, Copernicus proposed that the Earth was not the center of the universe but in fact revolved around the Sun. It took over a century for the idea to sink in, a gradual and actually rather painless transformation. (The religious reformer Philipp Melanchthon, a collaborator of Martin Luther, opined that "some Christian prince" should suppress this madman, but aside from a few such salvos, the world was not particularly shaken by Copernicus himself.) The Copernican

Revolution did eventually have its own "shot heard round the world": Galileo's *Dialogue Concerning the Two Chief World Systems*, but it was not published until 1632, when the issue was no longer controversial among scientists. Galileo's projectile provoked an infamous response by the Roman Catholic Church, setting up a shock wave whose reverberations are only now dying out. But in spite of the drama of that epic confrontation, the idea that our planet is not the center of creation has sat rather lightly in people's minds. Every schoolchild today accepts this as the matter of fact it is, without tears or terror.

In due course, the Darwinian Revolution will come to occupy a similarly secure and untroubled place in the minds—and hearts—of every educated person on the globe, but today, more than a century after Darwin's death, we still have not come to terms with its mind-boggling implications. Unlike the Copernican Revolution, which did not engage widespread public attention until the scientific details had been largely sorted out, the Darwinian Revolution has had anxious lay spectators and cheerleaders taking sides from the outset, tugging at the sleeves of the participants and encouraging grandstanding. The scientists themselves have been moved by the same hopes and fears, so it is not surprising that the relatively narrow conflicts among theorists have often been not just blown up out of proportion by their adherents, but seriously distorted in the process. Everybody has seen, dimly, that a lot is at stake.

Moreover, although Darwin's own articulation of his theory was monumental, and its powers were immediately recognized by many of the scientists and other thinkers of his day, there really were large gaps in his theory that have only re-

cently begun to be properly filled in. The biggest gap looks almost comical in retrospect. In all his brilliant musings, Darwin never hit upon the central concept, without which the theory of evolution is hopeless: the concept of a *gene*. Darwin had no proper *unit* of heredity, and so his account of the process of natural selection was plagued with entirely reasonable doubts about whether it would work. Darwin supposed that offspring would always exhibit a sort of blend or average of their parents' features. Wouldn't such "blending inheritance" always simply average out all differences, turning everything into uniform gray? How could diversity survive such relentless averaging? Darwin recognized the seriousness of this challenge, and neither he nor his many ardent supporters succeeded in responding with a description of a convincing and well-documented mechanism of heredity that could combine traits of parents while maintaining an underlying and unchanged identity. The idea they needed was right at hand, uncovered ("formulated" would be too strong) by the monk Gregor Mendel and published in a relatively obscure Austrian journal in 1865, but, in the best-savored irony in the history of science, it lay there unnoticed until its importance was appreciated (at first dimly) around 1900. Its triumphant establishment at the heart of the "Modern Synthesis" (in effect, the synthesis of Mendel and Darwin) was eventually made secure in the 1940s, thanks to the work of Theodosius Dobzhansky, Julian Huxley, Ernst Mayr, and others. It has taken another half-century to iron out most of the wrinkles of that new fabric.

The fundamental core of contemporary Darwinism, the theory of DNA-based reproduction and evolution, is now beyond dispute among scientists. It demonstrates its power every day, contributing crucially to the explanation of planet-sized facts of geology and meteorology, through middle-sized facts of ecology and agronomy, down to the latest microscopic facts of genetic engineering. It unifies all of biology and the history of our planet into a single grand story. Like Gulliver tied down in Lilliput, it is unbudgeable, not because of some one or two huge chains of argument that might —hope against hope—have weak links in them, but because it is securely tied by hundreds of thousands of threads of evidence anchoring it to virtually every other area of human knowledge. New discoveries may conceivably lead to dramatic, even "revolutionary" *shifts* in the Darwinian theory, but the hope that it will be "refuted" by some shattering breakthrough is about as reasonable as the hope that we will return to a geocentric vision and discard Copernicus.

Still, the theory is embroiled in remarkably hot-tempered controversy, and one of the reasons for this incandescence is that these debates about scientific matters are usually distorted by fears that the "wrong" answer would have intolerable moral implications. So great are these fears that they are carefully left unarticulated, displaced from attention by several layers of distracting rebuttal and counter-rebuttal. The disputants are forever changing the subject slightly, conveniently keeping the bogeys in the shadows. It is this misdirection that is mainly responsible for postponing the day when we can all live as comfortably with our new biological perspective as we do with the astronomical perspective Copernicus gave us.

Whenever Darwinism is the topic, the temperature rises, because more is at stake than just the empirical facts about how life on Earth evolved, or the correct logic of the theory that accounts for those facts. One of the precious things that is at stake is a vision of what it means to ask, and answer, the question "Why?" Darwin's new perspective turns several traditional assumptions upside down, undermining our standard ideas about what ought to count as satisfying answers to this ancient and inescapable question. Here science and philosophy get completely intertwined. Scientists sometimes deceive themselves into thinking that philosophical ideas are only, at best, decorations or parasitic commentaries on the hard, objective triumphs of science, and that they themselves are immune to the confusions that philosophers devote their lives to dissolving. But there is no such thing as philosophy-free science; there is only science whose philosophical baggage is taken on board without examination.

The Darwinian Revolution is both a scientific and a philosophical revolution, and neither revolution could have occurred without the other. As we shall see, it was the philosophical prejudices of the scientists, more than their lack of scientific evidence, that prevented them from seeing how the theory could actually work, but those philosophical prejudices that had to be overthrown were too deeply entrenched to be dislodged by mere philosophical brilliance. It took an irresistible parade of hard-won scientific facts to force thinkers to take seriously the weird new outlook that Darwin proposed. Those who are still ill-acquainted with that beautiful procession can be forgiven their continued allegiance to the pre-Darwinian ideas. And the battle is not yet over; even among the scientists, there are pockets of resistance.

Let me lay my cards on the table. If I were to give an award for the single best idea anyone has ever had, I'd give it to Darwin, ahead of Newton and Einstein and everyone else. In a single stroke, the idea of evolution by natural selection unifies the realm of life, meaning, and purpose with the realm of space and time, cause and effect, mechanism and physical law. But it is not just a wonderful scientific idea. It is a dangerous idea. My admiration for Darwin's magnificent idea is unbounded, but I, too, cherish many of the ideas and ideals that it *seems* to challenge, and want to protect them. For instance, I want to protect the campfire song, and what is beautiful and true in it, for my little grandson and his friends, and for their children when they grow up. There are many more magnificent ideas that are also jeopardized, it seems, by Darwin's idea, and they, too, may need protection. The only good way to do this—the only way that has a chance in the long run —is to cut through the smokescreens and look at the idea as unflinchingly, as dispassionately, as possible.

On this occasion, we are not going to settle for "There, there, it will all come out all right." Our examination will take a certain amount of nerve. Feelings may get hurt. Writers on evolution usually steer clear of this apparent clash between science and religion. Fools rush in, Alexander Pope said, where angels fear to tread. Do you want to follow me? Don't you really want to know what survives this confrontation? What if it turns out that the sweet vision—or a better one—survives intact, strengthened and deepened by the encounter? Wouldn't it be a shame to forgo the opportunity for a strengthened, renewed creed, settling instead for a fragile, sickbed faith that you mistakenly supposed must not be disturbed?

There is no future in a sacred myth. Why not? Because of our curiosity. Because, as the song reminds us, *we want to know why.* We may have outgrown the song's answer, but we will never outgrow the question. Whatever we hold precious, we cannot protect it from our curiosity, because being who we are, one of the things we deem precious is the truth. Our love of truth is surely a central element in the meaning we find in our lives. In any case, the idea that we might preserve meaning by kidding ourselves is a more pessimistic, more nihilistic idea than I for one can stomach. If that were the best that could be done, I would conclude that nothing mattered after all. . . .

* * *

At what "point" does a human life begin or end? The Darwinian perspective lets us see with unmistakable clarity why there is no hope at all of *discovering* a telltale mark, a saltation in life's processes, that "counts." We need to draw lines; we need definitions of life and death for many important moral purposes. The layers of pearly dogma that build up in defense around these fundamentally arbitrary attempts are familiar, and in never-ending need of repair. We should abandon the fantasy that either science or religion can uncover some well-hidden fact that tells us exactly where to draw these lines. There is no "natural" way to mark the birth of a human "soul," any more than there is a "natural" way to mark the birth of a species. And, contrary to what many traditions insist, I think we all do share the intuition that there are gradations of value in the ending of human lives. Most human embryos end in spontaneous abortion—fortunately, since these are mostly *terata*, hopeless monsters whose lives are all but impossible. Is this a terrible evil? Are the mothers whose bodies abort these embryos guilty of involuntary manslaughter? Of course not. Which is worse, taking "heroic" measures to keep alive a severely deformed infant, or taking the equally "heroic" (if unsung) step of seeing to it that such an infant dies as quickly and painlessly as possible? I do not suggest that Darwinian thinking gives us answers to such questions; I do suggest that Darwinian thinking helps us see why the traditional hope of solving these problems (finding a moral algorithm) is forlorn. We must cast off the myths that make these old-fashioned solutions seem inevitable. We need to grow up, in other words.

Among the precious artifacts worth preserving are whole cultures themselves. There are still several thousand distinct languages spoken daily on our planet, but the number is dropping fast (Diamond 1992, Hale et al. 1992). When a language goes extinct, this is the same kind of loss as the extinction of a species, and when the culture that was carried by that language dies, this is an even greater loss. But here, once again, we face incommensurabilities and no easy answers.

I began... with a song which I myself cherish, and hope will survive "forever." I hope my grandson learns it and passes it on to his grandson, but at the same time I do not myself believe, and do not really want my grandson to believe, the doctrines that are so movingly expressed in that song. They are too simple. They are, in a word, wrong—just as wrong as the ancient Greeks' doctrines about the gods and goddesses on Mount Olympus. Do you believe, literally, in an anthropomorphic God? If not, then you must agree with me that the song is a beautiful, comforting falsehood. Is that simple song nevertheless a valuable meme? I certainly think it is. It is a modest but beautiful part of our heritage, a treasure to be preserved. But we must face the fact that, just as there were times when tigers would not have been viable, times are coming when they will no longer be viable, except in zoos and other preserves, and the same is true of many of the treasures in our cultural heritage.

The Welsh language is kept alive by artificial means, just the way condors are. We cannot preserve *all* the features of the cultural world in which these treasures flourished. We wouldn't want to. It took oppressive political and social systems, rife with many evils, to create the rich soil in which many of our greatest works of art could grow: slavery and despotism ("enlightened" though these sometimes may have been), obscene differences in living standards between the rich and the poor—and a huge amount of ignorance. Ignorance is a necessary condition for many excellent things. The childish joy of seeing what Santa Claus has brought for Christmas is a species of joy that must soon be extinguished in each child by the loss of ignorance. When that child grows up, she can transmit that joy to her own children, but she must also recognize a time when it has outlived its value.

The view I am expressing has clear ancestors. The philosopher George Santayana was a Catholic atheist, if you can imagine such a thing. According to Bertrand Russell (1945, p. 811), William James once denounced Santayana's ideas as "the perfection of rottenness," and one can see why some people would be offended by his brand of aestheticism: a deep appreciation for all the formulae, ceremonies, and trappings of his religious heritage, but lacking the faith. Santayana's position was aptly caricatured: "There is no God and Mary is His Mother." But how many of us are caught in that very dilemma, loving the heritage, firmly convinced of its value, yet unable to sustain any conviction at all in its truth? We are faced with a difficult choice. Because we value it, we are eager to preserve it in a rather precarious and "denatured" state—in churches and cathedrals and synagogues, built to house huge congregations of the devout, and now on the way to being cultural museums. There is really not that much difference between the roles of the Beefeaters who stand picturesque guard at the Tower of London, and the Cardinals who march in their magnificent costumes and meet to elect the next Pope. Both are keeping alive traditions, rituals, liturgies, symbols, that otherwise would fade.

But hasn't there been a tremendous rebirth of fundamentalist faith in all these creeds? Yes, unfortunately, there has been, and I think that there are no forces on this planet more dangerous to us all than the fanaticisms of fundamentalism, of all the species: Protestantism, Catholicism, Judaism, Islam, Hinduism, and Buddhism, as well as countless smaller infections. Is there a conflict between science and religion here? There most certainly is.

Darwin's dangerous idea helps to create a condition in the memosphere that in the long run threatens to be just as toxic to these memes as civilization in general has been toxic to the large wild mammals. Save the Elephants! Yes, of course, but not *by all means*. Not by forcing the people of Africa to live nineteenth-century lives, for instance. This is not an idle comparison. The creation of the great wildlife preserves in Africa has often been accompanied by the dislocation —and ultimate destruction—of human populations. (For a chilling vision of this side effect, see Colin Turnbull 1972 on the fate of the Ik.) Those who think that we should preserve the elephants' pristine environment *at all costs* should contemplate the costs of returning the United States to the pristine conditions in which the buffaloes roam and the deer and the antelope play. We must find an accommodation.

I love the King James Version of the Bible. My own spirit recoils from a God Who is He or She in the same way my heart sinks when I see a lion pacing neurotically back and forth in a small zoo cage. I know, I know, the lion is beautiful but dangerous; if you let the lion roam free, it would kill me; safety demands that it be put in a cage. Safety demands that religions be put in cages, too—when absolutely necessary. We just can't have forced female circumcision, and the second-class status of women in Roman Catholicism and Mormonism, to say nothing of their status in Islam. The recent Supreme Court ruling declaring unconstitutional the Florida law prohibiting the sacrificing of animals in the rituals of the Santeria sect (an Afro-Caribbean religion incorporating elements of Yoruba traditions and Roman Catholicism) is a borderline case, at least for many of us. Such rituals are offensive to many, but the protective mantle of religious tradition secures our tolerance. We are wise to respect these traditions. It is, after all, just part of respect for the biosphere.

Save the Baptists! Yes, of course, but not *by all means*. Not if it means tolerating the deliberate misinforming of children about the natural world. According to a recent poll, 48 percent of the people in the

United States today believe that the book of Genesis is literally true. And 70 percent believe that "creation science" should be taught in school alongside evolution. Some recent writers recommend a policy in which parents would be able to "opt out" of materials they didn't want their children taught. Should evolution be taught in the schools? Should arithmetic be taught? Should history? Misinforming a child is a terrible offense.

A faith, like a species, must evolve or go extinct when the environment changes. It is not a gentle process in either case. We see in every Christian subspecies the battle of memes—should women be ordained? should we go back to the Latin liturgy?—and the same can also be observed in the varieties of Judaism and Islam. We must have a similar mixture of respect and self-protective caution about memes. This is already accepted practice, but we tend to avert our attention from its implications. We preach freedom of religion, but only so far. If your religion advocates slavery, or mutilation of women, or infanticide, or puts a price on Salman Rushdie's head because he has insulted it, then your religion has a feature that cannot be respected. It endangers us all.

It is nice to have grizzly bears and wolves living in the wild. They are no longer a menace; we can peacefully coexist, with a little wisdom. The same policy can be discerned in our political tolerance, in religious freedom. You are free to preserve or create any religious creed you wish, so long as it does not become a public menace. We're all on the Earth together, and we have to learn some accommodation. The Hutterite memes are "clever" not to include any memes about the virtue of destroying outsiders. If they did, we would have to combat them. We tolerate the Hutterites because they harm only themselves—though we may well insist that we have the right to impose some further openness on their schooling of their own children. Other religious membes are not so benign. The message is clear: those who will not accommodate, who will not temper, who insist on keeping only the purest and wildest strain of their heritage alive, we will be obliged, reluctantly, to cage or disarm, and we will do our best to disable the memes they fight for. Slavery is beyond the pale. Child abuse is beyond the pale. Discrimination is beyond the pale. The pronouncing of death sentences on those who blaspheme against a religion (complete with bounties or rewards for those who carry them out) is beyond the pale. It is not civilized, and is owed no more respect in the name of religious freedom than any other incitement to cold-blooded murder.[2] ...

Long before there was science, or even philosophy, there were religions. They have served many purposes (it would be a mistake of greedy reductionism to look for a single purpose, a single *summum bonum* which they have all directly or indirectly served). They have inspired many people to lead lives that have added immeasurably to the wonders of our world, and they have inspired many more people to lead lives that were, given their circumstances, more meaningful, less painful, than they otherwise could have been....

Religions have brought the comfort of belonging and companionship to many who would otherwise have passed through this life all alone, without glory or adventure. At their best, religions have drawn attention to love, and made it real for people who could not otherwise see it, and ennobled the attitudes and refreshed the spirits of the world-beset. Another thing religions have accomplished, without this being thereby their *raison d'être*, is that they have kept *Homo sapiens* civilized enough, for long enough, for us to have learned how to reflect more systematically and accurately on our position in the universe. There is much more to learn. There is certainly a treasury of ill-appreciated truths embedded in the endangered cultures of the modern world, designs that have accumulated details over eons of idiosyncratic history, and we should take steps to record it, and study it, before it disappears, for, like dinosaur genomes, once it is gone, it will be virtually impossible to recover.

We should not expect this variety of respect to be satisfactory to those who wholeheartedly embody the memes we honor with our attentive—but not worshipful—scholarship. On the contrary, many of them will view anything other than enthusiastic conversion to their own views as a threat, even an intolerable threat. We must not underestimate the suffering such confrontations cause. To watch, to have to participate in, the contraction or evaporation of beloved features of one's heritage is a pain only our species can experience, and surely few pains could be more terrible. But we have no reasonable alternative, and those whose visions dictate that they cannot peacefully coexist with the rest of us will have to quarantine as best we can, minimizing the pain and damage, trying always to leave open a path or two that may come to seem acceptable.

If you want to teach your children that they are the tools of God, you had better not teach them that they are God's rifles, or we will have to stand firmly opposed to you: your doctrine has no glory, no special rights, no intrinsic and inalienable merit. If you insist on teaching your children falsehoods—that the Earth is flat, that "Man" is not a product of evolution by natural selection—then you must expect, at the very least, that those of us who have freedom of speech will feel free to describe your teachings as the spreading of falsehoods, and will attempt to demonstrate this to your children at our earliest opportunity. Our future well-being—the well-being of all of us on the planet—depends on the education of our descendants.

What, then, of all the glories of our religious traditions? They should certainly be preserved, as should the languages, the art, the costumes, the rituals, the monuments. Zoos are now more and more being seen as second-class havens for endangered species, but at least they are havens, and what they preserve is irreplaceable. The same is true of complex memes and their phenotypic expressions. Many a fine New England church, costly to maintain, is in danger of destruction. Shall we deconsecrate these churches and turn them into museums, or retrofit them for some other use? The latter fate is at least to be preferred to their destruction. Many congregations face a cruel choice: their house of worship costs so much to maintain in all its splendor that little of their tithing is left over for the poor. The Catholic Church has faced this problem for centuries, and has maintained a position that is, I think, defensible, but not obviously so: when it spends its treasure to put gold plating on the candlesticks, instead of providing more food and better shelter for the poor of the parish, it has a different vision of what makes life worth living. Our people, it says, benefit more from having a place of splendor in which to worship than from a little more food. Any atheist or agnostic who finds this cost-benefit analysis ludicrous might pause to consider whether to support diverting all charitable and governmental support for museums, symphony orchestras, libraries, and scientific laboratories to efforts to provide more food and better living conditions for the least well off. A human life worth living is not something that can be uncontroversially measured, and that is its glory.

And there's the rub. What will happen, one may well wonder, if religion is preserved in cultural zoos, in libraries, in concerts and demonstrations? It is happening; the tourists flock to watch the Native American tribal dances, and for the onlookers it is folklore, a religious ceremony, certainly, to be treated with respect, but also an example of a meme complex on the verge of extinction, at least in its strong, ambulatory phase; it has become an invalid, barely kept alive by its custodians. Does Darwin's dangerous idea give us anything in exchange for the ideas it calls into question?

... [T]he physicist Paul Davies proclaim[ed] that the reflective power of human minds can be "no trivial detail, no minor by-product of mindless purposeless forces," and [I] suggested that being a by-product of mindless purposeless forces was no disqualification for importance. And I have argued that Darwin has shown us how, in fact, *everything* of importance is just such a product. Spinoza called his highest being God or Nature (*Deus sive Natura*), expressing a sort of pantheism. There have been many varieties of pantheism, but they usually lack a convincing *explanation* about just how God is distributed in the whole of nature.... Darwin offers us one: it is in the distribution of Design throughout nature, creating, in the Tree of Life, an utterly unique and irreplaceable creation, an actual pattern in the immeasurable reaches of Design Space that could never be exactly duplicated in its many details. What is design work? It is that wonderful wedding of chance and necessity, happening in a trillion places at once, at a trillion different levels. And what miracle caused it? None. It just happened to happen, in the fullness of time. You could even say, in a way, that the Tree of Life created itself. Not in a miraculous, instantaneous whoosh, but slowly, slowly, over billions of years.

Is this Tree of Life a God one could worship? Pray to? Fear? Probably not. But it *did* make the ivy twine and the sky so blue, so perhaps the song I love tells a truth after all. The Tree of Life is neither perfect nor infinite in space or time, but it is actual, and if it is not Anselm's "Being greater than which nothing can be conceived," it is surely a being that is greater than anything any of us will ever conceive of in detail worthy of its detail. Is something sacred? Yes, say I with Nietzsche. I could not pray to it, but I can stand in affirmation of its magnificence. This world is sacred.

NOTES

1. I will not devote any space [here to] cataloguing the deep flaws in creationism, or supporting my peremptory condemnation of it. I take that job to have been admirably done by others.

2. Many, many Muslims agree, and we must not only listen to them, but do what we can to protect and support them, for they are bravely trying, from the inside, to reshape the tradition they cherish into something better, something ethically defensible. *That* is— or, rather, ought to be—the message of multiculturalism, not the patronizing and subtly racist hypertolerance that "respects" vicious

and ignorant doctrines when they are pro- pounded by officials of non-European states and religions. One might start by spreading the word about *For Rushdie* (Braziller, 1994), a collection of essays by Arab and Muslim writers, many critical of Rushdie, but all de- nouncing the unspeakably immoral "fatwa" death sentence proclaimed by the Ayatollah. Rushdie (1994) has drawn our attention to the 162 Iranian intellectuals who, with great courage, have signed a declaration in support of freedom of expression. Let us all distribute the danger by joining hands with them.

POSTSCRIPT

Is Science Hazardous to Human Values?

The conflict between science and religion is deep and broad. Scientific skepticism is always a threat to established authority: It challenges old truths; it revises and replaces beliefs, traditions, and power structures; and religion is not immune to the attack.

Does this mean that science is a threat to society? Those who share the beliefs perceived to be under attack often think so. They may believe that the Bible or the Koran is a much better guide to the nature of the world than science is. They may believe in crystal power and magic spells. They may even believe that science is just a "useful myth," no different than any other fiction. Or they may (like Callahan) wish that there were some segment of society with sufficient stature to sit in judgment over science, to criticize it and perhaps to rein it in, certainly to keep it from arrogantly quashing other views, such as those of religion. And although most Americans welcome the benefits of science and technology, they are often leery of the unrestricted inquiry that characterizes science and challenges tradition. See Janet Raloff, "When Science and Beliefs Collide," *Science News* (June 8, 1996) and Gerald Holton, *Einstein, History and Other Passions: The Rebellion Against Science at the End of the Twentieth Century* (Addison-Wesley, 1996). Even some scientists feel threatened by the conflict between their professional and private beliefs. Some have therefore spent a great deal of effort searching for ways to reconcile science and religion. For instance, Leon Lederman titles his book about the quest for the most fundamental fragment of the atom *The God Particle* (Dell, 1994). And Stephen W. Hawking, in *A Brief History of Time,* expresses the thought that science might lead humanity to "know the mind of God."

Can these scientists be speaking in more than metaphorical terms? Perhaps not, for science deals in observable reality, which can provide at best only hints of a designer, creator, or God. Science cannot provide *direct* access to God, at least as the nature of God is currently understood. Still, it is not only creationists who see signs of design. Some scientists find the impression of design quite overwhelming, and many feel that science and religion actually have a great deal in common. Harvard astronomer and evangelical Christian Owen Gingerich says that both are driven by human beings' "basic wonder and desire to know where we stand in the universe." It is therefore not terribly surprising to find the two realms of human thought intersecting very frequently or to find that many people in both realms are concerned with reconciling differences.

On the other hand, some scientists find attempts to reconcile science and religion strange. Eugenie Scott of the National Center for Science Education insists that "science is just a method" and that people who see God in the complexity of biology or astronomy are "going beyond their data" and mis-using science "to validate their positions." Paul Gross, former director of the Woods Hole Marine Biological Laboratory and coauthor of *Higher Superstition: The Academic Left and Its Quarrels With Science* (Johns Hopkins University Press, 1994), even finds those who see God in science frightening.

To learn more about the history and context of scientific creationism, an invaluable source is Ronald L. Numbers's *The Creationists: The Evolution of Scientific Creationism* (Alfred A. Knopf, 1992). To learn more about the opposi-tion between science and religion, see Stephen Jay Gould's "The Persistently Flat Earth," *Natural History* (March 1994), in which Gould makes the valuable point that irrationality and dogmatism serve neither well: "The myth of a war between science and religion remains all too current and continues to impede a proper bonding and conciliation between these two utterly different and powerfully important institutions of human life."

ISSUE 4

Will the Information Revolution Benefit Society?

YES: John S. Mayo, from "Information Technology for Development: The National and Global Information Superhighway," *Vital Speeches of the Day* (February 1, 1995)

NO: James H. Snider, from "The Information Superhighway as Environmental Menace," *The Futurist* (March/April 1995)

ISSUE SUMMARY

YES: John S. Mayo, president emeritus of Lucent Technologies Bell Laboratories, formerly AT&T Bell Laboratories, argues that the information revolution will benefit society by slowing migrations from rural to urban areas, aiding economic development, and improving access to education, health care, and other social services.

NO: Political scientist James H. Snider argues that because the information superhighway will make it possible for more people to leave the city for rural areas, human impact on the environment will become more pervasive and more difficult to control.

Not all the effects of technological development are foreseeable. New technologies may promise—and even deliver—wondrous capabilities. They may make their inventors and developers rich beyond their wildest dreams. They may also create social problems and harm or even destroy some subgroups of society. The mechanization of the textile industry in the nineteenth century, for example, led directly to oppressive child labor and wage slavery. Railroads were a boon to farmers and ranchers, but they hastened the destruction of the American Indian cultures. Agricultural mechanization drove blacks from small farms to the industrialized cities, where other forces destroyed community and family cohesiveness. And when the automobile moved many high-paying jobs from cities to suburbs, inner-city residents were denied hope of escape from poverty and ghettoes were created. (See Robert C. Johnson, "Science, Technology, and Black Community Development," *The Black Scholar*, March/April 1984). Even refrigeration has been charged, specifically with helping to disempower women (see Corlann Gee Bush, "Women and the Assessment of Technology," in Joan Rothschild, ed., *Machina ex Dea*, Teacher's College Press, 1983).

Technology also has environmental effects. Something as ordinary as agriculture leads to wastelands, deserts, dust bowls, erosion, pesticide-poisoned water, and more. The printing press created a demand for paper that has helped to drive the clearing of forests. Paper-making machinery boosted that demand; added demands for toilet paper, tissues, and paper towels; and contributed enormously to water pollution. The automobile created both air and water pollution, as did the discovery and application of electricity, which also added the problem of nuclear waste. And refrigerators, air conditioners, and aerosol cans helped to create the hole in the Earth's protective ozone layer.

The list is endless. It is also unavoidable to a huge extent, for it is impossible to do anything without affecting the environment around us. What we can do is be aware of the potential for damaging side effects of our technologies and strive to keep them to a minimum.

The latest technology to spread rapidly through society is "information technology," best known to many of us as computers and the "information superhighway" (the National Information Infrastructure, or NII) or the Internet. Using telephone lines at present (and soon cable TV lines or direct links to orbiting satellites), the superhighway moves electronic data—words, numbers, voices, music, images—very rapidly in and out of the home and office. It increases access to information, education, and entertainment for everyone who is hooked up to the system. And that access is spreading rapidly, for not only does the technology become more capable every year, it also becomes cheaper.

What are the environmental effects of the information revolution? For one, transmitting information uses much less energy than transporting commuters, so it should be less polluting. Also, improved access to information should improve decision making in general and thereby help to minimize the environmental effects of human actions. "Virtual reality" even hints at a day when national parks and wilderness areas will be less congested because people will be "visiting" via computer simulations.

John S. Mayo has been intimately involved in the development of the information revolution. He sees the future in just such rosy terms, saying that the information revolution will stimulate development throughout the world, reduce the environmental problems posed by urbanization, and increase human welfare.

Political scientist James H. Snider argues that some of the advantages of the electronic revolution have ominous implications. His chief concern is that if information-processing workers can process information from home, they will not need to live within commuting range of an office. They will then be free to spread out across the countryside, causing a myriad of environmental problems.

YES

John S. Mayo

INFORMATION TECHNOLOGY FOR DEVELOPMENT: THE NATIONAL AND GLOBAL INFORMATION SUPERHIGHWAY

Delivered at the National Research Council/World Bank Symposium, Marshalling Technology For Development, Technology Trends And Applications Session, Irvine, California (by video), November 28, 1994

[In late 1995 and early 1996, AT&T underwent restructuring that resulted in three separate companies. The new systems and technology company is called Lucent Technologies. All references to AT&T in this selection should be considered synonymous with Lucent Technologies.—Ed.]

I plan to discuss major trends in information technology by first examining the driving forces propelling the emerging multimedia communications revolution and the evolution of the so-called information superhighways— to use the popular term. Then I will glance at this multimedia revolution and at AT&T's vision of information superhighways. And I will conclude by touching on the impact of all this information technology on developing countries.

Now, it's clear that the key underlying information technologies are the prime drivers and the key enablers behind the emerging multimedia communications revolution and the evolution of information superhighways—as well as a host of other advances that together are changing the way we live, work, play, travel and communicate. Because these key information technologies are changing the work and home environments, these same technologies are helping to address customer needs. The more they can do, the more new products and services the customer wants. It has been an upward spiral that has lasted over three decades, and will surely last at least one or two decades more.

What are these key underlying information technologies? They are silicon chips, computing, photonics or lightwaves, and software. And we've seen technology capabilities doubling every year in a number of such domains—

From John S. Mayo, "Information Technology for Development: The National and Global Information Superhighway," *Vital Speeches of the Day* (February 1, 1995). Copyright © 1995 by *Vital Speeches of the Day*. Originally delivered at the National Research Council/World Bank Symposium, Marshalling Technology for Development, Technology Trends and Applications Session, Irvine, California (by video), November 28, 1994. Reprinted by permission.

for example, in computing and photonics —and doubling every 18 months in silicon chips. Even software—once a "bottleneck" technology because of quality and programmer-productivity problems—is beginning to advance rapidly in major areas like telecommunications, thanks to advanced programming languages and reuse of previously developed software modules.

To cite perhaps the most widely known example, we've witnessed explosive growth in the power of silicon chips —one measure of which is the number of transistors we can cram onto a chip the size of a fingernail. And this number, now in the millions, is moving steadily toward known physical limits. In the early part of the next century, today's familiar solid state devices may mature with transistors measuring about 400 atoms by 400 atoms each—the smallest such transistors likely to operate reliably at room temperature. The new frontier then will not be in making the devices smaller, but in creatively and economically using the vast increase in complexity and power made possible by this remarkable technology.

The amazing progress of silicon chips forms a microcosm of the broad thrust of information technology and all the associated forces that are leading to the multimedia communications revolution and the evolution of information superhighways. Let's look at the progress and impacts of these related driving forces.

After the invention of the integrated circuit, every time the number of transistors on a silicon chip increased by a factor of a thousand, something had to be reengineered—that is, something had to be radically changed or improved, because it was a new ball game. So the first reengineering that we did—as we headed toward that first thousand-fold increase —was to change all of our design processes, which had been based on discrete components.

When we reached a thousand transistors per chip, we used the new digital circuitry to reengineer our products from analog to digital, as did many other industries. Let me stress that this early progress toward digital products, enabled by silicon chips and software, brought about the digitalization of most systems and services—domestically and, more and more, globally. This digitalization created a powerful force that is driving us toward multimedia communications and information superhighways.

Then, about a decade ago, we reached toward a million transistors per chip— and powerful microcomputers became possible, along with all the periphery related to microcomputers and the needed software systems. All this led to an explosion of advanced communications services that forced the judicial process that led to the reengineering of our company: from a company that provided largely voice and data-on-voice telecommunications services to a company focused on universal information services. The theme of universal information services is voice, data and images anywhere, anytime with convenience and economy. Providing advanced services on an increasingly intelligent global network was the beginning of multimedia communications, now emerging as the revolution of the 1990s and beyond.

We are currently in the era of yet another thousand-fold increase in transistors per chip. And reengineering has now extended beyond our company and is leading to the merging of communications, computers, consumer electronics and entertainment. The bringing together of these four industries has started out in obvious ways—that is, through joint projects, joint ventures, mergers, acquisitions and some new start-up companies. This reengineering of our industry appears to be the next-to-the-last step of the information revolution brought on by the invention of the transistor.

The last step, and one that may go on forever, is the reengineering of society— of how we live, work, play, travel and communicate. It will create a whole new way of life. For example, it will change education through distance learning and school at home; it will change work life through virtual offices and work at home; and it will diminish the need to transport our bodies for work or routine tasks such as visiting and shopping. Let me quickly add, however, that it will take social change as well as technology to make many of these changes happen.

Another driving force toward multimedia communications and information superhighway evolution is the worldwide push toward common standards and open, user-friendly interfaces that will encourage global networking, and maximum interoperability and connectivity.... [S]ervice providers and customers will be able to use equipment from many different vendors without worry about compatibility. This will facilitate the upgrading of existing networks and the construction of new networks on a worldwide basis.... Similar standards in domestic networks will enable digital communications to the workplace and home, and will make possible high data-rate services.

But let me be clear on this point: although we have a lot of good work on standards, universal connectivity and interoperability will remain a big challenge as the communications and computing industries merge....

Now, the pacing force behind the multimedia and information superhighway revolution is not so much the technology as it is marketplace demands. For the greater part of this century, the user willingly accepted whatever technological capabilities we were able to achieve. Thus, the telecommunications industry was supplier-driven, and the suppliers managed the evolution of the industry and the information highways. But, as you may know, the technology became so rich that it made many more capabilities possible than the user could accept. To put it differently, we could design a lot more products and services than the customer was willing to pay for. That marked the transition from a supplier-driven industry to today's customer-driven industry—from supplier push to marketplace pull.

And, importantly, the global transfer and assimilation of information technology are combining with political and regulatory forces such as the move to privatization of telecommunications around the world—in both developed and developing countries. The result is the growth of ever-stronger global competition in the provision of communications products and services. Such emerging competition is another force driving the evolution of both multimedia communications and information superhighways. And there is an on-going challenge to public policy— not just in the U.S., but globally—to provide a framework for that evolution to occur, a framework that ensures full and fair competition for all players.

These, then, are some of the important forces driving us into the multimedia communications revolution and the associated evolution of information superhighways.

Let's look a bit further into these subjects and start with the multimedia revolution. After all, the pursuit of multimedia is creating social pressures on the evolution of information superhighways—both here and around the world. So what is "multimedia?" A reasonable working definition is that the term "multimedia" refers to information that combines more than one medium, where the media can include speech, music, text, data, graphics, fax, image, video and animation. And we at AT&T tend to focus on multimedia products and services that are networked; that is, connected over a communications and information network.

Examples of such networked multimedia communications range from videotelephony and videoconferencing; to real-time video on demand, interactive video and multimedia messaging; to remote collaborative work, interactive information services such as electronic shopping, and multimedia education and training. Eventually, we will have advanced virtual reality services, which will enable people to indirectly and remotely experience a place or an event in all dimensions.

Now, we are excited about multimedia because public switched networks—or information highways, if you will—can presently accommodate a wide array of networked multimedia communications, and the evolutionary directions of those networks will enable them to handle an increasingly vast range of such communications. Moreover, there is also a potentially vast market for multimedia hardware and supporting software. Although actual projections differ widely, the most commonly quoted projection for the total worldwide market for multimedia products and services is roughly $100 billion by the year 2000.

We at AT&T are playing a major role in facilitating the emerging multimedia revolution—as a service provider, as a provider of network products to local service providers, and as a provider of products to end users. These are familiar roles for AT&T, so let me briefly describe another, perhaps less familiar, major role we are studying in relation to the multimedia revolution. That is the role of what we call "the missing industry"— and that role is a "host" for a wide variety of digital content and multimedia applications developed by others. Hosting is a function that connects end users to the content they seek. Customers will gain easy, timely and convenient access to personal communications, transactions, information services and entertainment via wired and wireless connections to telephones, handheld devices, computers and eventually television sets. Independent sources for this digital content eventually will range from publishers to large movie studios to small cottage-industry software houses.

This role is also of interest here because of the key information superhighway challenge it illustrates—specifically, because openness of critical interfaces and global standards are vital to this complex hosting function. The entertainment industry, for example, must have software systems that are compatible with those of the hosting industry, and these software systems must, in turn, be compatible with those of the communications and information-networking industry, which then must be compatible with the customer-premises equipment industry.

In addition, the tremendous growth in available information and databases will stimulate the need for personal intelligent agents. These "smart agents" are software programs that are activated by electronic messages in the network, and that find, access, process and deliver desired information to the customer. They can perform many of the time-consuming tasks that have discouraged a number of users from taking advantage of on-line services and the emerging electronic marketplace. "Smart agents" are one feature of AT&T's recently announced enhanced network service called AT&T PersonaLink^{SM} Services.

Let me say I'm looking forward to these "smart agents"—software that can take the hassle out of life. Shopping for the best mortgage, or finding the best new car deal, or finding out which store has the item I want is a hassle, and has people at the interface who add negative value. Just last week I needed a replacement part. I called the store twice and got no satisfactory response to my calls. So I went to the store, waited in line, and then the salesperson queried the database and said, "We don't have it in stock." My "smart agent" could have queried their database and saved them and me a big investment in a zero-revenue operation. There was never a problem with the database; the problem was that people were inadvertently in the way of my ability to access it—adding negative value, but diligently trying to do their jobs. A "smart agent" could simply have done it better.

Now, it's important to note that in the age of multimedia communications, people who are geographically separated from each other will not, for example, just play games together over networks —they will visit and find what is emotionally nourishing, and build their relationships. According to AT&T's vision, in this evolving age, consumers and business associates will seek new relationships based on telepresence, a new type of community, and a social experience independent of geography. This potential for interactive networks is quite unlike that found in the proposed availability in the U.S. of 500 pre-programmed TV channels on the CATV cable. The beauty is that people will have the freedom to choose any subject or service from the intelligent terminals in their homes and offices. A key point is that they will be able to network clusters of friends or associates to enjoy such services as a group.

I must stress that networked multimedia communications will dramatically change the nature of work, and will therefore have a broad impact on business—first in developed nations and eventually in developing nations. Videoconferencing, for example, is first coming into businesses to enhance productivity, save time, and reduce travel. And current developments in multimedia telephony are making the possibility of remote collaborative work more and more realistic. In a few years, for example, a person could be working with colleagues or suppliers in branch offices in New York, Irvine, Hong Kong, Paris, and Sydney. Working in real time, they could accomplish the combined task of producing printed materials, presentation slides, and a videotape introducing a new product line.

As I noted, the pursuit of multimedia communications is driving social issues relating to the evolution of the information superhighway. Now, what is AT&T's vision of the information superhighway?

Our vision is to bring people together, giving them easy access to each other and to the information and services they want and need—anytime, anywhere. In our view, the information superhighway is a seamless web of communications and information networks —together with other elements of our national information infrastructure, such as computers, databases, and consumer electronics—which will put vast amounts of information at the fingertips of a variety of users. And we see the information superhighway, quite simply, as a vast interoperable network of networks —embracing local, long distance and global networks, wireless, broadcast and cable, and satellites. In addition, the information superhighway also embraces the Internet.... Importantly, the information superhighway is *not* a uniform end-to-end network developed and operated by government or any one company. It is the totality of networks in our nation, interconnected domestically and globally. And it is an important part of evolving global information superhighways.

Now, let's turn to the impacts of these technology trends on developing nations. These advanced information technology trends, multimedia communications and information superhighways will have a variety of broad, beneficial social impacts on developing nations, including the following:

Item 1. Advanced communications, growing in ubiquity, could slow the migration of rural people to urban areas— a traditional problem in countries such as The People's Republic of China.

Item 2. Access to jobs and services. People living in rural areas would be less inclined to move to the cities if advanced communications systems gave them access to jobs and sophisticated social services where they already live. (In the U.S., for example, our pervasive communications infrastructure has enabled information-intensive businesses to flourish anywhere in the country.)

Item 3. Information superhighways could alleviate congestion and commuter-traffic pollution in cities by making telecommuting possible—by bringing good jobs to people, wherever they are. (In the U.S., as you know, the work-at-home movement is gaining momentum, and trials with certain types of jobs show that employees can be even more highly productive without leaving their homes. One side benefit here is reduced costs for urban office space.)

Item 4. Information superhighways could also revolutionize education and eliminate differences in quality between rural and urban education systems—by enabling a limited number of the very best teachers and professors to reach huge numbers of students. Both students and teachers could be located practically anywhere, in "virtual" classrooms—and they could enhance learning by accessing multimedia network databases on a great variety of content areas.

Item 5. Information superhighways could also revolutionize medical care by helping to deliver high-quality medical care far from large population centers. Advanced communications would permit frequent meetings between rural health workers and physicians located in more populated areas. The same capability would also permit direct doctor-to-patient consultation and follow-up.

Item 6. Advances in information technology are stitching together a truly global society and a global economy —which developing nations would be able to participate in fully.

Item 7. Peoples and countries would be able to retain their ethnic and cultural identities, but at the same time they would be able to communicate, transact and interact seamlessly across geographic and political boundaries.

Item 8. In addition to these capabilities, a modern information infrastructure would help strengthen the ties that hold a nation's people together. In a large country such as China, for example, the huge distances between cities and regions, and the enormous complexity of regional dialects, have made communication among the Chinese people exceptionally difficult. So an information superhighway would have the potential to help lessen both the obstacle of distance and the barrier of language. And information technology will also eventually make possible real-time translation of languages.

These, then, are some of the social impacts of information technology on developing nations. In addition to social impacts, the key information technology trends, multimedia communications and information superhighways will have some broad public-policy impacts on developing nations, including the following:

Item 1. In general, investment in communications infrastructure would contribute greatly to a nation's overall economic development. Moreover, the new technologies that developing countries would be investing in are becoming more and more cost-effective. So there is a strong need to ensure sufficient investment in construction and management of a country's communications infrastructure.

Item 2. There is an opportunity to choose a technology path that would move a developing nation into the information age most directly. The opportunity is to "leapfrog" many of the older technologies that preceded today's advanced network systems—for example, to install glass fiber in local distribution networks. A country thus has the opportunity to economize on scarce capital resources by investing in a national information superhighway in the initial stages.

Item 3. There is technology to "jump-start" a developing nation. For example, cellular radio can provide telephony almost overnight and serve large markets while the fiberoptic infrastructure is put in place.

Item 4. In addition, there is a need for heavy investment in the development of the *human* infrastructure, not just the *physical* infrastructure. The global leaders of the 21st century will be those countries that have not only invested in the right technologies, but also in the intellectual growth of their people.

Item 5. Information technology is vital to economic reform and development —to improving the economic and social life of a nation's people, and to attracting and meeting the needs of foreign investors.

Item 6. Information technology would also enhance financial management— for example, by enabling a country to move away from a cash economy to one in which electronic transactions are not only faster, but also provide for much greater visibility into economic activity.

Item 7. Information technology would both *facilitate and complicate* the job of governing; *facilitate* by making available to decision-makers vastly expanded resources of timely information; *complicate* by vastly expanding the numbers of people who would be informed about important issues and who would inevitably want to play a role in deciding them.

These are some of the broad public-policy impacts of information technology on developing nations. Although the government of the U.S. clearly does not have all the answers, some of our steps, as well as missteps, might be helpful for such nations to consider.

As you know, the U.S. government has played a crucial role in nurturing rapid technological progress, as well as rapid application of new technologies in the marketplace. In the communications sector, for example, the government has established a clear set of national objectives—such as universal service, technological leadership, and broadband capability into all population centers. The government has also created a strong, independent regulatory structure designed to ensure that private companies serve the public interest in a fair and competi-tive marketplace—although we still have a long way to go toward genuine and effective competition in the local exchange. Many, if not most, developing nations are still evolving their policies, laws and regulations governing the communications industry. And I cannot overemphasize the importance of this task.

In summary, rich information technology, the worldwide push toward global standards, ever-increasing customer demands, and growing global competition are key driving forces behind the emerging multimedia communications revolution and the evolution of national information superhighways. The growth of multimedia communications and the further competitive evolution of these information superhighways, as well as of global information superhighways promise a broad range of Information Age benefits to virtually every citizen of our nation. And they also promise to extend these Information Age benefits to virtually every citizen of the world, including the developing nations.

NO

James H. Snider

THE INFORMATION SUPERHIGHWAY AS ENVIRONMENTAL MENACE

Over the years environmentalists have cautioned us against threats to the environment—the population explosion, nuclear radiation, pesticides, aerosols, nonrecyclable garbage, and automobile exhaust, to name just a few. But what they haven't noticed yet is the environmental menace posed by the information superhighway.

If you look at the literature of some of the organizations concerned with preserving the land, such as the Wilderness Society or the Sierra Club, you don't see the information superhighway listed as a threat. On the contrary, the information superhighway is supposed to help the environment by reducing the need for automobile and airplane travel and all the pollution they bring. In fact, some of the most-ardent environmentalists also happen to be ardent advocates of the information superhighway.

U.S. Vice President Al Gore is a prime example. In his book *Earth in the Balance* (Houghton Mifflin, 1992), Gore attempts to recount the present dangers to the environment. In the chapter, "A Global Marshall Plan," he advocates building an information superhighway to facilitate telecommuting as a partial solution to our problems. This, he believes, will reduce the demand for cars and the pollution that cars inevitably bring. He notes that, for "a dozen years, I have been the principal author and advocate of a proposal to build a national network of information superhighways."

More recently, the Clinton administration has directed the U.S. Environmental Protection Agency and the Department of Transportation to promote telecommuting, largely to improve air quality, reduce future environmental risks, and conserve energy resources. High-population centers such as New York City, Los Angeles, and Chicago are among the areas targeted. Among the many policy proposals are tax incentives for employers and individuals to change to home-based telecommuting arrangements, as well as "flexiplace" incentives similar to current "flexitime" ones.

Yet, unbeknownst to the advocates of telecommuting, the coming information superhighway portends an environmental disaster of the first magnitude. In the United States, where population growth is relatively subdued, it may

From James H. Snider, "The Information Superhighway as Environmental Menace," *The Futurist*, vol. 29, no. 2 (March/April 1995). Copyright © 1995 by The World Future Society. Reprinted by permission of *The Futurist*, World Future Society, Bethesda, Maryland.

lead to the massive destruction of the remaining forests, open land, and wild flora and fauna over the next few decades.

RURAL VS. METROPOLITAN

Despite the huge increase over the last few hundred years, the world's population has been highly concentrated on a limited landmass. Only about 2% of the earth's land surface is covered by cities and towns. Though human beings affect much landmass through farming, tree growing, pollution, or other means, the mass of humanity has tended to congregate in metropolitan (urban or suburban) areas. Even now, the ratio of people living in metropolitan vs. rural areas continues to increase, substantially reducing the pressure on open spaces that would otherwise ensue from population increases.

In the United States, the population is also highly concentrated. About 80% of Americans live in metropolitan areas, which cover just 16% of the contiguous states. The number of Americans living in rural areas has decreased not just because of population increases in other areas, but because of changing job opportunities. In 1800, more than 90% of U.S. jobs were agricultural. Today, that figure is under 2%, and the vast majority of the remaining jobs can only be done in metropolitan areas.

Thanks to the information superhighway, this hundred-year-old trend toward metropolitan areas is about to reverse. In fact, a recent *Wall Street Journal* article argues that, "Like the coming of the railroad a century ago and the arrival of the interstate highway system in the 1950s, telecommunications is dramatically rearranging rural life.... Almost unnoticed are recent census figures showing an abrupt turnabout in the rural diaspora.... In all, during the first two years of the 1990s, rural counties gained nearly 900,000 new residents."

TRANSPORTATION AND POPULATION DISPERSION

Throughout history, transportation technology has largely determined where people live. Before the Industrial Age, when boats dominated the movement of people and goods, major population centers were located next to major bodies of water. During the nineteenth century, railroads opened up the hinterlands and led to a vast dispersion of towns and cities clustered around railroad stops and junctions.

As transportation historian Stephen Goddard says in *Getting There: The Epic Struggle Between Road and Rail in the American Century* (Basic Books, 1994), the West was worthless until the railroads "opened up the West to settlement. Pioneers rode the rails into the wilderness and seemingly overnight built new towns with supplies manufactured in the East. Towns called Omaha, Tulsa, and Wichita grew from tiny settlements to cities overnight."

In the twentieth century, the automobile led to the massive growth of suburbs surrounding traditional urban areas, as well as the growth of new cities along the interstate highway system. The interstates, says Goddard, altered "beyond recognition where and how Americans lived. They allowed a breadwinner to commute double the distance in the same time. Sleepy farming villages at the outskirts of cities doubled their population within a decade as their cornfields gave way to row upon row of tract houses."

The information superhighway could potentially spread people out much farther than the train or automobile ever could. People may have created new urban areas or moved to suburban areas, but the difficulty of driving to "civilization" has kept them within relatively narrow distances. By eliminating the remaining transportation barriers, the information superhighway threatens a massive migration out of metropolitan areas to the relatively unspoiled hinterlands.

THE DEATH OF RURAL AMERICA

Public officials representing rural areas throughout the United States (including Alaska, Idaho, Iowa, Maine, Montana, Nebraska, North Carolina, and Vermont) are advocating the information superhighway in order to stimulate business in their states. For example, U.S. Senator Conrad Burns of Montana explains in the *Congressional Record* his rationale for accelerating its building:

> Workers will travel to work on the information highways instead of our traditional highways. The cars on these information highways will be bits of information which can travel anywhere in the world instantly....
>
> Think of it, a stockbroker could live in Circle, Montana, with a population of 931, and be in instant contact with anyone, anywhere, anyway. That person wouldn't have to burn thousands of gallons of fossil fuel each year to drive to and from work.... And, best of all, that person will be able to live and work in rural America.

Burns also expects the information superhighway to stem the historical outflow of population from rural Montana to metropolitan areas in other states:

> In Montana, many of our graduating seniors want to stay in our beautiful state where the skies are blue, the water is crisp, the air is healthy, and the quality of life is good. But they are forced to leave the state to find jobs. We need to keep our best and brightest at home.

Until now, a large number of jobs have only been available in metropolitan areas. Occupations such as accounting, law, advertising, management consulting, and architecture tend not to thrive in more-rural areas. In occupations such as movie production, book publishing, and international finance, only a few metropolitan areas hold the vast majority of jobs.

Similarly, most cultural activities have only been available in metropolitan areas. Movies, theaters, playhouses, video stores, sports events, concerts, high-quality schools, and pools of potential friends are still heavily concentrated geographically. In the future, the information superhighway will make high-quality entertainment and education increasingly available in the home or anywhere else on the planet. And as "virtual" communities sprout, the need to be physically close to friends and relatives will continue to diminish.

At the same time, the allure of open spaces is unlikely to diminish. In *A Fierce Green Fire* (Hill and Wang, 1993), a history of the environmental movement, author Philip Shabecoff says, "The migration to the suburbs was, for many if not most of the families who moved, an environmental choice for open space, greenery, cleaner air, less noise, and a generally healthier place to live." More than ever, environmental quality is seen as an integral part of a search for a higher standard of living. With economic and cultural restrictions removed from the quest to live in open spaces, such a quest is likely to reach a new and environmentally destructive phase.

"Every survey shows that more people want to live in small towns than can find jobs there," says Calvin Beale, a senior demographer for the U.S. Department of Agriculture. "If you wire them, they will come."

"THE NEW YORKERS ARE COMING! THE NEW YORKERS ARE COMING!"

So what will happen if the information superhighway is built and the population can disperse evenly throughout the land? Let's take Vermont, the self-described "Green Mountain State." The *Wall Street Journal* recently rated metropolitan Burlington, Vermont, as the best place in the United States to raise a family. What would happen if the relatively nearby inhabitants of New York City could find good work in Vermont (whose current population is 560,000)? Would this attract millions of people to not just visit but live in Vermont?

No definitive answer can be found. I did ask this question to half a dozen of my friends in Manhattan. All of those with families told me that they'd readily move to Vermont if only they could find good work and a solid career. Whether justified or not, it certainly can be said that Vermonters live in constant fear of an onslaught of "flatlanders" from the south. Vermont is widely perceived as a highly desirable place to live. Much of its 50% increase in population since 1950 has resulted from out-of-staters seeking the quality of life that Vermont's environment makes possible. By 1994, a majority and ever-increasing proportion of Vermont's voting-age population were out-of-staters. Vermont's governor and U.S. representative are both transplanted New Yorkers.

If we allow the information superhighway to be built, it does seem reasonable to believe that it could absolutely blight this little gem of a state. Already the few suburban areas in Vermont are chock full of expatriates from nearby metropolitan areas such as New York City and Boston. But that is merely a trickle compared with the millions who are likely to come if the information superhighway flourishes. The best and brightest will leave the urban blights and turn Vermont into one huge and spread-out suburb. They will spoil Vermont, but it will still be far better than where they came from. They will telework from their home or nearby office. Maybe Vermont will become one of the premium telelifestyle locations, but the destruction visited upon its land will not be unique.

If all Americans succeed in getting their dream homes with several acres of land, the forests and open lands across the entire continental United States will be destroyed. Even if the U.S. population were to quadruple to 1 billion, the havoc wrought on the land would not be as great as from a more even dispersal of its present 250 million. Today's one-acre apartment building with 200 families will turn into 200 five-acre homesteads spread out over 1,000 acres. Even if the average home lot only increases from a quarter of an acre to an acre, the environmental destruction would be huge.

In the past, environmentalists have not been oblivious to the environmental impact of new communications technologies. Many, for example, have bemoaned the tendency of the car to destroy open spaces and ecosystems. Shabecoff recounts Lewis Mumford's warning that "the swelling size and power of the cities was overwhelming the countryside." For Mumford, "the automobile filled in the last open spaces and was the true Frankenstein's monster of the twentieth century, surpassed only in its destructive potential by the hydrogen bomb, but more dangerous because more complacently indulged." More recently in *Healing the Planet* (Touchstone, 1990), Paul Ehrlich calls for "a near absolute ban on the building of new freeways and roads." But environmentalists have yet to discover that the information superhighway might not only be destructive, but far more so than the physical highways of the past.

PRESERVING OPEN SPACES

The emerging information superhighway offers the potential to dramatically improve education, consumer information, democracy, entertainment, and economic growth. But it also has the potential to be the most environmentally destructive technology of the early twenty-first century.

Is there any way to gain the benefits of the information superhighway while preserving the earth's open spaces? The ideal solution would be to strengthen land-conservation incentives and laws. The government could buy or protect more land. Zoning laws could be tightened and more strictly enforced. Many such efforts are currently under way in the United States, but the pace will have to be dramatically accelerated to ward off the new onslaught on the land.

The paradox is that the very reason the land is threatened is because having open space around one's home is equated with a high standard of living. People's environmental values lead them to want to leave crowded cities and suburbs. But in doing so, they destroy the environment that attracts them there in the first place. The tendency to want a homestead with at least an acre is deeply rooted, and efforts to preserve open spaces will come into conflict with this powerful drive and the economic forces that cater to it.

This leads to pessimism that traditional land-conservation measures will be enough to hold back the flood of spreading humanity. The only way to stop the flood might be to dam it at its source—to prevent information superhighways, just like interstate highways, from being built in environmentally important areas. This is the path I urge upon land conservationists—at least until traditional land-conservation measures are significantly strengthened.

POSTSCRIPT

Will the Information Revolution Benefit Society?

Consider where people live. In the past, they have concentrated along river valleys, around river mouths, and along caravan routes. The availability of water was a critical factor, for it was needed for cooking, drinking, washing, and irrigation. It also provided one of the earliest "highways," an avenue for the movement of people, trade goods, and information. Where rivers and seas were lacking, the caravans took over.

We no longer travel much by water (though freight does). We have faster and more convenient highways and railways and airports. But a look at the map shows that the human populace is still clustered along rivers and coasts. Those highways, railways, and airports were built to link older settlements, and the patterns remain.

As Snider notes, past improvements in transportation have led to increased dispersal of the human population; the automobile is notorious for the part it has played in this. Improvements in communications have surely assisted, but the chief aid to dispersal has been easier, faster, cheaper transportation both of people and of the goods they need to survive. Communication has improved along with transportation, but until very recently it did not raise the possibility of dispersing the populace even further, for work was still done in central locations. Today, Snider notes, much work can be done at home, far from the office, and people can flee the cities and suburbs, taking their environmental impacts wherever the roads may reach.

Whether this is good or bad depends on what one thinks is important. Developing countries and impoverished regions of developed countries tend to be more concerned with jobs than with the environment. They see anything that brings in money as good, even if it does do a bit of harm in the process.

In broader terms, the issue is whether or not the information revolution serves the "public interest," which some people see less in terms of development versus the environment than in terms of social equity. The Telecommunications Policy Roundtable, for instance, has said that the National Information Infrastructure should support public applications such as education, libraries, public health, and delivery of government information and services; universal access (meaning minorities and the poor should not be excluded); and protection of basic rights such as privacy, freedom of speech, and intellectual property. See "Renewing the Commitment to a Public Interest Telecommunications Policy," *Communications of the ACM* (January 1994) and Fred W. Weingarten, "Public Interest and the NII," *Communications of the ACM* (March 1994).

PART 2

The Environment

As the damage that human beings do to their environment in the course of obtaining food, wood, ore, fuel, and other resources has become clear, many people have grown concerned. Some of that concern is for the environment—the landscapes and living things with which humanity shares its world. Some of that concern is for human welfare, focusing more on the ways in which environmental damage threatens human health or even human survival.

Some environmental issues, such as overpopulation, global warming, and fossil fuel exhaustion, are well known. Other environmental issues are less familiar to the general population but are perhaps no less worthy of concern. All have provoked extensive debate over details and degrees of certainty, what can or should be done to prevent future difficulties, and even whether or not the issues are real.

- Can Human Population Stabilize Before Disaster Strikes?

- Can the Sun and Wind Supply Our Energy Needs?

- Should Society Be Concerned About Global Warming?

- Is Ozone Depletion a Genuine Threat?

ISSUE 5

Can Human Population Stabilize Before Disaster Strikes?

YES: Stephen L. Gillett, from "Population, the Demographic Transition, and 'Biological Imperatives,'" *Analog* (January 1996)

NO: Thomas A. Easton, from "Trapped Between Damnations: The True Meaning of the Population Crisis," *Analog* (January 1996)

ISSUE SUMMARY

YES: Geoscientist Stephen L. Gillett argues that because human beings adapt their behavior to circumstances very readily, human population will probably stabilize before it exceeds the capacity of the environment to support it.

NO: Biologist Thomas A. Easton argues that humanity is now on the verge of a catastrophic mismatch between population and the food supply, largely because people do not adapt their behavior to circumstances readily enough.

In 1798 the British economist Thomas Malthus published his *Essay on the Principle of Population.* In it, he pointed with alarm at the way the human population grew geometrically (a hockey-stick curve of increase) while agricultural productivity grew only arithmetically (a straight-line increase). It was obvious, he said, that the population would inevitably outstrip its food supply and experience famine. Contrary to the conventional wisdom of the time, Malthus argued, population growth was not necessarily a good thing. Indeed, it led inexorably to catastrophe.

For many years, Malthus was something of a laughingstock. The doom he forecast kept receding into the future as new lands were opened to agriculture, new agricultural technologies appeared, new ways of preserving food limited the waste of spoilage, and the birth rate dropped in the industrialized nations (the "demographic transition"). The food supply kept ahead of population growth and seemed likely—to most observers—to continue to do so. Malthus's ideas were dismissed as irrelevant fantasies.

Yet overall population kept growing. In Malthus's time, there were about 1 billion human beings on Earth. By 1950—the year that Warren S. Thompson wrote that civilization would be endangered by the rapid growth of Asian and Latin American populations during the ensuing five decades ("Population," *Scientific American,* February 1950)—there were a little over 2.5 billion. By 1997 the tally will have hit 6 billion. Although global agricultural production has also increased, it has not kept up with rising demand, and, because of the loss of topsoil to erosion, the exhaustion of aquifers for irrigation water, and the high price of energy for making fertilizer (among other things), the prospect of improvement seems to many observers exceedingly slim. The statistics presented in *World Resources 1996–97* (Oxford University Press, 1996), a report of the World Resources Institute in collaboration with the United Nations Environment and Development Programmes, are positively frightening.

Some people are still laughing at Malthus and his forecasts of doom that two centuries never saw come to pass. Among the scoffers is economist Julian Simon, who believes that more people on Earth means more talent available for solving problems and that humans can indeed find ways around all possible resource shortages (see his essay "Life on Earth Is Getting Better, Not Worse," *The Futurist*, August 1983).

But more and more people—including some economists—are coming to realize that Malthus's error lay not in his prediction but in his timing. There is a growing consensus that he was quite correct to say that a growing population must inevitably outrun its food supply. The only question is how long human ingenuity can stave off the day of reckoning.

How long *can* human ingenuity stave off the day of reckoning? The World Resources Institute sets the global human population at about 8.5 billion in 2025. By 2050 the population is expected to hit 10 billion *and to still be rising;* some estimates peg the 2050 population at 12.5 billion. The United Nations expects that *if* human fertility can be controlled, the population may stabilize in the neighborhood of 11.5 billion by 2150.

Can population really go that high? If it does, can it be fed? There are famines in the world *today.* Won't they grow far worse long before the population doubles—indeed, well before it hits the 10 billion (or more) mark in 2050? Stephen L. Gillett, a geoscientist at the University of Nevada, Reno, believes that because human behavior is ruled by culture (including science and technology) rather than by biology, we will not breed ourselves into disaster. Population growth will slow, even as technology improves humanity's ability to thrive.

Thomas A. Easton, a biologist at Thomas College in Waterville, Maine, fears that it is already too late to stave off catastrophe. The world harvest is at best stagnant, he argues, while population continues to increase, and agriculture seems to have lost its ability to increase production as it has in the past. The per capita food supply is already declining, Easton contends, and disaster seems inevitable.

YES

Stephen L. Gillett

POPULATION, THE DEMOGRAPHIC TRANSITION, AND "BIOLOGICAL IMPERATIVES"

It is *not* in an organism's interest to have as many offspring as possible.

... [T]he difference is by no means semantic, because having as many offspring *survive* as possible generally means *not* having as many as possible.

OF R AND K

Ecologists call the naïve "breed-as-fast-as-you-can-and-damn-the-consequences" approach *r-strategy*, "*r*" for "rapid." Rabbits are *r*-strategists....

One risk of *r*-strategy is of becoming a resource for... predators. Look at salmon! Maybe one egg in a hundred thousand ever turns into a new breeding salmon. *R*-strategy also makes you extremely vulnerable to population booms and crashes.

... [A]nother way [is] *K-strategy*, named from fitting yourself into a population that's already at the limit, at that somewhat ill-defined number *K* that reflects the carrying capacity of the environment.

K-strategists are specialists. Because there are only so many slots available, you have to be very, very good at what you do to fit into one. Thus, *K* strategists typically have only a handful of offspring; better to put a lot of energy into preparing a few offspring and make sure of preserving your genes, than to have too many and lose all. For this reason they also show a tendency toward caring for their young, to better prepare them for that niche. They also typically—maybe even intrinsically—have high levels of direct intraspecific conflict.

Most higher animals are *K*-strategists.... Their populations are typically more stable, too, absent such major environmental perturbations as (say) a local volcanic eruption. Without such crises, *K* is not a variable!

From Stephen L. Gillett, "Population, the Demographic Transition, and 'Biological Imperatives,' " *Analog* (January 1996). Copyright © 1996 by Stephen L. Gillett, Department of Geographical Sciences, University of Nevada, Reno, NV 89557. Reprinted by permission of the author. Notes and references omitted.

CULTURE, TECHNOLOGY, AND K

It should be obvious what sort of strategists human beings are. Even the most fecund human female has difficulty bearing more than a dozen or so offspring in her lifetime. Just among vertebrates, mice, doves, or salmon do vastly better! And our absurdly protracted infancy and childhood drives the point home even more.

Thus, just from sheer biological considerations, the natural condition of human populations is *stable*. K is not a function of the rate of population increase. But this whole new human innovation of extragenetic information processing: technology, culture, and all that, raises some new issues. It turns out K *is* a strong function of culture and technology. Humans' profound innovation is to have kept upping K, and population then follows to reach a new steady state.

It's happened at least twice previously in human history, in the transitions from hunter-gatherers to peasant societies, and later from peasant to industrial societies. Obviously these innovations haven't occurred uniformly, and a major part of the current population boom simply results from industrialization spreading across the planet.

... [I]t also follows historically that when you *can* manage to support more people the society gets wealthier, because of the increase in the labor force (and the soldiering force, though that's not always mentioned). This is why economic growth has followed population increase. This is also why traditional economists view population growth as a Good Thing. (Of course, they oversimplify; the population growth doesn't "cause" economic growth, but an innovation allowing population growth becomes synergistic with further economic growth.)

We might wonder whether this correspondence of higher population with formidability will remain true. Consider, for example, that in the few centuries extending from about 1500 to 1900, a handful of Europeans managed to dominate the entire world—not merely the sparsely populated Americas and Australia, but the ancient and populous societies of Asia. Obviously, relative population sizes was not the controlling variable here.

WHY WOMEN AND CHILDREN AREN'T FIRST

If human populations are naturally stable, what enforces that stability? Social constructs. Traditional cultures have been caught in a tight trade-off between having *enough* people (to till the soil, herd the stock, and fight off their neighbors—all labor-intensive activities), and having so many people they crowd the available resources too much. There's also the not-so-minor matter of *training* children, which is a costly and long-term process.

So you have to have, not just the right number of children, but also a robust arrangement for raising them for an extended period of time. And the problem is compounded because (again up till very recently indeed) quite a number of those children are going to die before adulthood. Thus, for insurance you need to encourage fecundity, but only within a rigid social arrangement that ensures that the children can be reared and trained.

Such subtleties are not always appreciated. Some SF writers, mixing naïve biology with a sort of social Darwinism, have asserted "women and children first" as a fundamental law, and it's been suggested this is the "biological imperative" behind the current population explosion.

This is not true. For one thing, many hunter-gatherer and primitive agricultural societies had extremely strong taboos against adultery, which were enforced with savage penalties usually involving a painful and humiliating death: consider the ancient Jews, the Bronze-age peoples of northern Europe, or the Apaches....

Another example is the prevalence of infanticide in many traditional cultures. Indeed, traditional Inuit (Eskimo) culture practiced *female* infanticide. Now, this was a highly sophisticated culture living as close to the edge of survival as humans ever have managed. If there weren't a pressing survival reason for killing girl babies, it wouldn't have happened. (The reason, probably, was that it took several male adults to support a single child. Again, if you have too many children, you risk losing all—the classic *K* conundrum. In a small, closely related group, moreover, there's no biological conflict of a childless adult working to support children not his own, as many of his genes are being carried by his collateral relations.)

Even in modern times, many cultures discriminate against girls, and female infanticide has not vanished by any means. This stems from sheer biology: females bear the offspring. In turn, this biological fact is typically expressed by social and economic structures. Boys are assets, for example, not only because of their labor but because they remain part of the family and thus will be around to care for their aging parents. Girls, however, will leave, and furthermore commonly cost a dowry when they do. (From a biological standpoint, too, you

can propagate your genes with sons as easily as daughters—more easily, in fact, because you don't incur the cost of child-raising.)

Many proto-urban or early urban cultures have also taken measures to limit children; e.g., infanticide in ancient China or Greece, or infant abandonment in medieval and early modern Europe. Economic considerations play a role here as well: because traditional farming was extremely labor-intensive, children were an asset on the farm. Children aren't nearly so valuable in an urban setting, though. Until the 20th century, cities were population *sinks*. The people to replenish them came from rural areas.

Thus there's more to survival, for human populations as well as cultures, than just child*bearing!* In fact, children are cheap, biologically speaking. What is not cheap is raising them. In any society, the most valuable members are not "women and children" but its young adults, of either sex—traditionally, people from about 16 to maybe 30 or so. (These limits have been rising of late.) The culture has made its maximum investment in them, and now they need to produce. McNeill points out that the Old World plagues were especially devastating when introduced to the Americas because they preferentially killed young adults. By contrast, Old World cultures, including the Europeans', had adapted to losing *children* to the diseases. Smallpox, for example, was an endemic childhood disease; and in the Middle Ages, small children weren't really considered part of the family till they'd survived it.

(Just to forestall any misunderstandings: I'm not being deliberately callous; I'm a parent, too. I'm simply reiterating cold historical fact.)

SIMPLE ARITHMETIC—OR
SIMPLISTIC ARITHMETIC?

A great deal of the "population explosion" literature makes much of "exponential growth." Because exponentials are easy to work with, it's trivial to make entertaining but irrelevant projections of when (say) Earth's population will reach n (where n is large), or when the mass of the Earth has been entirely converted into people, or whatever. These are typically followed by the ponderous observation that "exponential growth can't continue forever in a finite world." (Of course it can't! So what?)

In fact, real populations are describable by exponentials only over extremely short intervals. The famous S-curve, or *logistic curve*, in which an initially exponential growth tapers off to an asymptotic limit, is a much better model of the real world. This in fact is where the parameters r and K come from. Such a curve is a very general result of a system in which further growth is inhibited by the increasing population density.

To be sure, it can also be simplistic. The approach to K is not always smooth, and under some circumstances large and erratic oscillations of population around the K value may occur. Such underdamping typically occurs if: (1) there are large time lags in response to the increasing density; or (2) the organism is highly specialized, so that it cannot shift to alternative resources if its food becomes exhausted. Examples of this latter situation include parasitic wasps on grain beetles in grain elevators, or lynxes vs. snowshoe rabbits. For human beings only case (1) is potentially a concern, both because humans have long generation times and also because of social inertia. However, since humans are also the most flexible creatures on the planet—in utter contrast to case (2)!—oscillations are certainly not a necessary consequence.

THE DEMOGRAPHIC TRANSITION:
THE APPROACH TO K

So the rapid growth in human numbers right now is an extremely temporary phenomenon. Social structures adapted to a regime of high birth and death rates that were still tied to extremely labor-intensive peasant agriculture are lagging the new realities of low death rates, especially of children, and urbanization. We see this particularly because the locus of population increase is in the developing world. Birthrates *have* dropped in the industrialized world, in many cases to below the replacement level.

This decline is called the "demographic transition." It began in France in the 18th century and spread spottily over the rest of Europe through the next century or so, and thence to the rest of the industrialized (and industrializing) world. The fundamental biological cause is the approach of K, but (as is usual with human beings) it's expressed by a slew of proximate social causes. One such, which has long been recognized, is affluence —although not "simply," because the benefits of affluence must be broadly distributed. Another is social stability and low infant mortality; when children aren't assets, people won't have so many; but they nonetheless have to have a good chance of surviving. Yet another is women's status, as the total fertility rate (TFR) is well correlated with the education of women. They will have fewer children and take better care of them.

Broadly, such factors reflect the increasing specialization of the "niches" available, such that offspring require more and more preparation—and thus more and more economic outlay—to better their chances, not only of surviving but of prospering. Hence fewer offspring makes good biological sense. It's the best way to insure that genes are propagated—indeed, it's classic *K*-strategy.

For humans this strategy is further buttressed by economics. For one thing, as children become perceived as costs rather than assets people will have fewer of them. Even when children remain assets, as when they are still their parents' source of support in old age, the greater investment required to train and educate those children mandates having fewer of them. In Thailand, for example, one place that's recently arrived at the demographic transition, interviews indicate that people are fully aware that two children with secondary school training are much more likely to prosper than six or eight with no schooling at all, and thus are much more likely to be able to support their parents in later years.

A demographic transition thus requires new economic and social structures to limit birthrates. It also requires *time*, as social attitudes take a few generations to shift. One interesting study describes the gradual spread of birth-control practices among the landowner, merchant, and peasant classes in a town in (thoroughly Catholic) Sicily. It's particularly striking the degree to which a norm of few children became internalized among the "lower classes," so that a couple was willing to spend a lifetime practicing *coitus interruptus* to avoid pregnancies, because of the Church's proscriptions on "mechanical" birth control. The stress was made even worse, of course, by the strict taboos against sexual practices that could not result in pregnancy.

"Fare Sacrifici" ("[One must] make sacrifices"), they said. Indeed! So even without cheap birth control techniques, social attitudes *will* change under the pressure of gritty economic realities. As Barnes noted, people aren't stupid—they are very good at perceiving their own interests. It is simply not true that people will just keep having children willy-nilly, despite the predictions of Malthus and such follow-ups as the "Marching Morons" scenario. That makes no biological or economic sense....

"OVERSHOOT" AND K

The more sophisticated gloom 'n' doomers realize that the complexity of the real world is not described by exponentials, however impressive and mathematically tractable they may be. They claim, however, that the final population level will be unsustainable because the resources to support so many people don't exist. Such "overshoot" after consumption of the Earth's "natural capital," will then inevitably be followed by a catastrophic population crash. One author has even called modern *H. sapiens* a "detritovore," in analogy to scavengers feeding on detritus. On finding a rich deposit, such species can have a spectacular population boom, followed by an equally spectacular crash as the resource is exhausted. The implication is that not only can't we achieve US-level affluence for the entire world, but even our own affluence is doomed.

Many in this school of thought also note that the industrialized countries, with their low, even sub-replacement birth rates, have a disproportionate impact due to their consumption of resources and output of pollution, so they're still "overpopulated."

All such scenarios, however, confound the limitations of current engineering practice with laws of nature. (There's a perverse element of wishful thinking involved here, too.) Present technologies are extremely primitive, as should be obvious by comparison with the capabilities of biological systems (something biologists, of all people, should realize!). As we move away from these technologies and ultimately toward nanotechnologies, low-impact affluence will become possible, not just for the industrialized countries, but for all. The impact of technology on the bio-sphere can become arbitrarily low as technology becomes arbitrarily sophisticated. Indeed, one could use level of impact as a criterion of the sophistication of a technology. (Elsewhere, Erhlich and his coworkers seem, in part, to recognize such considerations.)

This also puts to rest another strawman scenario, the idea that to make the developing world "wealthy" would involve building them enough roads/cars/discos/suburbs/etc. *now*. This is extraordinarily naïve. Even the First World will have to change to new technologies as the oil runs out. There is absolutely no point in implementing any more of the old technologies now than we need to. Insofar as possible, it makes far more sense to move toward the technologies of the future.

DESPERATELY SEEKING K

"The problem is not population growth per se, [but] when the rate of population growth exceeds the rate at which technology and social change can compensate."

— Bruce Wilcox

To take the other tack; if a demographic transition will happen eventually in the Third World, why then should we even worry? In particular, why bother to encourage an early demographic transition, of compressing into a single generation what took Europe over a century?

Several reasons. One is that the technologies that will achieve affluence for the teeming billions aren't ready yet— and buying some time is vital. Second, raw labor is not nearly so valuable any more, as more and more of the grunt work of primary production is taken up by machines. So, the paradigm of "more people, more labor," which has previously rewarded population growth, is obsolete. In modern "cyberwar," the unskilled masses aren't even useful as cannon fodder any more—look at the Gulf War.

Because of this Ehrlich is certainly correct, and economist Julian Simon is wrong, in that people, *per se*, are *not* the "ultimate resource." Ehrlich is also wrong, though. In the information economy, what *is* the ultimate resource is not so much the "inherited capital of the Earth," as he claims, but the education and skills of those people. Those are expensive and time-consuming to acquire, and becoming more so, as we've seen. (To be sure, the stored knowledge and experience of humanity —"information capital," if you will, is also vital.)

The last reason is esthetic and ethical. More things are possible in a world less utterly dominated by humans; for one thing, backcountry permits will be easier to get! More non-human life forms will survive, too; not only is this an ethical consideration, there's a strong element of self-interest, too, from the knowledge that can be gained from these organisms and the communities they live in.

Since a demographic transition involves profound *social* changes, education—especially of women—is critical, although raising living standards and furnishing contraceptives are also important. Of course, educating women puts what David Brin calls the "macho" cultures in a bind: they can't ignore education, because the outlets for unskilled or semi-skilled labor are dwindling so rapidly, and a country that expects to survive needs a highly educated work force. Yet when they *do* educate people (not just women), their archaic social structures become strained.

The developing nations *are* dominated by young people, true. This is commonly regarded as a demographic disaster in the making, because the population is dominated by the highly fertile, who can continue childbearing for years. But there's also a bright spot: young populations can be a lot more flexible, and cultural attitudes can change a lot more quickly, because domination by the young can attenuate the cultural continuity between generations, particularly in an era of cheap mass communication.

I will make a note on how *not* to do it. A "triage" approach, in which the First World simply writes off large parts of the developing world, will backfire spectacularly. Even worse would be what might be euphemistically described as "active measures." Hardin describes the necessity of shooting most of a starving deer herd on an overcrowded island, with at least the implication that something similar may be required for people. Aside from the appalling ethical problem here—who decides who should be "culled"?—he seems to forget that deer can't shoot back but people can! Even with the "best" intentions, too, the staggering potential for abuse in any sort

of "culling" program should require its dismissal *a priori*. Consider how the 20th century has largely been characterized by mass murder in support of "necessary" political agendas.

Even worse: if you wanted to encourage a bunker mentality of "us agin them," you could hardly go about it better. And that is likely to make for an unpleasant world indeed. *Lots* of nukes are out there, with the collapse of the Soviet Union— and anyway, as Heinlein noted, you can't classify the laws of physics. Check out Martin van Creveld's *The Transformation of War* for the flavor of the international politics of the 21st century. His predictions of domestic terrorism in particular seem eerily prophetic. . . .

No, of course terrorists won't be able to destroy the US or even the rest of the First World. But they could make it uncomfortable. In fact, I think the severe curtailment of civil liberties that is likely to result under such a scenario would do more long-term damage than any number of terrorist bombs.

Last and most ironically, "culling" is unlikely to have any long-term effect on population. Mass mortality is *not* a way to encourage lowering the fertility rate. Quite the reverse, in fact; it's the historical encouragement for high fertility; "compensatory mortality," in the ecologists' phrase. (Ecologists like Ehrlich, who warned that pesticides would have little long-term effect against insect pests, should realize this!)

"PEOPLE AS THE PROBLEM"

"Development is something that happens because of the poor, not in spite of the poor."

— Idriss Jazairy

"We" have to "solve" the population "problem." "Governments" must "provide" services "for" more and more new people. Etc.

You hear phrases like this a lot, and I suggest this is a completely counterproductive approach. Despite confident predictions and 50 years of AI [artificial intelligence] research, we still have no clue as to how to make a system with even rudimentary intelligence, much less the flexibility, autonomy, and power of a human. Why on Earth, then, are these autonomous, self-programming entities not viewed as part of the *solution?* As the economists point out, every one of those new mouths to feed comes with a pair of hands attached—and, it might be added, a brain as well.

Many of the interim things that could be done in the developing world are labor-intensive. One example is intensive agriculture, in which much labor goes to maintaining the land, such as in the Machakos district of Kenya. Yet, alas, in much of Africa, heartbreakingly perverse *political* disincentives to increasing small farmers' food production are the rule. The vast conurbations growing in the Third World, with all their vast problems, also contain a vast labor pool that could potentially address at least some of their problems. Consider road building, garbage collection....

I've implied it above, but I'll say it again: population is as much a *social* issue as "economic," "ecological," or "technological." And a focus on helping people help themselves is much more likely to be effective than "solving" the "problem" from on high.

THE LIMITS TO BIOLOGY

The alert reader will have noticed a problem in talking about K strategy. Why should birthrates drop *below* replacement? That makes no biological sense! Indeed, how can we talk of "forcing" a demographic transition, of reaching a "lower" K? K is one number, right?

In theory, sure. But in fact it's time to acknowledge: humans are not driven only by biology. Sure, human nature is not infinitely pliable; the ignominious collapse of state-sponsored socialism demonstrates that. Nonetheless, cultural conditioning does have a profound effect.

Amusingly, it's quite common for people to make what they think are "biological" arguments that merely demonstrate the depth of their cultural conditioning. Here's an example from Heinlein's essay "The Pragmatics of Patriotism," in which he described a young husband and a tramp who both were killed by a train while trying to free the wife's foot from a switch: Heinlein tried to make this a parable of the "biological" truism of "Women and children first"—and it's nothing of the sort. Obviously no biological imperative holds the tramp there—getting himself killed in a vain attempt to save a stranger will not help his genes propagate. Quite the reverse, in fact!

But the exact same analysis is true of the husband: rather than kill himself, he too should find a new mate so his genes can propagate. This is the *real* biological imperative, and Dawkins gives a number of natural examples. The doe, losing the battle to protect her fawn, will suddenly save herself and leave the fawn to its fate. There is absolutely no point, biologically, in getting yourself killed in a probably vain attempt to save an offspring. If you stay alive, you may have a chance for more offspring, so the thing to do is cut your losses.

But this analysis violates our most profound cultural conditioning—which is exactly my point. We *are*, after all, capable of carrying out programs—even unto death—that nothing whatsoever in our biological makeup has prepared us for.

TOWARD THE HOPEFUL FUTURE

Overshoot remains possible; certainly the perversity of human history suggests that it could happen. But equally certainly, it is not inevitable.

Humans and their societies have long since reached a level of complexity in which the interactions are so multitudinous, and so non-linear, that the system(s) can exhibit unexpected behavior indeed. Because humans are a young species, moreover, these interactions have hardly settled down. Any student of human evolution can rattle off

many more such epiphenomena resulting from an unexpected confluence of factors: e.g., music as inspired by the mother's heartbeat; overhand throwing as leading to planning, through the necessity of "preprogramming" ballistic movements, which in turn makes such skills as piano playing possible; and so on and so on.

And of course, changes aren't slowing down. Biological evolution has become essentially irrelevant to human beings; it works on timescales of tens to hundreds of thousands of years, whereas human societies are overturning themselves within decades. But of course this is old hat to *Analog* readers, who are familiar with Vernor Vinge's idea of the Singularity.

The point of all this is that birthrates might go very low indeed. Perhaps human beings will become too interested in other things to bother with breeding —children are *work*, after all. "If you give people access to contraceptives and abortion they practically stop having children."

NO

Thomas A. Easton

TRAPPED BETWEEN DAMNATIONS: THE TRUE MEANING OF THE POPULATION CRISIS

It is not news that the global population is rising and will continue to rise. The United Nations projects that it will reach 8.5 billion in 2025 and 10 billion in 2050. Some estimates put the world's population at 12.5 billion in 2050, when children born today will be merely middle-aged.

In 1950, when I was six years old, the world population was just over 2.5 billion. That is, by the time the century that began in 1950 ends, in the span of a single long lifetime, the world population will have increased four or five-fold. The result will be vastly increased demand for water, food, metals, energy, wood, and all other resources. In consequence, many expect, forests will be destroyed, species will vanish, and the air and water will grow foul.

The litany is familiar. It may even be accurate. But it is really beside the point. The true meaning of the population crisis is something else again—an ironic paradox that very few people appreciate. Not to put too fine a point on it, if we don't rein in our numbers, Mother Nature will, and the old dame is not known for her gentle hand.

That is, for the sake of our children, we *must* have fewer of them. Birth control is essential, and those who oppose it—from the Pope to the demonstrators outside the local abortion clinic—act in a way that is more "pro-death" than anything Hitler or Stalin ever did.

Such statements are provocative. To some they must be infuriating. But they are also inescapable if we look at the numbers that relate world population, grain production, and the amount of grain available per person per day, from 1950 to the present, and then attempt to project the numbers into the future. "Grain" includes wheat, rice, corn (maize), barley, oats, sorghum, millet, rye, and some other crops; because grain comprises the bulk of the human diet almost everywhere, its production is often used as a stand-in for overall food production. The statistics for other foods show similar patterns; for some, such as seafood, the prognosis is worse.

From Thomas A. Easton, "Trapped Between Damnations: The True Meaning of the Population Crisis," *Analog* (January 1996). Copyright © 1996 by Thomas A. Easton. Reprinted by permission. The author has slightly modified his article for this edition of *Taking Sides: Science, Technology, and Society*.

The world's grain harvest increased tremendously between 1950 and 1994. It in fact increased more than enough to keep up with the growth in population, and the amount of grain available to the average resident of Earth each day grew from 680 grams (about 1.5 pounds, or 2700 kilocalories) to 840 grams (about 1.8 pounds, or 3400 kilocalories) today. Since about 40 percent of the grain harvest goes for animal feed—producing meat, eggs, milk, leather, wool, pets, animal labor, and even entertainment (e.g., horse races, zoos, and circuses)—the average human's share of the harvest now amounts to about 2000 kilocalories of wheat flour, corn meal, corn on the cob, oatmeal, rice, barley, and so on. Other foods—meat, fish, dairy, fruits, and vegetables—supply the rest of the 2000–3000 kilocalories adults need each day to live healthy, vigorous lives.

Unfortunately, the grain harvest peaked in 1990, and the grain available per capita peaked in 1984, over a decade ago. Because the number of mouths to be fed has increased while the food supply has held relatively steady, the per capita grain ration has already slipped noticeably.

What does the future hold? It is very simple to calculate that if the world population does indeed reach 10 billion in 2050, and if the average citizen of the planet is to have as much grain available each day as he or she averaged from 1965 to 1994 (870 grams; 3500 kilocalories), the world grain harvest will have to be about 3200 million tons. Since in some parts of the world, many people are not adequately fed today, we should increase the harvest even more. If standards of living are to rise in the nine tenths of the world we call undeveloped or developing, we will need much, much more. Recent analyses note that increasing prosperity in China alone promises to demand by 2030 all the grain available on the export market. Of course, demand will be increasing in other areas at the same time.

That is, in 2050 the world will have to produce nearly twice as much grain as it does now. In terms of percentage increase, we did even better between 1950 and 1994, but in terms of sheer tonnage the necessary increase in production is absolutely unprecedented.

It is also probably unachievable. Three chief limits on our ability to produce food are already apparent:

- Most prime farmland is already being farmed. What remains is marginal land whose fertility is exhausted after very few years of use.
- A third of the world's harvest comes from irrigated land. Irrigation water often comes from underground aquifers, many of which are already seriously depleted of their water and will not remain useful for more than a few more decades. At the same time, irrigation deposits mineral salts in soil; when the salt builds to high enough levels, crops do not grow. About 1.5 million hectares (3.7 million acres) are lost to salt build-up every year.
- We are losing farmland. As population grows, we preempt it for housing, factories, roads, and other construction. In addition, erosion removes vast amounts of topsoil every year. "During the last 40 years," wrote David Pimentel and his coauthors in the February 24, 1995, *Science*, "nearly one-third of the world's arable land has been lost by erosion and continues to be lost at a rate of more than 10 million hectares per year." In the U.S. alone, erosion

causes some $44 billion worth of damage per year. On a worldwide basis, it costs us each year the capacity to produce about 20 million tons of grain, a little more than one percent of the current world grain harvest.

These effects—and others, including the impacts of global warming—will of course be fought. We may even win the battle. However, the harvest is already levelling off and there are reasons to think it may decline. Let us consider four scenarios:

A. The world grain harvest increases steadily toward the 3200 million ton 2050 harvest that will mean people are no worse off than they were between 1965 and 1994.
B. We hold the line and harvests do not decline below the 1994 level.
C. We manage a few record harvests before losses of fertile soil and irrigation water, as well as salinization, begin in 2005 a steady one percent per year decline (*less than* the loss in productivity due to erosion alone; the actual decline could easily be worse, begin sooner, and last longer). In this scenario (for the sake of optimism), we halt the decline after 20 years.
D. The one-percent slide continues; please note that even this is *not* a worst-case scenario.

The exact effect of these scenarios on per-person food supply depends on whether population growth turns out to be "high," "medium," or "low." My "high" estimate is 12.5 billion in 2050; it is worth noting that this requires a decrease in the world's population growth rate; if growth were to continue at its present rate, we would top 14 billion by 2050. "Medium" is the United

Nations projection of 8.5 billion in 2025 and 10 billion in 2050. My "low" estimate is 8 billion in 2050; it comes from the UN population conference, held in Cairo, Egypt, in September 1994, which declared as a goal the stabilization of world population at a level of 7.8 billion by 2050; I assume the figure will inflate at least a little.

With scenario A (the highest harvest projection), the smallest population is better off than we have ever been before, at least in terms of grain supply. The largest is about as well fed as we were in 1950. The middle population is as well fed as people averaged between 1964 and 1994.

The *lowest* harvest (scenario D) gives in 2050 a mere 1033 million tons of grain, about the same as the 1967 harvest, when the population was 3.5 billion and the average daily ration was 810 grams. This picture is quite bleak. Even the smallest population is only half as well fed as people were in 1950. A population of 10 billion people will "enjoy" a daily ration of 280 grams (1100 kilocalories) of grain each, well below subsistence levels. The result will surely be widespread starvation.

The two other harvest scenarios—constant (B) and 20-year-slide-and-hold (C)—offer intermediate conclusions, but in both cases even the smallest (8 billion) population winds up worse off than people were in 1950. Larger populations will suffer hunger, starvation, and—because malnutrition weakens defenses—disease. Demographic experts also expect mass migrations and war.

There may be ways to improve the food supply. In 1994, 38 percent of the world's grain harvest was used as feed for livestock. Perhaps half of this grain could be liberated for human consumption if people ate less meat. However, as standards of living increase, people want more animal products, not fewer. Further, eating less meat may well have no net effect at all. If fossil fuels become (as expected) less available, animal labor—and the need for feed grain—can be expected to become more widespread rather than less.

We would gain a great deal of lost ground if we returned more organic wastes to our fields instead of burying them in landfills or burning them in incinerators. Unfortunately, there already exist demonstration projects to turn such wastes into fuels and thus deprive the soil of essential organic material. Worse yet, the diversion of grain (maize) to fermentation of alcohol to be used as vehicle fuel (in gasohol) is already growing; it will more and more deprive people of necessary food.

Genetic engineering will undoubtedly provide us with high-yield crops, but even they will need soil. And despite all the high expectations of the fans of genetic engineering (including me), it is proving excruciatingly slow to make the necessary kind of progress. We cannot count on it.

Another improvement may lie in pest control. Estimates of the amount of the world's crops lost to mice, rats, insects, and fungi range up to 50 percent. If we could prevent all or some of the loss, we could clearly increase the food available for human consumption. Unfortunately, the use of pesticides leads inexorably to pesticide resistance and rapidly declining effectiveness of control efforts. Fungi—blights, rusts, and smuts—offer similar resistance to fungicides. And rodents are notorious for getting around the barriers we set in their way.

Some think that the crisis is so far off that we will have time to develop new technologies—perhaps based on nano-engineering—that will permit everyone to be fed.

However, many experts are less sanguine. K. O. Emery, writing in the March 1994 *Population and Environment*, tells us that, "the conclusion... is nearly completely avoided: that Malthus was correct." Thomas Malthus wrote in 1798 that because food supply cannot be increased as rapidly as population, the human population must inevitably outstrip its food supply and experience famine. Contrary to the conventional wisdom of the time, population growth was not necessarily a good thing. Indeed, it led inexorably to catastrophe.

Emery argues that we confront the Malthusian crisis *now*, today, in the lifetimes of ourselves and our children. If we are to survive, we must somehow increase the amount of food available. If we cannot do that, we must decrease the number of mouths that need filling. That is, we must reduce and *reverse* the population growth rate.

Projections of 2050 populations of 10 or 12.5 billion already assume a steady decline in the growth rate. If the world is to be as well fed in 2050 as it is today, and if we cannot keep the harvest growing, we must therefore improve even on these growth rate projections. If we do not, nature will do the job for us. We may even see a precipitous decline in human numbers, a Great Die-Off, that could reduce the world's population to well below current numbers. This is what happens when other organisms overrun the resources they need to survive. We are no different.

The effect will of course be worse in those countries that today have barely enough food for their people. We hardly dare to consider the consequences if a year's harvest is diminished by drought, flood, or other natural disaster, especially since world carryover grain stocks (the amount of grain in storage at the beginning of harvest, and hence available for famine relief if the crop fails) are now sufficient to feed the world for less than two months.

To prevent catastrophe will call for drastic measures. Some people think that trying to freeze population size by restricting couples to two children—zero population growth, or ZPG—is drastic enough. If it isn't, then certainly China's famous one couple–one child approach is, insofar as it lives up to its name (China's actual fertility rate is 2.2 children per woman, very close to ZPG; the country expects to grow by almost half by 2030.) However, neither can work in the short term. Thirty-two percent of the current world population is less than 15 years old, and only 6.5 percent is over 65. Those young reproducers will replicate their numbers long before the population can lose an equal number of oldsters, and their children can be expected to do the same. If the number of births per woman dropped today to the ZPG level, world population would still hit 8 billion before levelling off.

Some areas, such as North America and Europe, have their fertility rates at or below the replacement level. In fact, the U.S. Census Bureau estimates that net immigration now accounts for 28 percent of population growth in the United States and will account for *all* growth by the 2030s if present trends continue. In a June 1992 *Omni* interview, Garrett Hardin, Emeritus Professor of Human Ecology at the University of California in Santa Barbara noted that

"The quickest, easiest, and most effective form of population control in the U.S., that I support wholeheartedly, is to end immigration."

Thinking more of the world's population problem than of the U.S.'s, Virginia Abernethy, Professor of Psychiatry and Anthropology at Vanderbilt University School of Medicine, goes even further. She argues persuasively that "traditional" societies long existed in balance with the ability of their environment to support them. The popularization of the idea that prosperity and economic development lead to small family size has produced since World War II a "flood of international aid and generous immigration policies" and "Ample evidence indicts the demographic transition model for fueling the 20th century over-population debacle." She argues that people reduce their fertility when times grow difficult, as in the former Soviet Union (Russia's birth rate reportedly dropped below the death rate in 1992), but as long as they see a promise of better times ahead—talk of sharing resources from the industrialized nations, open-door immigration policies, and the like—they will continue to be fertile and there will be a population explosion that defeats the effort to help.

Abernethy's startling conclusion is that reducing efforts to "help" will in the long run do more good than harm. The U.S. should therefore halt almost all immigration and large-scale foreign aid in order to help the rest of the world rediscover a sense of limits and thereby ease the worldwide population problem.

It follows that if nothing is done and population continues to grow until disaster strikes, that will teach the world the necessary sense of limits and the birth rate will drop. Unfortunately, while people are certainly capable of not having babies even without the Pill, condoms, and other modern birth control techniques, their methods can be as brutal as Mother Nature's. In China, many couples still use infanticide—especially of female infants—to keep within their one-child allotment.

Some people refuse to admit that we face a problem. Writing in the May–June 1995 *Society*, Nicholas Eberstadt calls overpopulation a myth; the term has no defensible definition, he says, and indeed, some countries we call overpopulated are actually declining in population. He does not seem to see that when population overruns its resource base, decline is inevitable.

Others grant that there is a problem but think we will be able to cope. David Norse, a research associate for the Overseas Development Institute in London and a research fellow at the Environmental Change Unit at the University of Oxford, believes that it is possible to improve food production and distribution enough to support a population much larger than today's, although he recognizes that if population growth is not brought under control eventually, the best we can do is to stave off the day of reckoning. John Bongaarts, vice president and director of the research division of the Population Council in New York City, has a very similar view.

Charles Westoff says that our hope must lie in making family planning more widely available, creating a demand for small families, and encouraging later marriages. Such measures would undoubtedly help, but they will be difficult to implement rapidly enough to prevent disaster. Part of the difficulty lies in widespread resistance to family planning, which surfaced very clearly in the September 1994 UN population

conference, which shied away from any mention of birth control (including abortion) in favor of vowing that the proper path is to educate women and give them control over their lives. It is true that educated, empowered women have fewer children, but education and empowerment take decades to show large effects; the process has to start when the women are children; it also takes time to train teachers.

If we truly wish to rein in population, we will have to find more rapid, more drastic measures. Indonesia uses powerful government pressure—more stringent than China's—to keep births down, an approach Eberstadt fears as "a foretaste of the future." Yet what other approaches might work quickly enough to prevent the Great Die-Off?

Mass murder? No one can seriously suggest that, but a genetically engineered sterility plague might do the job, even if it does seem more at home in science fiction than in the real world. Perhaps we will agree on mandatory sterilization for all after their first child (India tried it on men in the 1970s), or for all refugee immigrants (who are likely to be fleeing regions where the problems of overpopulation are worst; there are currently some 10 million environmental refugees in the world, and another 17 million political, religious, and ethnic refugees; by 2050, according to Norman Myers, there may be 150 million environmental refugees alone, 1.5 percent of the world's population).

Unfortunately, many governments and individuals see every measure with much hope of actually working as tyrannical and/or inhumane, on a moral par with the Nazi Holocaust. It was largely objections from religious groups such as the Catholic church and Moslem fundamen-

talists that kept the UN population conference from endorsing birth control. We can detect similar sentiments in the cries of hysterical activists that urging birth control on developing countries (where birth rates are highest) is a form of genocide, and even in American attitudes toward Chinese "fertility refugees" (the one couple–one child policy violates the purported basic human right to have all the children one wishes).

If we permit such attitudes to interfere with effective action, we can expect to encounter worse tyranny, worse inhumanity, and worse genocide from starvation, disease, and even war. And here is the crux. Inaction condemns us to the damnation of the biblical four horsemen. Yet action, effective action, means measures that offend against all that most of us think is kind, moral, ethical, decent, and right, measures that, if we adopt them, will leave us feeling that our souls are forever stained.

Perhaps more to the political point, if the U.S. were to follow Dr. Abernethy's prescription[1], it would become the target of vigorous attacks, both verbal and physical (probably including some from terrorists with suitcase nukes). Yet if we do nothing effective, we may prove responsible by our inaction for billions of deaths in a Great Die-Off. Our souls will be stained even blacker.

We are trapped between damnations, between the rock and the hard place, and there seems no way out of the trap. People are not likely to change their attitude until the Great Die-Off is in progress—this is an obvious corollary of Abernethy's point—and by then it will be too late. Nature will be solving the problem for us, and in a way for more brutal than anything we might do to ourselves in the name of survival.

Or will it? Nature need not be quite that brutal. There is at least one gentler natural process developing today that may help if we do not fight it: a natural sterility plague, chlamydia. It is among the most widespread of sexually transmitted diseases, with an estimated 5 million new cases in the U.S. every year. It can produce pain and even death, but many of its victims are barely aware that they are infected until they try to have children. Then one of its main effects appears: in women, chlamydial infections often scar the uterine (Fallopian) tubes and block the movement of the egg to the uterus; the blockage may be complete or partial, preventing pregnancy entirely, making it less likely, or even forcing it to take the dangerous ectopic form (the fertilized egg implants in the tube or elsewhere in the abdomen). That is, chlamydia reduces fertility; this may be a tragedy for the individual, but it is a boon for an overpopulated world.

Unfortunately, few people are likely to stand by while chlamydia infringes their right to have babies. Yet the "right" to have babies is well worth questioning. The unrestricted exercise of that "right" is threatening humanity with suffering and death on a scale unprecedented in all of history. It therefore may be a wiser choice *not* to try to prevent or undo those side-effects of human behavior that diminish human fertility. In a very real sense, they may save us from ourselves.

If we do not restrict the "right" to have babies in some fashion, we can expect nature to remind us that we are just as much biological beings as pandas, whales, and elephants. We are no less subject to natural laws. We are not exempted from the consequences of our folly by the gods we profess to believe in.

NOTES

1. It wouldn't be difficult. The U.S. has a strong isolationist tradition, and Congress is already trying to cut foreign aid in the name of deficit reduction, while border states such as California and Florida are crying for relief from immigrant hordes.

POSTSCRIPT

Can Human Population Stabilize Before Disaster Strikes?

The concept of "carrying capacity" is basic to the population issue. It is defined as the size of the population that the environment can support or "carry" indefinitely, through good years and bad. It does not mean how many people can prosper in good times alone, for such a large population must suffer catastrophically when droughts, floods, or blights arrive or the climate warms or cools. It is thus a long-term concept, where "long term" does not mean decades nor generations, nor even centuries, but millennia or more.

What is the Earth's carrying capacity for human beings? It is surely impossible to set a precise figure on the number of human beings the world can support for the long run, but many population biologists agree with Sandra Postel, who, in the Worldwatch Institute's report *State of the World 1994* (W. W. Norton, 1994), says, "As a result of our population size, consumption patterns, and technology choices, we have surpassed the planet's carrying capacity. This is plainly evident by the extent to which we are damaging and depleting natural capital" (including land and water).

Later in the Worldwatch volume, project director Lester R. Brown says, "As the nineties unfold, the world is facing a day of reckoning. Many knew that this time would come, that at some point the cumulative effects of environmental degradation and the limits of the earth's natural systems would start to restrict economic expansion." In *State of the World 1996* (W. W. Norton, 1996), Brown states that that point is coming too fast for political systems to cope, due in large part to the addition of nearly 100 million people to the world's population each year. According to Brown, "The demands of our generation [already] exceed the... sustainable yield of the earth's ecological endowment."

Two books worth reading are E. G. Nisbet's *Leaving Eden: To Protect and Manage the Earth* (Cambridge University Press, 1991) and Paul R. Ehrlich and Anne H. Ehrlich's *Healing the Planet: Strategies for Resolving the Environmental Crisis* (Addison-Wesley, 1991). Both hold out some hope that we can learn how to live within the means the Earth provides. A third source is the Worldwatch Institute's *Vital Signs* series, which each year reports a wealth of trend data —some alarming, some encouraging—for the world's population, economy, and environment.

Students who wish to find more information on the Internet will find this site a useful starting point: http://drseuss.lib.uidaho.edu:70/docs/egj02/groat01.html.

ISSUE 6

Can the Sun and Wind Supply Our Energy Needs?

YES: Christopher Flavin, from "Power Shock: The Next Energy Revolution," *World Watch* (January/February 1996)

NO: Chauncey Starr, Milton F. Searl, and Sy Alpert, from "Energy Sources: A Realistic Outlook," *Science* (May 15, 1992)

ISSUE SUMMARY

YES: Christopher Flavin, vice president for research at the Worldwatch Institute, argues that the world is on the verge of a massive shift to renewable energy sources, with hydrogen filling the need for a portable fuel.

NO: Chauncey Starr, Milton F. Searl, and Sy Alpert, researchers at the Electric Power Research Institute, argue that renewable (solar) energy is limited particularly by its intermittency and lack of portability; thus, the hydrogen solution is of no practical interest.

A *renewable resource* is one whose supply is constantly replenished. Fresh water is one, for it is renewed as rapidly as the rain falls from the sky. Solar energy is another, for the Earth receives a new shipment every day.

It is possible to overuse a renewable resource by using it faster than it is renewed. The fresh water available for use includes not only the runoff from each day's rain but also past days' rain stored in underground aquifers that may have taken thousands of years to fill. If these reserves are drained for such uses as irrigation (as indeed is the case in many regions of the world), then their renewability is largely theoretical.

Oil, coal, and natural gas were once living organisms and therefore embody the solar energy those organisms captured when alive. They can therefore be called "reserves" of solar energy. However, considering that it took many millions of years to produce the Earth's stocks of fossil fuels and that people have been rapidly consuming them over the course of the past couple of centuries, in reality they must be called "nonrenewable." It will be a long, long time before the world forms new deposits of oil or coal.

The energy crisis that struck in the 1970s did not surprise everyone. A few people were aware that supplies of fossil fuels are finite and that if fossil fuels must be used to heat homes and power cars, then they must eventually run out. A few were also aware that as long as the United States and Canada remain dependent on other nations for much of their energy—North America in 1991 imported 61 percent of its liquid fuel and 53 percent of its total energy used—the countries are necessarily at the mercy of others who have their own interests at heart.

In 1973 an oil embargo imposed by the Organization of Petroleum Exporting Countries (OPEC) brought the same points to the attention of the general citizenry and their political representatives. Among the results was a massive effort to fund research into "energy independence," including ways to get oil from oil shales, to make oil from coal, to squeeze more oil from old oil wells, and to make renewable energy sources more acceptable.

The search for alternative energy sources led to many developments: the market for woodstoves boomed; small hydroelectric power plants were built along rivers where mills of the nineteenth century had left dams that could be reused; entrepreneurs generated electricity by burning sawmill waste and garbage; windmills sprouted like dandelions across the country; many people added energy-producing solar panels to the roofs of their houses; and cars, trucks, and buses were modified to run on hydrogen gas despite the danger of hydrogen's high flammability.

Then OPEC lost its political muscle: new, large oil fields were found; prices fell; and dependence on oil supplies seemed less chancy. As a result, the U.S. government decided it was a waste of money to fund alternative energy research. Research projects and demonstration plants were thus abandoned. However, there were some lasting benefits. For example, energy conservation —from increased building insulation to more efficient lightbulbs, refrigerators, and cars—became almost a cause and indeed reduced energy demand significantly. Photovoltaic cells, which utilize electromagnetic waves (such as those found in visible light) to generate electricity, became the power source for millions of hand-held calculators and other gadgets. And windmills were designed for greater efficiency and durability and were installed by utilities where the wind blew strong and steady.

The world remains enormously dependent on fossil fuels, and their supply remains finite. Can future energy crises far worse than the panics of the 1970s be avoided? Christopher Flavin, vice president for research at the Worldwatch Institute, says yes, maintaining that the world has the necessary technology to meet most of its energy needs from renewable sources, which is already competitive in price in many circumstances and being put to ever wider use. Solar-generated hydrogen, he says, will fulfill the need for a portable fuel. Chauncey Starr, Milton F. Searl, and Sy Alpert of the Electric Power Research Institute argue that renewable (solar) energy is too limited and that increases in energy efficiency and decreases in pollutant (including carbon dioxide) emissions will keep fossil fuels competitive well into the next century.

YES

Christopher Flavin

POWER SHOCK: THE NEXT ENERGY REVOLUTION

Historians of technology may one day argue that by the mid-1990s, the world energy economy was already in the early stages of a major transition. One sign, for example, is that relatively small, efficient jet engines are coming to dominate the power industry, sweeping aside less efficient coal-fired models. Another is that advanced electronics have improved the efficiency of lighting by as much as four-fold. Meanwhile, the fastest growing energy market in the early 1990s isn't oil, coal, or even natural gas—it is wind power, which expanded from 2,000 megawatts in 1990 to 4,500 megawatts in 1995.

Around the world, advanced electronics, new kinds of synthetic materials, and the techniques of mass production are allowing engineers to substitute clever technologies for brute force. The result is a variety of new modular, mass-produced energy systems that have the potential to be more economical and flexible than the traditional energy systems they replace.

Here, as in the mercurial worlds of computers and telecommunications, it is impossible to predict the future. But the broad outlines of a new energy economy are beginning to emerge. Its chief feature is likely to be a radical decentralization, akin to the computer industry's shift from mainframes to PCs. The new technologies will make it possible to decentralize power generation, even down to the household level, harness the world's most abundant energy resources—solar energy and wind power—and greatly reduce the burden that current energy systems place on the world's atmosphere.

But these changes may add up to more than the sum of their parts. Using technologies such as fuel cells and mass-produced solar generators, it should be possible in the long run to replace virtually all fossil fuels with a hydrogen-based energy system, something that author Jules Verne dreamed of more than a century ago. The hydrogen would be produced using sunlight harnessed on rooftops as well as in remote desert collectors, and would be conveyed to homes and industries via pipeline. Although this vision may sound futuristic, most of the inventions needed to make it real have already been made.

From Christopher Flavin, "Power Shock: The Next Energy Revolution," *World Watch*, vol. 9, no. 2 (January/February 1996). Copyright © 1996 by The Worldwatch Institute. Reprinted by permission.

PUNCTUATED EQUILIBRIUM

... For nearly a century after Charles Darwin wrote *Origin of Species*, biologists thought of evolution as an exceedingly gradual process, with an almost infinite number of incremental stages between one species and its successor. During the 1970s, Harvard biologist Stephen Jay Gould proposed an alternative theory: that most evolutionary change occurs in sudden bursts—driven in part by changing climates and other environmental influences that force species to change rapidly in order to survive. According to Gould, these bursts may be preceded by long periods of stasis—giving the impression that evolution is glacially slow. Gould's theory, known as "punctuated equilibrium," has since earned broad acceptance among biologists.

In the evolution of technology, the same pattern of punctuated progress can be seen. The telephone, for example, developed rapidly in the late nineteenth century and then changed very little through the middle decades of the twentieth century. Now the telephone is again in a period of explosive transition—simultaneously becoming digital, wireless, and portable, while also becoming a carrier not only of voices but of a wide variety of other kinds of communications—from facsimile pages to debit card transactions.

To those who make a living out of projecting future energy trends, the current system appears close to immutable. For more than 70 years it has been dominated by big oil refineries, internal combustion engines, and steam-cycle power plants, devices that have become more efficient and larger, but have never been displaced. It is no wonder that these analysts see the future as marked by increasingly small refinements to the existing system.

Reflecting this bias, official energy projections published by the International Energy Agency, the World Energy Council, and various national governments conclude that future energy systems will merely be more efficient versions of the current one. Their studies suggest that our grandchildren will still be driving automobiles powered by internal combustion engines—and using electricity generated by power plants that waste two-thirds of the coal they consume—well into the 21st century.

These prognosticators are mesmerized by how little energy systems have changed in recent decades, but ignore the fact that in the more distant past, energy systems have changed rapidly. The energy economy we have today was created in an explosion of invention between 1890 and 1910. During that short period, many cities were dramatically transformed, with horse-drawn carriages replaced by automobiles, and gas lamps by electric lights.

The carriages and gas lamps had prevailed for centuries, but once the conditions for rapid change were present, the old technologies were replaced with breathtaking speed. Today, we may be at a similar turning point, as revolutionary new energy technologies emerge at the same time that consumers demand a cleaner environment and more flexible, less costly ways of meeting their energy needs. The technological upheavals sweeping so many other industries are unlikely to leave the old energy system intact.

Today, even the conservative business press is beginning to take such ideas seriously. In its October 7 issue, *The Economist* magazine stated: "Once [renewable energy] was the province of mad scientists and dreamers... No longer. Little noticed, the costs of many renewables have recently been tumbling. Fossil fuels are still almost always cheaper, but a battle has begun on the fringes of the mighty $1-trillion-a-year fossil-fuel industry that could force it into retreat early in the coming century."

ROOFTOP POWER

One of the most neglected "fringes" of the world energy economy is made up of thousands of rural villages that are home to some 2 billion people who lack access to electricity or other modern fuels. Yet these villages are now at the center of one of the most revolutionary new developments: during the past ten years, silicon cells that turn sunlight directly into electricity have been installed on or adjacent to at least 250,000 homes, mostly in remote areas of countries such as Sri Lanka, China, and Mexico.

In Kenya, in 1993, more homes were electrified using solar cells than by extending the grid. In Brazil, utility companies are starting to support solar electrification in the Amazon and other areas where it is impractical to extend power lines. In South Africa, the government has launched a major effort to provide solar power to millions of people. And in Vietnam, where only 14 million of the country's 72 million people currently have electricity, the Vietnam Women's Union has launched a solar electrification program.

Solar electric systems are also beginning to appear on the roofs of posh suburban homes in industrial countries. In Sacramento, California, for example, the municipal utility is putting shiny blue solar electric panels on 100 homes each year;

their rooftop systems are connected to the utility's electric grid, so that power not needed within the home can be sold to other consumers. Consumers pay for the systems via their monthly power bill, at a rate that is only slightly higher than their neighbors'....

A product of the electronic revolution, solar cells bypass the mechanical generators now used by virtually all power plants, whether they run on fossil fuels, hydropower, or nuclear energy. First used to power orbiting satellites in the U.S. space program in the 1960s, solar cells are a close relative of the microprocessors that make today's computers possible. The cells consist of semiconductors—usually made of silicon—that emit electrons when struck by sunlight, thereby producing an electric current.

Japanese, Swiss, and U.S. manufacturers have designed experimental "solar tiles" that shelter occupants while also powering their appliances. In Europe, Flachglas, a leading producer of architectural glass, has developed a semitransparent "curtain wall" that provides filtered light as well as electricity. In a joint venture in the United States, Corning Glass and Siemens Solar are developing a similar product.

The cost of solar cells has declined from more than $70 per watt in the 1970s (in 1994 dollars) to $4 per watt today, and is expected to drop to between $1 and $2 per watt within a decade, according to the National Renewable Energy Laboratory in Colorado. As a result, the potential applications have multiplied. The world market went from 34 megawatts in 1988 to an estimated 90 megawatts in 1995.

Aerial photographs show that even in the cloudy climate of the British Isles, putting solar cells on all the country's existing flat roofs could generate 68,000 megawatts of power on a bright day—about half the United Kingdom's current peak power demand. With a strong push by governments and private investors, it is possible that rooftops alone could provide as much as a quarter of the world's electricity by the middle of the next century.

POWER FROM THE BASEMENT

Another technology that may soon allow individual buildings to produce their own power is the fuel cell. First used to provide electricity for orbiting U.S. spacecraft in the 1960s, fuel cells are battery-like devices that efficiently convert a fuel —usually hydrogen—to electricity. Compared to today's generators, which are mechanical devices, fuel cells produce minimal air pollution and virtually no noise. And because they are small and can be located inside buildings, their waste heat can be productively used, rather than vented to the atmosphere as occurs in most of today's power plants....

During the past five years, the imperative to improve urban air quality has produced a surge of investment in fuel cells. Several companies have successfully demonstrated the pollution avoidance benefits of fuel-cell generators by installing them in hospitals and other buildings. Typically, such fuel cells are used to provide around-the-clock electricity, with waste heat captured for water and space heating.

In the United States, the race is on. Last September, ONSI Corporation, a division of United Technologies, launched the world's first commercial fuel cell factory, which will initially turn out some 50 fuel cells each year, at less than half the cost of earlier fuel cells. Meanwhile, Allied Signal has been working on a

5- to 10-kilowatt fuel cell for home-scale use, relying on technologies it developed in its aerospace business. And IBM announced last summer that it is applying its expertise in multi-layer ceramic substrates to make less-expensive fuel cells in a joint venture with the Dow Chemical Company. In Canada, Ballard Power Systems has developed a fuel cell that is designed specifically for use as a bus engine.

Such commitments suggest that a commercial takeoff for fuel cells is likely within the next decade. And as the volume of production grows, costs are expected to plummet. If this technology flourishes, we may soon approach the day when a city that is now served by three or four power plants may have thousands of small networked generators connected to it. In a sign of things to come, the Netherlands already gets one-third of its power from industrial and commercial co-generators. Low cost fuel cells could one day push that figure to two-thirds or more....

WINDS OF CHANGE

Another modular power technology, the wind turbine, has begun to change the electric power landscape from the northern coasts of Europe to the plains of southern India. The world had more than 25,000 wind turbines operating at the end of 1995, producing nearly 5,000 megawatts of power. California has 1,700 megawatts, generating enough electricity to supply all of San Francisco's residents, and Germany has more than 1,000 megawatts, supplying over 5 percent of the electricity in the state of Schleswig-Holstein.

After a slow period in the late 1980s, the world market for wind turbines has exploded since 1990. Following the laws of technological progress and large-scale manufacturing, the cost of wind-generated electricity has fallen by more than two-thirds over the past decade, to the point where it is lower than that of new coal plants in many regions. Within the next decade, it is projected to fall to 3 to 4 cents per kilowatt-hour, making wind the least expensive power source that can be developed on a large scale worldwide.

The new wind turbines aren't the quaint old "wind mills" we remember from past generations; they are sleek, high-tech fiberglass models with gearless, variable speed transmissions and advanced electronic controls. The larger machines have blade spans of 50 meters (160 feet) and more. Unlike large conventional power plants, new wind turbine models enter the market as frequently as new laptop computers do. And, like laptops, they deliver services in small units; the latest wind machines generate 300 to 750 kilowatts per turbine—one-thousandth the size of a typical coal plant.

Europe is now the world's hottest wind power market. Its wind boom is led by Germany, which now has thousands of gleaming white wind turbines sprinkled across the flat farmland of Lower Saxony and other coastal states. The tenfold rise in wind power in Germany since 1990 resulted from an investment boom stirred up by generous tax credits and the 1991 "electricity infeed law" for renewables.

Not far behind are several other European nations, including Denmark, Great Britain, the Netherlands, and Spain. If development continues at the recent frenzied pace, wind power could become a major source of European electricity within the next decade.

In India, a wind energy rush began in 1994 as the government opened up the power grid to independent developers and offered tax incentives for renewable energy development. Indeed, India is now second only to Germany in the number of annual wind power installations. By early 1995, some 300 megawatts of wind power were in place, much of it resulting from joint ventures with European and U.S. manufacturers, some of whom are building assembly plants in India. Already, land values in windy regions have jumped dramatically. Other countries with sizable wind power projects underway include Brazil, China, Greece, and Mexico.

Although wind power provides less than 0.1 percent of the world's electricity today, it is fast becoming a proven power option that is reliable enough for routine use by electric utilities. It is not inconceivable that two decades from now, millions of turbines will be spread across windy areas of the world, providing 20 or 30 percent of the electricity in some areas. In the United States, three Great Plains states could in theory supply all the country's electricity, and for China, the same can be said of Inner Mongolia, which is located within a few hundred kilometers of Beijing.

The formula used for wind energy—independent developers installing collections of small generators in resource-rich areas—is proving viable for solar energy as well. In the Mojave Desert, some 350 megawatts of parabolic dish solar collectors already provide power for Southern California Edison's power grid, and similar projects are being eyed in Australia and the Middle East. Similarly, the Houston-based Enron Corporation announced in late 1994 that it plans to build large collections of grid-connected solar photovoltaic generators in the desert regions of China, India, and the United

States. As costs fall, these could become a leading source of electricity.

SMART ENERGY?

As regional power systems go from relying on 10 or 20 power plants to networking thousands of small generators, broader changes in the energy system are likely to follow. Recent advances in two-way communications make it possible to precisely monitor and control the power system using microprocessors. With such controls, each solar rooftop, fuel cell, and air conditioner can be linked to a utility's computers via copper or fiber optic lines so that the grid operates as a single "smart" system, turning various devices on and off as needed.

In an experiment in the Chenal Valley neighborhood of Little Rock, Arkansas, the local electric utility, Entergy, has installed unobtrusive, wall-mounted computers that look like fancy thermostats. They provide two-way communication between home and utility and permit on-site optimization of energy use. As demand fluctuates, the utility can provide "real time" pricing to customers, who can program their appliances to turn on when demand is low and electricity is available at less expensive rates. For example, a house can be cooled down just before a period of peak temperatures—and peak power prices.

Entergy projects that real-time pricing, combined with electronic controls, will increase the efficiency of the system by reducing peak power demand and, with it, the need for spare generating capacity. For each new household Entergy hooks up in Chenal Valley, at a cost of $1,050, the utility estimates that it avoids $1,757 worth of power supply costs over the next 20 years. Globally, such systems could eliminate the need to build hundreds of large power plants over the next few decades....

The dramatic changes now in prospect for the power industry were acknowledged in last September's *Financial Times Energy Economist:* "Just as the networking personal computer has replaced the mainframe in the office, so we may be seeing a trend towards the imploding of the centralised, integrated utility in sophisticated economies... In short we are at the beginnings of a revolution in power supply."

FORCES OF CHANGE

From some perspectives, the mid-1990s are a dark time for the world energy system. Oil consumption is approaching the record levels of the late 1970s, with demand in some countries growing at rates as high as 10 percent per year. Even the use of coal is still expanding in many nations, pushing emissions of carbon dioxide, the leading greenhouse gas, to more than 6 billion tons per year. Emissions are growing particularly rapidly in China and India, but even the United States and Canada are failing to hold carbon dioxide emissions steady as they are supposed to under the Rio climate convention.

Although most energy analysts view such trends as convincing evidence that the world energy system won't change anytime soon, the reverse may be true. As Stephen Jay Gould's theory suggests, evolutionary bursts are usually precipitated by strong pressures. Today, three major forces of change are bearing down on the world energy economy— new technologies, industry restructuring, and tougher environmental policies—all of which are likely to be intensified by incipient climate change.

New technologies are the most obvious. As noted earlier, advanced electronics, new materials, and biotechnology are now being put to use in energy systems.... Thanks to such developments, spurred by two decades of strong government support for R&D [research and development] on new energy technologies, it will soon be possible to harness solar and wind energy on a much larger scale.

Industry restructuring is also spurring change. In the past, most electric power systems have been operated as government-owned or controlled monopolies that manage everything from constructing power plants to reading the meters attached to customers' homes. These monopolies have been drawn to giant plants and inefficient, entrenched technologies, and have had little incentive to pursue innovation.

But today, all that is changing. In Brazil, India, Poland, Great Britain, Japan, and the United States, utility systems are being broken up and sold to private investors. In many nations, the generation of electricity is increasingly provided by independent power producers that have no monopoly franchise on the business. Local distribution utilities and industrial users buy power from those producers, using the electricity transmission system as a common carrier, in the same way that railroads and telephone lines are used.

This restructuring has led to an unprecedented wave of innovation, as independent producers find that in order to be competitive, they have to build ever more efficient and less expensive plants. Such producers are pursuing smaller and less environmentally damaging energy sources than did their utility brethren. In

the United States, for example, a power plant built in the early 1990s has a capacity of 100 megawatts on average, compared to 600 megawatts less than a decade earlier. Most of the latest plants now are fueled with natural gas rather than coal or nuclear power.

India provides a particularly strong example of the impact of restructuring. As the state utility monopolies were broken in the early 1990s, independent power generation blossomed. Scores of projects are now underway, in a competitive rush to reduce the country's chronic power shortages. Although many of the new plants are coal- and gas-fired, dozens of wind and solar energy projects are also underway, attracting foreign investment and creating a manufacturing boom.

The third force driving rapid change is the growing reach of policies intended to protect the earth's embattled environment. In many countries, emissions and waste-disposal laws have greatly added to the cost of building coal-fired power plants, and nuclear generators have essentially been ruled out as having unacceptably high costs and risks. These changes have boosted the market prospects for efficient natural gas and renewable energy generators.

To help protect the environment, some governments have changed tax and utility laws to level the playing field between dirty and clean technologies. India, for example, allows a full income tax deduction for renewable energy investments, and the United States offers a 1.5 cents per kilowatt-hour subsidy to renewable power. In Germany, renewable power generators have been granted the right to sell power to utilities at a rate of 0.17 DM (12 cents) per kilowatt-hour —about what Germans pay for coal and nuclear power, but well above current prices for the latest natural gas-based power systems—thereby priming the pump for renewables.

As more countries enact similar changes, the boom in renewable energy development now taking place in Germany and India is likely to spread. Japan, for example, has just opened its power grid to independent generators, with special incentives for renewables. Brazil is opening the gates to independents as well, and renewable energy developers are reported to be exploring the coasts and deserts of the country's northeast, which has prime wind and solar sites.

THE HYDROGEN AGE

In elaborate studies churned out by governments and corporations each year, powerful computers are used to project future energy trends. Although the results of such studies are received by many policymakers as gospel, they are generally based on a narrow band of oil price and economic growth assumptions. Indeed, what passes for energy analysis today is dominated by a preoccupation with econometrics and the geopolitics of the Persian Gulf, leaving unquestioned the assumption that we will stay hooked on oil until it is gone, and that coal's role must expand simply because coal is abundant.

Economists who conduct such studies often ignore ongoing technological trends, let alone the broader policy environment. If earlier forecasters had used similar techniques, they would have concluded that we—in the 1990s—would still be driving around in horse-drawn carriages and writing on typewriters. After all, we never ran out of either hay or paper. Rather, people found ways of meeting their needs more conveniently and economically.

What was true for transportation toward the end of the 19th century and for communications toward the end of the 20th will be no less true for energy at the start of the 21st: when breakthroughs alter the relative competitiveness of a long-dominant resource, its continued abundance becomes suddenly irrelevant. The age of oil, for example, was ushered in not by the discovery of petroleum, which had been found much earlier, but by the development of an internal combustion engine that made oil much more useful. Overnight, 25 million horses were rendered obsolete.

Just as our forefathers at the turn of the last century had a hard time envisioning what was to come, so we now have a hard time seeing what lies beyond the age of fossil fuels. Do all of the changes described above add up to more than an efficient version of the current system? The answer appears to be yes. A number of scientists and other experts have been able to offer at least a glimpse of what we are moving toward: a solar hydrogen economy.

Hydrogen is the simplest of the chemical fuels, and unlike methane, the cleanest fuel used today, is entirely carbon-free. Hydrogen is the lightest of the elements as well as the most abundant. Three-quarters of the mass of the universe consists of hydrogen, which of course is also a principal constituent of water. When the time comes to use the hydrogen as fuel, it is combined with oxygen to produce water, releasing energy but no pollution.

Scientists have foreseen the possibility of a transition to hydrogen for more than a century, and today it is seen as the logical "third wave" fuel—hydrogen gas following liquid oil, just as oil replaced coal decades earlier. The required technology—using electricity to split water molecules through electrolysis—is already being used commercially. (All the world's current energy needs could be met with less than 1 percent of today's fresh water supply, and hydrogen can also be produced from seawater.) Although many people worry that hydrogen is dangerous, if properly handled, it will probably be safer than fuels like gasoline that are widely used today.

The challenge now holding up the transition to hydrogen is finding inexpensive sources of energy to split water. This may seem circular—the need to find cheap energy in order to produce an affordable fuel. But the key to the puzzle lies in the possibility of storage and transportation. Wind and solar energy are often found in the wrong place at the wrong time, but those energy sources can be used to feed the electricity grid when power demand is high, and to produce storable hydrogen when it is not.

In fact, hydrogen may provide the ideal means of storing and distributing these intermittent power sources. Additional hydrogen can be produced in homes and commercial buildings using rooftop solar cells. The hydrogen can then either be stored in a basement tank for later use in a fuel cell or conventional boiler, or be piped into a local hydrogen distribution system.

In either case, a decade or two from now, hydrogen could begin to enter the markets now dominated by oil and natural gas—including home heating, cooking, industrial heat, and transportation. In fact, scientists have determined that in the early stages, hydrogen fuel can be derived from natural gas, and that during the transition, consumers may use a mixture of hydrogen and methane gas. Experimental hydrogen-powered cars have already been developed by Mazda and Mercedes. With the advent of small fuel cells, such cars may become highly efficient and affordable. By the middle of the next century, oil and coal could be phased out.

Although renewable energy sources are more abundant in some areas than others, they are far less concentrated than oil, since two-thirds of proven petroleum reserves are in the Persian Gulf. Moreover, the coming solar-hydrogen economy is likely to be based on a diverse array of renewable resources, with the mix varying by region. The hydrogen can be carried to where it is needed through pipelines similar to those used to carry natural gas.

Over time, solar- and wind-derived hydrogen could transform the way energy is produced and used virtually everywhere. All of the world's major population centers are within reach of sunny and wind-rich areas. The Great Plains of North America, for instance, could supply much of Canada and the United States with electricity and hydrogen fuel. For Europe, solar power plants could be built in North Africa, with hydrogen transported along existing gas pipeline routes. In China, hydrogen could be produced in the country's vast western deserts and shipped to population centers on the coastal plain.

Many people assume that producing sufficient hydrogen from solar and wind energy requires huge swaths of land, but these technologies actually use less than one-fifth as much land to produce a given amount of energy as does hydropower, which now supplies nearly a third of the world's electricity. Moreover, while much of the land used for hydropower has to be condemned for flooding (often of prime cropland), the tracts used for wind farms can still be used for crops and grazing.

What then would a solar-hydrogen energy system look like? One of its chief advantages is that it would be largely invisible. Fuel cells... would be hidden in peoples' basements; solar rooftops would be nearly indistinguishable from conventional rooftops; and hydrogen pipelines would be buried underground, as are today's natural gas pipelines. Some rural farming areas may be sprinkled with wind turbines, but most of the larger wind and solar power plants are likely to be located in remote areas such as India's Thar Desert or Mexico's La Ventosa, where people rarely visit.

On first reflection, such an energy system may seem fanciful. But two decades ago, the idea of desktop computers and information superhighways would have seemed equally far-fetched. And arguably, what is most inconceivable is that an information-age economy will be powered by a primitive industrial age energy system.

As corporate and government decision makers begin to understand just how economical and practical a zero-emission, carbon-free energy system can be, and just how inefficient and dirty the current system is, they may finally summon the sort of effort that made the last great energy transition possible—a hundred years ago.

NO

Chauncey Starr, Milton F. Searl, and Sy Alpert

ENERGY SOURCES:
A REALISTIC OUTLOOK

Projections to the middle of the next century indicate that unabated
historical global energy trends would lead to an annual global energy demand about four times present levels, primarily due to population and economic growth. But extensive global conservation and
energy-efficient systems might reduce this value by half. The cumulative effect of the coming half century's use may strain the world's
low-cost resources, particularly oil. The future fuel mix is further
complicated by the environmental thrust to reduce the global use of
carbon-based fuels. The interaction of the principal factors influencing future energy resource and technology options are projected.

The energy supply mix of the coming century will depend on the magnitude
of the demand growth for global energy, changing performance targets, and
the technologies available to meet them. . . .

The future adequacy of globally available fossil fuel resources will depend
on the total societal costs of extracting and delivering such fuels and on their
effectiveness in use to meet the broad performance objectives of energy systems. Projections of proven, probable, and speculative resources are often
updated as new discoveries or extraction techniques are developed, but professional conservatism has often resulted in underestimating future resource
expansion at acceptable costs. On a next century time scale, the traditional
question is whether the cumulative effect of the increasing rate of depletion
of these resources would result in a global constraint on energy systems,
particularly on the future supply of liquid fuel for vehicles and airplanes.
This question is technologically intriguing because of the now demonstrated
large-scale convertibility of all fossil fuels to gas or liquid forms and the implications of the application of this technology as an option for a global source
of liquid fuel derived from large coal resources.

The present global energy mix is likely to change substantially during
the next century as a result of several factors. First, comparative scarcity

From Chauncey Starr, Milton F. Searl, and Sy Alpert, "Energy Sources: A Realistic Outlook,"
Science, vol. 256 (May 15, 1992), pp. 981–986. Copyright © 1992 by The American Association for
the Advancement of Science. Reprinted by permission. Notes and references omitted.

attributable either to resource or to political constraints may increase the relative price of the most convenient fossil fuel, oil; second, the growing costs of reducing environmental degradation will alter the cost competition among fuels; and third, the potential threat of global climate change may stimulate a shift from carbon-based fuels to nonfossil alternatives. A resource perspective for the next century involves speculation on future energy demand, likely competitive supply alternatives, and possible changes in energy systems and technologies. Such speculations are shaped by the long time periods required to develop new or improved energy technologies and to deploy them commercially. Although long-range projections are unavoidably judgmental and are dependent on present knowledge and experience, they permit the scoping of alternative trends and outcomes and thus help guide current strategies. A projected global energy supply mix based on such judgmental factors provides a conceptual basis for considering the factors discussed below, which are likely to shape future trends.

It is of particular interest that the availability of liquid fuels in the coming century and beyond is likely to be maintained as the rising cost of conventional oil brings into competition higher cost sources such as coal conversion, tar sands, and oil shale. This transition, initially based on the technologies described in this paper, should be under way by the middle of the century.

FUTURE ENERGY DEMAND

Two major trends determine global future end use energy demand, population growth and economic growth. The primary energy input depends on the efficiency of conversion to end use, as determined by the choice of technology. Thus, if a permanent increase in the real price of primary fuel is expected, there exists an incentive to invest in more efficient or alternative technologies. The range of future energy demand and supply outcomes based on plausible projections of these factors has been studied by Starr and Searl. Two bounding efficiencies were applied to current trends: (i) maintenance of current conversion efficiencies and (ii) a full conservation concept, which assumed reduction of the present trend by one-third of all electricity use and by half of all direct energy (nonelectric) use. This full conservation was judged to be the maximum amount of conservation that could foreseeably be implemented without inhibiting economic growth.

... By the year 2060, if present trends continue without modification, total energy demand is projected to increase 4.4 times and electricity demand is projected to increase 7.0 times the 1986 reference levels. If full conservation is accomplished, the total energy demand increase is reduced to 2.5 times and electricity demand is reduced to 4.7 times. Most of the anticipated increases are the result of the higher population and economic growth rates of the less developed countries. These large increases are the result of a global population increase of 1.95 times and an average per capita gross national product (GNP) increase of 2.8 times, for a combined product growth of 5.5 times. With the full conservation case, this implies that the efficiency of global economic productivity per unit of primary energy will be improved 2.2 times....

FUTURE SUPPLY: ARE FOSSIL FUELS A CONSTRAINT?

There is little likelihood that serious scarcity of fuels will develop during the next century on a global scale because of the intraconvertibility of coals, oil, and gas. The major uncertainties arise from the constantly changing economic competition among the various sources and the eventual effects of environmental constraints and increased costs arising from the need to minimize undesirable effluents of fuel use. The prevalent situation that many reserves are only proven for several decades is an artifact of prudent investment in development of a future inventory.... The proven fossil reserves are nearly twice that needed to meet the projected cumulative global demand. The specific resource factors for near-term oil and gas have been recently discussed in some detail, suggesting that low-cost oil will become scarcer after the next few decades. Of course, the speculative higher cost resources are uncertain but may be large. In fact, the real resource cost of energy is lower today than at the beginning of this century, even though the world's population has tripled and its economic output increased by an order of magnitude. Economic incentives and technology have historically overcome perceived resource limitations.

However, it is likely that real primary energy costs from the conventional oil and gas sources will eventually increase. The average cost of exploration and development of new oil fields has risen steadily. At some increasing price level, unconventional oil sources gradually become competitive but require large capital investments. For example, at an oil price of about $30 to $40 per barrel (1990 dollars), large high-cost oil resources (for example, tar sands) become economically viable. Even the direct use of oil shales in utility boilers becomes marginally economic. Such oil-bearing bodies are the energy equivalent of giant oil fields, sufficiently large to provide the liquid fuel needs of the next century but require much higher capital investment for the same flow rates. This would change the character of the liquid fuel production industry.

The most abundant fossil fuel is coal, representing about 90% of all known conventional fossil resources. Its convertibility to both liquid and gaseous hydrocarbons has been demonstrated. The production of complex hydrocarbons by coal conversion has been commercially deployed worldwide.... The famous Sasol plant in South Africa has been producing liquid transportation fuel for decades from indigenous coal. The true costs have been stated to be marginally competitive currently but would be more competitive at higher oil prices. In the past 6 years, a plant in New Zealand has demonstrated the feasibility of converting methane into gasoline with a large-scale zeolite process. Low-cost and large natural gas reserves discovered in some remote locations have stimulated the investment in on-site conversion of natural gas to liquid fuel, so as to economically ship the product to a distant transportation market. It is thus obvious that if the price of oil becomes sufficiently high, coal conversion to liquid fuel can enter the oil industry investment structure. Estimates for producing liquid fuel from coal or gas indicate that $50 to $60 billion over the next 30 to 40 years would be required to satisfy 5% of projected U.S. demand for transportation fuel. This should be compared with the present worldwide expenditure of the oil and gas companies of more than $50 billion annually for exploration and production, and the roughly $500 billion of annual crude oil sales.

A direct use of coal conversion to gas for the generation of electricity has already been demonstrated with the 100-MW integrated gasification combined cycle (IGCC) power plant at the cool water station of Southern California Edison. This is the cleanest coal-fueled technique developed.... The advanced cycles now have a marginally higher capital cost, but continuing development will eventually make them competitive, particularly because of environmental factors.

A major future improvement in the efficiency of fossil fuel-based electricity generation will come from the ongoing development of the fuel cell.... The molten carbonate fuel cell is the current focus of development.... If successful, the commercialization of the fuel cell would eventually decrease the electricity component of the global demand for coal to about two-thirds of that based on present power plant practice, reducing annual carbon emissions.

NONFOSSIL AND RENEWABLES: SIGNIFICANT OR MARGINAL?

The potential role of the nonfossil and renewables in the future global energy mix depends on their developing economic competitiveness. This category includes biomass, solar, wind, geothermal, and the two commercial electricity sources, hydro and nuclear. Only hydro and nuclear are significant contributors today, with hydro about 20% of global electricity and nuclear about 17%. There are practical upper bounds for the potential contri-

bution of the nonfossil and renewable sources summarized here.

Both the energy input to manufacture the renewables and their initial capital cost are the issues. A basic consideration is net energy output, or the output minus the energy input from other resources required for their manufacture. This is particularly relevant to biomass, where the energy input for their growth (for example, fertilizer and irrigation) and processing are substantial. Both factors determine the competitive lifetime cost per unit of delivered end-use energy. As yet, renewables such as solar, wind, and biomass have been able to penetrate only limited niche markets, with much uncertainty about their net energy contribution.

The economic issues for hydro and nuclear are understood the best out of the renewables. Both require about the same capital investment per plant— about twice that for a coal-based unit. Compared to coal, hydro has no fuel cost and a low maintenance and operating cost; nuclear has a low fuel cost and a high maintenance and operating cost. Depending on the treatment of capital costs, hydroelectricity is usually cheaper than coal. In the industrial countries, nuclear electricity is now generally competitive with coal. The upper limit for global hydro growth is about four times the present level. Nuclear is limited only by available capital and manufacturing facilities. Both are constrained by environmental considerations. Hydro expansion involves flooding large areas and altering river flows and probably will not grow significantly for environmental reasons. Nuclear, when operating as designed, has small environmental impact but faces serious public concerns about the risk of off-design accidental release of radioactivity from either the reactor or spent fuel, and thus, nuclear has high administrative penalties. This has stimulated the current engineering concentration on reducing the probability of such accidents. Nuclear growth depends on the future public perception of the comparative benefits, costs, and risks of alternative energy sources. Based on the comparative evaluations of tangible risks to public health, safety, and environment, nuclear appears to be a better choice than coal. The intangible risk comparisons are more uncertain. Historically, such perceptions have changed with time. A century ago oil was perceived as too inflammable to replace coal, retarding its use in naval vessels for decades. During the recent decades, large naval ships turned to nuclear power because of its fuel longevity. Similarly, public opinion may shift with the changing priorities of the issues—costs, pollution, safety, global warming, among others. In the meanwhile, nuclear is slowly expanding worldwide, now providing 17% of world electricity.

Biomass is an unusual case. Much of the population in the underdeveloped regions has historically depended on noncommercial biomass energy sources, such as wood, shrubs, agricultural wastes, and animal dung, because these required no capital, only labor. In the industrial world, wastes from the paper, pulp, and lumber industries are used as on-site fuel. Less than 2% of the global energy supply is estimated to be from such noncommercial sources. The true cost of the noncommercial sources in the underdeveloped world is speculative because they are not market priced. However, in labor-hours required for their collection, noncommercial sources are costly. If the economic growth of the underdeveloped countries continues, the shift of this labor pool

to more economically productive activity will result in a corresponding shift from noncommercial to commercial fuels, probably petroleum products initially.

The concept of commercial biomass fuel production through managed agriculture and forestry has been studied in great detail. The production of ethanol from sugar cane in Brazil is a massive demonstration of this potential. Although it was initially undertaken for internal social and trade balance objectives, ethanol now appears embedded in that nation's structure and may continue for that reason. However, it does not appear to be economically competitive with petroleum products in a world market. From a net energy view, estimates range from marginal to providing about 20% more energy than it consumes. The tropical zone, including Brazil, is the optimum area for biomass production and provides the basis for the most optimistic estimates of managed forestry. As a feasible, although optimistic upper estimate, biomass might supply a fourth of the fuel for the electricity demand in 2060 with full conservation, provided that transmission to markets from such biomass plants is available. Hall et al. suggest a slightly more optimistic estimate of the potential. If reduction of carbon emission becomes a global priority, managed biomass deserves a high weighting because it will either recirculate atmospheric carbon or sequester it. This capability suggests that managed biomass (that is, forestry) be encouraged to sequester carbon rather than use it as a fuel, particularly because of its uncertain net energy contribution.

The key technological issue for solar and wind is epitomized by the windmill-driven old-fashioned well-water pump and tank (once common on farms). It represents the ideal theoretical arrangement —an intermittent source coupled to storage end use. Its only handicap was the catastrophic windless drought that occurs for extended periods almost every year. Windmills were abandoned when power lines became available for reliable electrical pumping. Analogously, solar sources face the uncertainty of heavy cloud cover and reduced output. Nevertheless, the immensity of the solar energy available both by direct radiation and from wind is such that, even with low-efficiency conversion systems of a few percent, it is seductively apparent that most of the future global energy needs could be met. The big barrier is the technical and economic feasibility of overcoming their intermittent nature with energy storage and the required expanded collectors.

Solar and wind have made minimal entries to the present energy structure. Several windmill demonstrations have been installed on utility systems. Subsidized solar generators are supplying electricity during the peak hours, which roughly coincide with the diurnal cycle. As yet, their competitiveness is marginal. Both direct thermal absorption and photovoltaic systems should improve with development. Both have high capital costs per unit of electricity, which will be multiplied many times if their intermittent nature is compensated by the addition of energy storage facilities. Unless a low-cost electricity storage device is developed, the large-scale participation of solar and wind sources will be limited to a 12% maximum of the total network capacity of fuel-based electrical systems. However, this is not inconsiderable. By the middle of the next century this limited fraction would be equivalent to about 60% of today's world electricity generation. Solar and wind in combination with batteries can today economically fill small power niches, such as remote signaling devices. This may establish a base for future improvements and growth.

Solar enthusiasts have suggested that solar electricity be used to dissociate water for the production of hydrogen as a transportation fuel. This would achieve the ideal system goal of energy storage, no carbon emissions or pollutants, and an eternal primary energy resource. Although scientifically sound, the practical barriers of economics and operable technologies are large. Many billions of cubic feet of pure hydrogen are routinely produced in the world's oil refineries, at costs that are a fraction of electrolytic hydrogen. Nevertheless, there are no indications that a transition from conventional end-use systems to hydrogen-based systems has been of practical interest. There are no developments now visible that are likely to remove these economic and technical barriers, although the obvious merits of hydrogen combustion producing only water as a byproduct provides a tantalizing target....

TECHNOLOGY TRANSITION—WHY DOES IT TAKE SO LONG?

In considering advanced energy systems that might supply future energy needs, many decades will be required for a significant transition from today's conventional systems. Only in a crisis is it feasible to compress research, development, demonstration, and deployment into a decade or less. This has been accomplished in wartime by overriding all normal priorities and economic constraints. The history of energy fuel transitions (wood-coal-oil) shows that in a peacetime commercial environment almost a half century is required to significantly shift fuel patterns.

A projection of modern industrial experience to the future of advanced coal technologies suggests the typical time sequence of energy research, development, demonstration, and deployment....

The long time required for these transitions has serious implications for global energy strategies. It is likely that this time scale of three to five decades for significant energy contribution will also apply to the renewables, with the eventual limitations already described. By the middle of the next century perhaps a third of the global electricity-generating capacity might be advanced technology, and by the end of the century most of it should be. In the industrial countries, the entry of advanced technologies is limited by the slow obsolescence of existing plants (with a usual lifetime of 40 years) and by the rate at which additional capacity is needed. At a typical long-term annual growth rate of 2%, it takes 35 years to double total capacity. For the undeveloped countries obsolescence is less an issue than the scarcity of capital and the avoidance of performance risk. Thus, they are likely to purchase only well-proven conventional plants. Nevertheless, they are in particular need of small and dispersed power growth, providing a special opportunity for small solar, wind, and conventional fossil-fueled units.

POSTSCRIPT

Can the Sun and Wind Supply Our Energy Needs?

Starr, Searl, and Alpert use a key phrase when they say that a shift to hydrogen fuel has not "been of practical interest." Perhaps the flow of energy from the sun to Earth *is* sufficient to meet the needs of society, and perhaps there are ways around the drawbacks, but as long as society can continue to use the physical infrastructure it has developed to deal with oil—even if this means, for instance, converting coal to a synthetic oil—nothing else will be "practical." This remains true even if society chooses to develop techniques for using solar energy to produce liquid fuels other than hydrogen, such as synthetic gas, or syngas. See Israel Dostrovsky, "Chemical Fuels from the Sun," *Scientific American* (December 1991). The question thus comes down to how long fossil fuels will remain practical energy sources.

How could a shift toward renewable sources of energy be achieved? Flavin says that the shift is already under way. The prices of some renewable-energy technologies have been dropping steadily. These technologies have also been finding favor in many parts of both the developed and the developing world, and installed wind-energy generating capacity has been increasing by about 20 percent per year since 1990. Installed photovoltaic capacity has been increasing almost as fast. See *Vital Signs 1995* (W. W. Norton, 1995). The following warning from *World Resources 1994–95* (Oxford University Press, 1994) already seems out of date: "Without leadership in developing and actively promoting advanced energy technologies... it is unlikely that these technologies will be speedily adopted [by developing nations, which] do not command sufficient technical and financial resources to drive research and development, and they harbor institutional biases favoring conventional fossil fuel and hydroelectric approaches." The combination of market forces and available technology is doing the job.

Yet powerful forces continue to support fossil fuels. As noted in *World Resources 1994–95*, "Worldwide commercial energy production was 35 percent higher in 1991 than in 1971.... Liquid fuels, primarily derived from petroleum, continue to dominate the world's energy mix."

To learn more about the use of hydrogen as a fuel, see James J. MacKenzie, *Electric and Hydrogen Vehicles* (World Resources Institute, 1994) and Keith L. Kozloff and Roger C. Dower, *A New Power Base: Renewable Energy Policies for the Nineties and Beyond* (World Resources Institute, 1993).

Students who wish to find information on the Internet will find this site a useful starting point: http://www.nrel.gov/research/nrel_research.html.

ISSUE 7

Should Society Be Concerned About Global Warming?

YES: Ross Gelbspan, from "The Heat Is On," *Harper's Magazine* (December 1995)

NO: Wilfred Beckerman and Jesse Malkin, from "How Much Does Global Warming Matter?" *The Public Interest* (Winter 1994)

ISSUE SUMMARY

YES: Journalist Ross Gelbspan argues that the evidence for global warming is incontrovertible, despite the disinformation campaign being waged by the fossil fuels industry, and that the effects on human society will be extreme. Action is therefore needed now.

NO: Economists Wilfred Beckerman and Jesse Malkin argue that global warming, if it even occurs, will not be catastrophic and warrants no immediate action; there are other worldwide concerns that are far more pressing.

Scientists have known for a century that carbon dioxide and other "greenhouse gases" (including water vapor, methane, and chlorofluorocarbons) help prevent heat from escaping the Earth. In fact, it is this "greenhouse effect" that keeps the Earth warm enough to support life. Yet there can be too much of a good thing. Ever since the dawn of the industrial age, humans have been burning vast quantities of fossil fuels, releasing the carbon they contain as carbon dioxide. Because of this, some estimate that by the year 2050, the amount of carbon dioxide in the air will be double what it was in 1850. By 1982 the increase was apparent. Less than a decade later, many researchers were saying that the climate had already begun to warm. Now there is a strong consensus that the global climate will continue to warm. However, there is less agreement on just how much it will warm or what the impact of the warming will be on human (and other) life.

The June 1992 issue of *The Bulletin of the Atomic Scientists* carries two articles on the possible consequences of the greenhouse effect. In "Global Warming: The Worst Case," Jeremy Leggett says that although there are enormous uncertainties, a warmer climate will release more carbon dioxide, which will warm the climate even further. As a result, soil will grow dryer; forest fires will occur more frequently; plant pests will thrive; and methane trapped in the world's seabeds will be released and will increase global warming much further— in effect, there will be a "runaway greenhouse effect." Leggett also hints at the possibility that the polar ice caps will melt and raise sea levels by hundreds of feet.

Taking the opposing view, in "Warming Theories Need Warning Label," S. Fred Singer emphasizes the uncertainties in the projections of global warming and their dependence on the accuracy of the computer models that generate them, and he points out that improvements in the models have consistently shrunk the size of the predicted change. There will be no catastrophe, he argues, and money spent to ward off the climate warming would be better spent on "so many pressing—and real—problems in need of resources."

These scientists are not alone on their sides of the debate. In 1991 many scientists testified on "Global Climate Change and Greenhouse Emissions" before the House Subcommittee on Health and the Environment, Committee on Energy and Commerce. Some scientists maintained that the problem was real and potentially serious. See, for instance, Wallace S. Broecker, "Global Warming on Trial," *Natural History* (April 1992), in which the author asserts that past climate coolings have been so immensely disruptive that a cautious approach to the future would require doing all we can to decrease releases of greenhouse gases to ward off potential disaster.

Other scientists asserted that they were not impressed by the data and computer models assembled to date. For instance, Sallie Baliunas, deputy director of the Mount Wilson Observatory and chair of the Science Advisory Board at the George C. Marshall Institute in Washington, D.C., claimed that global warming in the next century will amount to no more than a few tenths of a degree, "indistinguishable from natural fluctuations in temperature." Richard Lindzen, in "Absence of Scientific Basis," *Research and Exploration* (Spring 1993), stated outright that there is no real evidence at all for global warming.

In the following selections, journalist Ross Gelbspan notes that the last few years have witnessed an alarming number of extremes in the weather. This, he asserts, is consistent with analyses that say global warming puts more energy into weather systems and thus drives rainstorms, droughts, floods, and even blizzards. The scientific consensus is therefore stronger today than it was just a few years ago. Those who still question "global warming," says Gelbspan, are serving a campaign of disinformation for the fossil-fuels industry. Oxford University scholar Wilfred Beckerman and writer Jesse Malkin insist that disaster is not imminent and that people can adapt to whatever changes may occur. They say that there are much better ways to spend money, such as on relieving world poverty, than in trying to ward off a nonproblem like global warming.

YES

Ross Gelbspan

THE HEAT IS ON

After my lawn had burned away to straw last summer, and the local papers announced that the season had been one of the driest in the recorded history of New England, I found myself wondering how long we can go on pretending that nothing is amiss with the world's weather. It wasn't just the fifty ducks near my house that had died when falling water levels in a creek exposed them to botulism-infested mud, or the five hundred people dead in the Midwest from an unexpected heat wave that followed the season's second "one-hundred-year flood" in three years. It was also the news from New Orleans (overrun by an extraordinary number of cockroaches and termites after a fifth consecutive winter without a killing frost), from Spain (suffering a fourth year of drought in a region that ordinarily enjoys a rainfall of 84 inches a year), and from London (Britain's meteorological office reporting the driest summer since 1727 and the hottest since 1659).

The reports of changes in the world's climate have been with us for fifteen or twenty years, most urgently since 1988, when Dr. James Hansen, director of NASA's Goddard Institute for Space Studies, declared that the era of global warming was at hand. As a newspaper correspondent who had reported on the United Nations Conferences on the environment in Stockholm in 1972 and in Rio in 1992, I understood something of the ill effects apt to result from the extravagant burning of oil and coal. New record-setting weather extremes seem to have become as commonplace as traffic accidents, and three simple facts have long been known: the distance from the surface of the earth to the far edge of the inner atmosphere is only twelve miles; the annual amount of carbon dioxide forced into that limited space is six billion tons; and the ten hottest years in recorded human history have all occurred since 1980. The facts beg a question that is as simple to ask as it is hard to answer. What do we do with what we know?

The question became more pointed in September, when the 2,500 climate scientists serving on the Intergovernmental Panel on Climate Change [IPCC] issued a new statement on the prospect of forthcoming catastrophe. Never before had the IPCC (called into existence in 1988) come to so unambiguous a conclusion. Always in years past there had been people saying that we didn't

From Ross Gelbspan, "The Heat Is On," *Harper's Magazine*, vol. 291, no. 1747 (December 1995). Copyright © 1995 by *Harper's Magazine*. Reprinted by permission. All rights reserved. Some notes omitted.

yet know enough, or that the evidence was problematical, or our system of computer simulation was subject to too many uncertainties. Not this year. The panel flatly announced that the earth had entered a period of climatic instability likely to cause "widespread economic, social and environmental dislocation over the next century." The continuing emission of greenhouse gases would create protracted, crop-destroying droughts in continental interiors, a host of new and recurring diseases, hurricanes of extraordinary malevolence, and rising sea levels that could inundate island nations and low-lying coastal rims on the continents.

I came across the report in the *New York Times* during the same week that the island of St. Thomas was blasted to shambles by one of thirteen hurricanes that roiled the Caribbean this fall. Scientists speak the language of probability. They prefer to avoid making statements that cannot be further corrected, reinterpreted, modified, or proven wrong. If its September announcement was uncharacteristically bold, possibly it was because the IPCC scientists understood that they were addressing their remarks to people profoundly unwilling to hear what they had to say.

That resistance is understandable, given the immensity of the stakes. The energy industries now constitute the largest single enterprise known to mankind. Moreover, they are indivisible from automobile, farming, shipping, air freight, and banking interests, as well as from the governments dependent on oil revenues for their very existence. With annual sales in excess of one trillion dollars and daily sales of more than two billion dollars, the oil industry alone supports the economies of the Middle East and large segments of the economies of

Russia, Mexico, Venezuela, Nigeria, Indonesia, Norway, and Great Britain. Begin to enforce restriction on the consumption of oil and coal, and the effects on the global economy—unemployment, depression, social breakdown, and war—might lay waste to what we have come to call civilization. It is no wonder that for the last five or six years many of the world's politicians and most of the world's news media have been promoting the perception that the worries about the weather are overwrought. Ever since the IPCC first set out to devise strategies whereby the nations of the world might reduce their carbon dioxide emissions, and thus ward off a rise in the average global temperature on the order of 4 or 5 degrees Celsius (roughly equal in magnitude to the difference between the last ice age and the current climatic period), the energy industry has been conducting, not unreasonably, a ferocious public relations campaign meant to sell the notion that science, any science, is always a matter of uncertainty. Yet on reading the news from the IPCC, I wondered how the oil company publicists would confront the most recent series of geophysical events and scientific findings. To wit:

- A 48-by-22 mile chunk of the Larsen Ice Shelf in the Antarctic broke off last March, exposing rocks that had been buried for 20,000 years and prompting Rodolfo del Valle of the Argentine Antarctic Institute to tell the Associated Press, "Last November we predicted the [ice shelf] would crack in ten years, but it has happened in barely two months."

- In April, researchers discovered a 70 percent decline in the population of zooplankton off the coast of southern California, raising questions about the survival of several species of fish that feed on it. Scientists have linked the change to a 1 to 2 degree C increase in the surface water temperature over the last four decades.

- A recent series of articles in *The Lancet*, a British medical journal, linked changes in climate patterns to the spread of infectious diseases around the world. The *Aedes aegypti* mosquito, which spreads dengue fever and yellow fever, has traditionally been unable to survive at altitudes higher than 1,000 meters above sea level. But these mosquitoes are now being reported at 1,150 meters in Costa Rica and at 2,200 meters in Colombia. Ocean warming has triggered algae blooms linked to outbreaks of cholera in India, Bangladesh, and the Pacific coast of South America, where, in 1991, the disease infected more than 400,000 people.

- In a paper published in *Science* in April, David J. Thomson, of the AT&T Bell Laboratories, concluded that the .6 degree C warming of the average global temperature over the past century correlates directly with the buildup of atmospheric carbon dioxide. Separate findings by a team of scientists at the National Oceanic and Atmospheric Administrations's National Climatic Data Center indicate that growing weather extremes in the United States are due, by a probability of 90 percent, to rising levels of greenhouse gases.

- Scientists previously believed that the transitions between ice ages and more moderate climatic periods occur gradually, over centuries. But researchers from the Woods Hole Oceanographic Institution, examining deep ocean sediment and ice core samples, found that these shifts, with their temperature changes of up to 7 degrees C, have occurred within three to four decades—a virtual nanosecond in geological time. Over the last 70,000 years, the earth's climate has snapped into radically different temperature regimes. "Our results suggest that the present climate system is very delicately poised," said researcher Scott Lehman. "Shifts could happen very rapidly if conditions are right, and we cannot predict when that will occur." His cautionary tone is underscored by findings that the end of the last ice age, some 8,000 years ago, was preceded by a series of extreme oscillations in which severe regional deep freezes alternated with warming spikes. As the North Atlantic warmed, Arctic snowmelts and increased rainfall diluted the salt content of the ocean, which, in turn, redirected the ocean's warming current from a northeasterly direction to one that ran nearly due east. Should such an episode occur today, say researchers, "the present climate of Britain and Norway would change suddenly to that of Greenland."

These items (and many like them) would seem to be alarming news—far more important than the candidacy of Colin Powell, or even whether Newt Gingrich believes the government should feed poor children—worthy of a national debate or the sustained attention of Congress. But the signs and portents have been largely ignored, relegated to the environmental press and the oddball margins of the mass media. More often than not, the news about the accelerating retreat of the world's glaciers or the heat- and insect-stressed Canadian forests comes qualified with the observation that the question of global warming never can be conclusively resolved. The confusion is intentional, expensively gift wrapped by the energy industries.

* * *

Capital keeps its nose to the wind. The people who run the world's oil and coal companies know that the march of science, and of political action, may be slowed by disinformation. In the last year and a half, one of the leading oil industry public relations outlets, the Global Climate Coalition, has spent more than a million dollars to downplay the threat of climate change. It expects to spend another $850,000 on the issue next year. Similarly, the National Coal Association spent more than $700,000 on the global climate issue in 1992 and 1993. In 1993 alone, the American Petroleum Institute, just one of fifty-four industry members of the GCC, paid $1.8 million to the public relations firm of Burson-Marsteller partly in an effort to defeat a proposed tax on fossil fuels. For perspective, this is only slightly less than the combined yearly expenditures on global warming of the five major environmental groups that focus on climate issues—about $2.1 million, according to officials of the Environmental Defense Fund, the Natural Resources Defense Council, the Sierra Club, the Union of Concerned Scientists, and the World Wildlife Fund.

For the most part the industry has relied on a small band of skeptics—Dr. Richard S. Lindzen, Dr. Pat Michaels, Dr. Robert Balling, Dr. Sherwood Idso, and Dr. S. Fred Singer, among others— who have proven extraordinarily adept at draining the issue of all sense of crisis. Through their frequent pronouncements in the press and on radio and television, they have helped to create the illusion that the question is hopelessly mired in unknowns. Most damaging has been their influence on decision makers; their contrarian views have allowed conservative Republicans such as Representative Dana Rohrabacher (R., Calif.) to dismiss legitimate research concerns as "liberal claptrap" and have provided the basis for the recent round of budget cuts to those government science programs designed to monitor the health of the planet.

Last May, Minnesota held hearings in St. Paul to determine the environmental cost of coal burning by state power plants. Three of the skeptics—Lindzen, Michaels, and Balling—were hired as expert witnesses to testify on behalf of Western Fuels Association, a $400 million consortium of coal suppliers and coal-fired utilities.[1]

An especially aggressive industry player, Western Fuels was quite candid about its strategy in two annual reports: "[T]here has been a close to universal impulse in the trade association community here in Washington to concede the scientific premise of global warming... while arguing over policy prescriptions that would be the least disruptive to our economy.... We have disagreed, and do disagree, with this strategy." "When [the climate change] controversy first erupted... scientists were found who are skeptical about much of what seemed generally accepted about the potential for climate change." Among them were Michaels, Balling, and S. Fred Singer.

Lindzen, a distinguished professor of meteorology at MIT, testified in St. Paul that the maximum probable warming of the atmosphere in the face of a doubling of carbon dioxide emissions over the next century would amount to no more than a negligible .3 degrees C. Michaels, who teaches climatology at the University of Virginia, stated that he foresaw no increase in the rate of sea level rise—another feared precursor of global warming. Balling, who works on climate issues at Arizona State University, declared that the increase in emissions would boost the average global temperature by no more than one degree.

At first glance, these attacks appear defensible, given their focus on the black holes of uncertainty that mark our current knowledge of the planet's exquisitely interrelated climate system. The skeptics emphasize the inadequacy of a major climate research tool known as a General Circulation Model, and our ignorance of carbon dioxide exchange between the oceans and the atmosphere and of the various roles of clouds. They have repeatedly pointed out that although the world's output of carbon dioxide has exploded since 1940, there has been no corresponding increase in the global temperature. The larger scientific community, by contrast, holds that this is due to the masking effect of low-level sulfur particulates, which exert a temporary cooling effect on the earth, and to a time lag in the oceans' absorption and release of carbon dioxide.

But while the skeptics portray themselves as besieged truth-seekers fending off irresponsible environmental doom-sayers, their testimony in St. Paul and elsewhere revealed the source and scope of their funding for the first time. Michaels has received more than $115,000 over the last four years from coal and energy interests. World Climate Review, a quarterly he founded that routinely debunks climate concerns, was funded by Western Fuels. Over the last six years, either alone or with colleagues, Balling has received more than $200,000 from coal and oil interests in Great Britain, Germany, and elsewhere. Balling (along with Sherwood Idso) has also taken money from Cyprus Minerals, a mining company that has been a major funder of People for the West—a militantly anti-environmental "Wise Use" group. Lindzen, for his part, charges oil and coal interests $2,500 a day for his consulting services; his 1991 trip to testify before a Senate committee was paid for by Western Fuels, and a speech he wrote, entitled "Global Warming: the Origin and Nature of Alleged Scientific Consensus," was underwritten by OPEC. Singer, who last winter proposed a $95,000 publicity project to "stem the tide towards ever more onerous controls on energy use," has received consulting fees from Exxon, Shell, Unocal, ARCO, and Sun Oil, and has warned them that they face the same threat as the chemical firms that produced chlorofluorocarbons (CFCs), a class of chemicals found to be depleting atmospheric ozone. "It took only five years to go from . . . a simple freeze of production [of CFCs]," Singer has written, " . . . to the 1992 decision of a complete production phase-out—all on the basis of quite insubstantial science."[2]

The skeptics assert flatly that their science is untainted by funding. Nevertheless, in this persistent and well-funded campaign of denial they have become interchangeable ornaments on the hood of a high-powered engine of disinformation. Their dissenting opinions are amplified beyond all proportion through the media while the concerns of the dominant majority of the world's scientific establishment are marginalized. By keeping the discussion focused on whether there is a problem in the first place, they have effectively silenced the debate over what to do about it.

Last spring's IPCC conference in Berlin is a good example. Delegations from 170 nations met to negotiate targets and timetables for reducing the world's carbon dioxide emissions. The efforts of the conference ultimately foundered on foot-dragging by the United States and Japan and active resistance from the OPEC nations. Leading the fight for the most dramatic reductions—to 60 percent of 1990 levels—was a coalition of small island nations from the Caribbean and the Pacific that fear being flooded out of existence. They were supported by most western European governments, but China and India, with their vast coal resources, argued that until the United States significantly cuts its own emissions, their obligation to develop their own economies outranked their obligation to the global environment. In the end, OPEC, supported by the United States, Japan, Australia, Canada, and New Zealand, rejected calls to limit emissions, declaring emission limits premature.

* * *

As the natural crisis escalates, so will the forces of institutional and societal denial. If, at the cost of corporate pocket change, industrial giants can control the publicly perceived reality of the condition of the planet and the state of our scientific knowledge, what would they do if their survival were truly put at risk? Billions would be spent on the creation of information and the control of politicians. Glad-handing oil company ads on the op-ed page of the *New York Times* (from a quarter-page pronouncement by Mobil last September 28: "There's a lot of good news out there") would give way to a new stream of selective finding by privatized scientists. Long before the

planet itself collapsed, democracy would break apart under the stress of "natural" disasters. It is not difficult to foresee that in an ecological state of emergency our political liberties would be the first casualties.

Thus, the question must be asked: can civilization change the way it operates? For 5,000 years, we have thought of ourselves as dependent children of the earth, flourishing or perishing according to the whims of nature. But with the explosion of the power of our technology and the size of our population, our activities have grown to the proportion of geological forces, affecting the major systems of the planet. Short of the Atlantic washing away half of Florida, the abstract notion that the old anomalies have become the new norm is difficult to grasp. Dr. James McCarthy of Harvard, who has supervised the work of climate scientists from sixty nations, puts it this way: "If the last 150 years had been marked by the kind of climate instability we are now seeing, the world would never have been able to support its present population of 5 billion people." We live in a world of man-size urgencies, measured in hours or days. What unfolds slowly is not, by our lights, urgent, and it will therefore take a collective act of imagination to understand the extremity of the situation we now confront. The lag time in our planet's ecological systems will undoubtedly delay these decisions, and even if the nations of the world were to agree tomorrow on a plan to phase out oil and coal and convert to renewable energies, an equivalent lag time in human affairs would delay its implementation for years. What too many people refuse to understand is that the global economy's existence depends upon the global environment, not the other way around. One cannot negotiate jobs, development, or rates of economic growth with nature.

What of the standard list of palliatives —carbon taxes, more energy-efficient buildings, a revival of public transportation? The ideas are attractive, but the thinking is too small. Even were the United States to halve its own carbon dioxide contribution, this cutback would soon be overwhelmed by the coming development of industry and housing and schools in China and India and Mexico for all their billions of citizens. No solution can work that does not provide ample energy resources for the development of all the world's nations.

So here is an informal proposal—at best a starting point for a conversation—from one man who is not an expert. What if we turned the deserts of the world into electricity farms? Let the Middle East countries keep their oil royalties as solar royalties. What if the world mobilized around a ten-year project to phase out all fossil fuels, to develop renewable energy technologies, to extend those technologies to every corner of the world? What if, to minimize the conflict of so massive a dislocation, the world's energy companies were put in charge of the transition—answering only to an international regulatory body and an enforceable timetable? Grant them the same profit margins for solar electricity and hydrogen fuel they now receive for petroleum and coal. Give them the licenses for all renewable energy technologies. Assure them the same relative position in the world's economy they now enjoy at the end of the project.

Are these ideas mere dream? Perhaps, but here are historical reasons to have hope. Four years ago a significant fraction of humanity overturned its Communist system in a historical blink of an eye. Eight years ago the world's governments joined together in Montreal to regulate CFCs. Technology is not the issue. The atomic bomb was developed in two and a half years. Putting a man on the moon took eleven. Surely, given the same sense of urgency, we can develop new energy systems in ten years. Most of the technology is already available to us or soon will be. We have the knowledge, the energy, and the hunger for jobs to get it done. And we are different in one unmeasurable way from previous generations: ours is the first to be educated about the larger world by the global reach of electronic information.

The leaders of the oil and coal industry, along with their skeptical scientists, relentlessly accuse environmentalists of overstating the climatic threat to destroy capitalism. Must a transformation that is merely technological dislodge the keystone of the economic order? I don't know. But I do know that technology changes the way we conceive of the world. To transform our economy would oblige us to understand the limits of the planet. That understanding alone might seed the culture with a more organic concept of ourselves and our connectedness to the earth. And corporations, it is useful to remember, are not only obstacles on the road to the future. They are also crucibles of technology and organizing engines of production, the modern expression of mankind's drive for creativity. The industrialist is no less human than the poet, and both the climate scientist and the oil company operator inhabit the same planet, suffer the same short life span, harbor the same hopes for their children.

NOTES

1. In 1991, Western Fuels spent an estimated $250,000 to produce and distribute a video entitled "The Greening of Planet Earth," which was shown frequently inside the Bush White House as well as within the governments of OPEC. In near-evangelical tones, the video promises that a new age of agricultural abundance will result from increasing concentrations of carbon dioxide. It portrays a world where vast areas of desert are reclaimed by the carbon dioxide-forced growth of new grasslands, where the earth's diminishing forests are replenished by a nurturing atmosphere. Unfortunately, it overlooks the bugs. Experts note that even a minor elevation in temperature would trigger an explosion in the planet's insect population, leading to potentially significant disruptions in food supplies from crop damage as well as to a surge in insect-borne diseases. It appears that Western Fuels' video fails to tell people what the termites in New Orleans may be trying to tell them now.

2. Contrary to his assertion, however, virtually all relevant researchers say the link between CFCs and ozone depletion is based on unassailably solid scientific evidence. As if to underscore the point, in May the research director of the European Union Commission estimated that last winter's ozone loss will result in about 80,000 additional cases of skin cancer in Europe. This fall, the three scientists who discovered the CFC-ozone link won the Nobel Prize for Chemistry.

NO

Wilfred Beckerman and
Jesse Malkin

HOW MUCH DOES
GLOBAL WARMING MATTER?

More than a billion people in developing countries have no access to safe drinking water, and at least twice that many have no access to adequate sanitation. Consequently, between 1 and 1.5 billion people suffer from water-related diseases such as schistosomiasis, hookworm, and diarrhea. Infant mortality attributable to diarrhea is estimated to be about 5 million per year.

But the environmental problems that dominate the media, that are given the most attention by environmentalist pressure groups, and that capture the imagination of the public, are the melodramatic issues. The myth of "scarce resources" is one.... Another is global warming—"the highest-risk environmental problem the world faces today," according to Vice President Al Gore. The public is bombarded by television images showing the earth surrounded by a layer of "greenhouse gases" (GHGs) that allow the sun's energy to penetrate, but block much of the outgoing radiation from the earth's surface. These images are accompanied by dire predictions that we shall all frizzle up and that the world will become a desert—despite concurrent predictions that rainfall will increase and sea levels will rise. Such scenarios of global warming are much more exciting for the viewer than pictures showing that what the world's population needs most are more lavatories and better sewage systems.

* * *

The "consensus" opinion on climate change, as embodied in the 1990 report of the International Panel on Climate Change (IPCC), is that a doubling of equivalent carbon dioxide [CO_2] (an index that summarizes the effect of all man-made GHGs), is likely to occur within the next fifty years if nothing is done to reduce CO_2 emissions. Because of the time lags in the dynamics of climate change—notably those caused by the inertia introduced into the

From Wilfred Beckerman and Jesse Malkin, "How Much Does Global Warming Matter?" *The Public Interest*, no. 114 (Winter 1994), pp. 3–16. Copyright © 1994 by National Affairs, Inc. Reprinted by permission of the author.

system as a result of the absorption of carbon dioxide by the oceans—the temperature increase associated with this warming commitment would not be realized until approximately 2100. At that point, the global mean surface temperature is predicted to increase by between 2° and 5° Celsius.

This conclusion has not gone unquestioned. To be sure, the scientific work that has gone into climate modeling represents a major intellectual achievement. Yet it is widely recognized that these estimates have a wide margin of error and that there are still great gaps in our understanding of how the climate is determined. The IPCC report itself contains hundreds of pages of misgivings about the potential temperature increase, and many climatologists have expressed skepticism about the reliability of the global climate models that forecast significant warming.

For example, equivalent CO_2 levels have increased by over 40 percent during the past 100 years, yet the climate has not responded in the manner predicted by the models. Consider the following anomalies:

- The amount of global warming that has occurred over the past century— roughly .45°C—is at least a factor of two less than that predicted by the most sophisticated models.
- The Northern Hemisphere, which the models say should have warmed more rapidly than the Southern Hemisphere, is no warmer than it was a half century ago.
- The models say warming should occur as a result of GHG buildup, but most of the warming during the past 100 years occurred prior to World War II—*before* most of the GHGs were emitted.

Clearly a dose of skepticism is warranted. But let us suppose that the skeptics are wrong—suppose the earth's temperature does rise by somewhere between 2°C and 5°C. How damaging is this likely to be?

* * *

There is one simple piece of evidence, which does not require vast computerized models of the world's climate or economy (our understanding of both being extremely limited), and which does at least refute the widespread notion that the human race is some tender plant that can only survive in a narrow band of plus or minus 3°C. This is the present dispersion of the world's population throughout widely different temperature zones. For example, taking the average temperatures in the coldest month in the countries concerned, 32.3 percent of the world's population lives in a band of 0°C to 3°C, whereas 18.8 percent live in a band of 12°C to 15°C, and 14.6 percent live in a band of 24°C to 27°C. Furthermore, across the world as a whole there appears to be no correlation at all between average temperatures and income levels. ...

Of course, it will be argued that such cross-country comparisons do not adequately take into account the difficulty of adjusting to relatively rapid changes in temperature. There is some truth in this. But as the distinguished economist Thomas Schelling has observed, the sort of rapid climate changes experienced throughout history by vast migratory movements of population were far greater than those predicted to occur during the next century as a result of global warming. The human race has always been a highly adaptable species, and is likely to become increasingly so, since most of its adaptability comes from its accumulation of technical knowledge.

Similar back-of-the-envelope calculations show that, for the United States at least, global warming could hardly have a significant impact on national income. For the sector most likely to be affected is agriculture, which constitutes 2 percent of U.S. gross domestic product (GDP). Most other sectors of economic activity are not likely to be affected at all, and some, such as construction, will probably be favorably affected. So even if the net output of agriculture fell by 50 percent by the end of the next century, this is only a 1 percent reduction in GDP.

Anyway, the net effect on U.S. agriculture is more likely to be negligible. In the northern states, growing periods would be longer and there would be less disruption by frosts. Further, the predicted rise in carbon dioxide—the most important greenhouse gas leading to global warming—is actually good for plant growth. Authoritative estimates put the impact on the net output of U.S. agriculture at somewhere between plus and minus $10 billion. Even the worst end of this range, minus $10 billion, is a trivial part of a U.S. GDP of about $6 trillion.

Similar estimates for the world as a whole (which, as far as we know, were not done on the back of an envelope) also show that agricultural output in some countries will be favorably affected by global warming, whereas others will lose; and that, on balance, the net effect is likely to be negligible. Of course, the effects depend partly on how climate change affects the regional distribution of rainfall. But this is even more difficult to predict than is the global climate change.

All in all, such estimates as have been made of the overall effect of a doubling of the CO_2 concentration on the world economy suggest that world output would be reduced by about 1 or 2 percent. Suppose that these estimates are much too conservative—as they may well be given that the models on which they are based are extremely shaky. Suppose instead that world output would be reduced by 10 percent by the end of the next century below what it otherwise would be.

Well, what would it otherwise be? Over the whole period 1950 through 1985, the annual average compound rate of growth of world output *per head* has been 1.9 percent. Given that the rate of growth of world population is slowing down and that, at the same time, there has been a rapid increase in the proportion of the world's population receiving higher education or engaged in scientific research—the mainsprings of technical progress—there is good reason to believe that this growth rate will be at least maintained, if not increased. But suppose that it is only, say, 1.5 percent a year. This means that by the year 2093 world output per head will be 4.4 times as great as it is now. If global warming cuts world GDP by 10 percent, then instead of it being 4.4 times as great as it is now, it would be only 3.96 times as great. Would this be such a disaster? Would it justify imposing vast costs on the present generation rather than devoting more resources to helping developing countries overcome the environmental problems that they are facing today?

*   *   *

So far we have limited our discussion to the effect of global warming on agriculture, since this is the most vulnerable sector. But what about sea level rise, the other eco-catastrophe most frequently associated with global warming?

In 1980 scientists predicted that global warming would lead to a sea level rise of as much as 8 meters. In early 1989 the prevailing estimate was down to about 1 meter. By 1990 (as in the IPCC report) the predicted sea level rise was about 65 centimeters, and current authoritative estimates put it as low as about 30 cm by the end of the next century, assuming a 4°C rise in average temperature by then. (If one were to extrapolate from trends in these estimates, the sea level would be predicted to fall, with consequences for many seaside resorts that would be as serious as sea level rises!)

But even if sea levels did rise appreciably, the economic consequences would not be disastrous. A few years ago, when the sea level was still predicted to rise by 1 meter, the U.S. Environmental Protection Agency estimated that it would cost about $100 billion to protect U.S. cities by building sea walls. Applying a 1.5 percent a year annual growth rate to the present U.S. GDP of $6 trillion gives a GDP of $26.2 trillion in 2093; so as a fraction of GDP in the year 2093, the once-and-for-all capital cost of the sea walls would be about .38 percent. As a fraction of cumulative GDP over the whole of the next 100 years—the time during which the work would have to be carried out —the amounts involved are, of course, trivial.

What about the rest of the world? Estimates by William Cline of the Institute for International Economics, also assuming a 1 meter rise in the sea level and that the costs of sea walls for other threatened coastal cities are comparable to those of the U.S., show costs of adaptation, plus the value of land lost in coastal areas, of about $2 trillion. On the above assumption concerning the growth rate, world GDP in the year 2093 will be about $115 trillion—so the one-time capital cost of the sea walls would still be only about 1.7 percent of one year's GDP. As a fraction of cumulative GDP over the whole period it would still be negligible. Given that the latest predictions of the rise in the sea level are about one third of those assumed in these estimates and that a given reduction in the estimated sea level rise implies more than a proportionate reduction in the costs of adaptation or the damage done through land loss, the costs for the world as a whole would be insignificant even if the above estimates are way off.

Now that may be very well for the world as a whole, but it is little consolation to the people of Bangladesh, where 20 percent of the land could be lost under the sea with a 1 meter sea level rise. But leaving aside the falling trend in the estimate of sea level rises, suppose, purely for the sake of illustrating the logic of the choices to be made, that measures to prevent the climate change and the consequent sea level rise would cost the world community $20 trillion —i.e. ten times as much as the cost of protection against the rising sea level. It would clearly be in everyone's interest, including the Bangladeshis', to strike some sort of a deal. For example, instead of incurring $20 trillion in costs to prevent the climate change and the associated sea-level rise, the rich countries would do better to hand over, say, a quarter of the resulting economy—that is, $5 trillion— to the people who would suffer from the sea-level rise. The Bangladeshis would then gain $5 trillion to carry out work costing only $2 trillion, and the rest of the world still saves $15 trillion.

In other words, the course of action that is being urged by environmentalists —to prevent rising sea levels at any cost—would mean that the world is being asked to incur costs of $20 trillion —or whatever the cost would be—to prevent the Bangladeshis from suffering the effects of the sea level rise when there would be a much cheaper way of sparing them from these effects. Developed countries could, for example, help Bangladeshis move away from threatened coastal areas, diversify their economy, or take some other protective action. They might even consider making it easier for Bangladeshis to export goods and emigrate. The point is that adaptation should not be viewed as an impossibility. After all, over half the population of the Netherlands and virtually all the people in Amsterdam live below sea level.

If the estimates of the costs involved in significant reductions of CO_2 emissions referred to above are anywhere near reality, it is clear that the world and the Bangladeshis would be far better off if adaptive policies were taken rather than drastic action to prevent threatened rises in sea levels. In any event, since it is suspected that far more land is being lost to soil erosion than through climate change, there are policies that could be undertaken to reduce land loss without draconian cuts in carbon dioxide emissions.

* * *

But what would it cost to implement CO_2 cuts by the most economical means, and how would one do it? One view, espoused by the Clinton administration among others, is that cuts can be achieved at no cost whatsoever to the public or private sector. The White House insists that its "Climate Change Action Plan," a collection of mostly voluntary public-private partnerships which purports to stabilize greenhouse gas emissions at 1990 levels by 2000, will save the private sector $207 billion in reduced energy costs by 2010.

Most economists, however, believe the administration is relying on astonishingly optimistic assumptions about energy savings. The reason is simple: If energy-efficiency investments really yield such fantastic returns, businesses and individuals would undertake them without the government's push. To accept the administration's savings estimates, one would have to believe that firms are very stupid indeed.

As many disappointed environmentalists have noted, voluntary measures of the sort in Clinton's plan are likely to have only a very limited effect on greenhouse gas emissions. Deep cuts will require stronger government action, namely a carbon tax or a system of internationally tradable emissions permits.

Making a rapid transition to a less carbon-intensive economy would be painful, but just how much so is unclear. The uncertainties about the magnitude of the costs are as great, if not greater, than those embodied in the scientific models to predict climate change. Nobody can predict with much accuracy the future pattern of economic growth over the next century in a manner that enables one to say how much fossil fuel would be burned and hence how much needs to be done to reduce fossil fuel use by any given amount. Nor can anyone say with any degree of reliability how sensitive the consumption of fossil fuels is to different levels of carbon taxes. The impact of carbon taxes depends in large part on the degree to which carbon-free energy sources like nuclear, wind energy, and photovoltaics become cheaper and easier to use than their fossil rivals.

Finally, there is the huge question of what is done with the revenues raised by carbon taxes. If they are refunded to the economy in a way that merely changes the pattern of fuel use rather than exerting a depressive effect on the economy as a whole, the effect could well be favorable. For example, there is a strong case for reducing government subsidies to the coal and oil industries apart from any considerations about global warming. If the savings from the elimination of those subsidies were used to pursue growth-enhancing policies, so much the better. If, on the other hand, carbon taxes were used to fund extra entitlements or low-return government "investment" programs, the effect would more likely be negative. A tax on a basic input to the economy, which is what fossil fuels are, could have a far more serious impact than other taxes such as those that are levied on different items of consumer expenditure, such as cigarettes or beer.

Vast computerized models tend to blind people with science and impress grant-giving institutions. Most of them produce a maximum amount of statistical "results" with a minimum input of ideas or insight. The estimates that they churn out of the cost of measures designed to cut CO_2 emissions are highly uncertain. Inevitably, different models lead to widely different results. But for what they are worth, it seems that the cost of freezing CO_2 emissions at 1990 levels would be somewhere in the region of 2 percent of output per year in advanced industrial countries and perhaps twice that in developing countries, which have fewer financial and technological resources with which to adapt. To put that in perspective, 2 percent of current U.S. GDP is about $120 billion. The large magnitude of the costs is not surprising since, again, it seems obvious—even without the aid of any sophisticated computerized models —that, if carried out quickly, a drastic cut in the use of fossil fuels would cause severe economic disruption.

* * *

The above discussion of the damage that might be done by a doubling of present concentrations of carbon in the atmosphere considers only the costs over a 100-year period. Some economists have pointed out that there is no reason to confine the analysis to a single century. Fossil fuels will probably continue to be used well after the year 2100, so it is likely that there will be greater atmospheric build-up of CO_2 and more global warming than that indicated by the century-long models. William Cline, for example, has shown that over a period of three centuries, atmospheric concentration of CO_2 might increase eight-fold and temperatures might rise 10°C to 13°C or more unless action is taken to reduce carbon dioxide emissions. This, he argues, could lead to a reduction of world GDP on the order of 10 percent.

Of course, the further one projects into the future the more uncertain the already shaky projections become. There have been vast technological changes in energy use in the last century. And these will probably be dwarfed by the changes that will take place in the next three centuries, during which an incomparably greater number of people will be engaged in technological and scientific research all over the world. Hence, nobody can suppose that the world of the 23rd century will bear much resemblance to the world that we know today. It is most unlikely that energy will still be produced on a large scale by the use of dirty and polluting substances such as coal.

One need only look at the past to see how difficult it is to make predictions over hundreds of years. Who could have predicted three centuries ago that sources of power would shift from wind, water, and wood to coal, oil, natural gas, and nuclear energy? Who could have imagined that modern gas-fired, combined-cycle power plants would be about ten times as energy efficient as power stations built at the beginning of the century, or that the thermal efficiency of steam engines would be about forty times that of the earliest engines, or that the most advanced fluorescent lights would be 900 times more energy efficient than the original kerosene lamp?

And progress is now being made in developing viable forms of renewable energy that emit no carbon at all. These include the photovoltaic cells that convert sunlight directly into storable electricity. They are regarded as having great promise for local power generation in developing countries. During the past twenty years the cost of photovoltaic-generated electricity has fallen from about $60 per kilowatt hour to about 30–50 cents, and is expected to fall to about 12–16 cents within the next few years as a result of further efficiency improvements that are already in the pipeline. Industry analysts say costs could go as low as 6 cents per kilowatt hour by 2020, little more than the price of electricity from a coal-fired station.

Similarly, the cost of wind-generated electricity has dropped from 50 cents per kilowatt hour in 1975, to 25 cents in 1980, to 7–9 cents in the best locations today. A new wind turbine under development is expected to bring costs down to 5 cents or less. The U.S. Department of Energy projects that over the next twenty years, costs in moderately windy sites could fall to 3.5 cents per kilowatt hour. Wind power's contribution will ultimately be limited by the number of suitable sites. The German Future Energies Forum, an energy research group, estimates that wind power can meet no more than 15 percent of the world's energy requirements.

Then there is always the possibility of a breakthrough in geothermal, solar thermal, hydrogen fuel, or nuclear fusion technology. It is impossible to determine the ultimate potential of technologies that are barely off the drawing board, but it would be foolishly pessimistic to assume that none of these carbon-free technologies will ever become cost-competitive with fossil fuels.

Even without any significant recourse to the many forms of renewable energy under investigation, there have been major reductions in the ratio of both energy use and carbon emissions to GDP. For example, from 1950 to 1985 the rate of growth of CO_2 emissions in the US was 1.9 percent a year, compared with a growth of GDP of 3.2 percent a year. This means that there was a 1.3 percent a year fall in carbon emissions per unit of GDP over the period 1950–1985. This is accounted for by a 0.8 percent a year decline in the rate of energy use per unit of output and a 0.5 percent a year decline in the rate of CO_2 emissions per unit of energy.

Cline does not make explicit his assumptions concerning these two influences on the growth of CO_2 emissions in his predictions. But based on his projections of GDP growth and CO_2 emissions, it is possible to work out what assumption is implied. It appears that he is assuming that the carbon emissions per unit of GDP will fall by only about 0.7 percent a year in the latter half of the twenty-first century—i.e. only about half the rate of decline in the U.S. between 1950 and 1985. Further, his estimates imply that the ratio of carbon emissions to GDP will fall even more slowly thereafter, and will actually rise during the last 75 years of the period covered in his projections.

Cline also assumes that every carbon dioxide molecule released into the atmosphere stays there for the duration of his three-century model. Calculating the effective lifespan of carbon dioxide is complex because CO_2 molecules are constantly exchanged between the atmosphere, the oceans, and the biosphere. Yet according to the IPCC Scientific Assessment, the "lifetime" associated with an individual CO_2 surge is only 50 to 200 years.

Adjusting Cline's assumptions yields dramatic changes. If we assume (a) that CO_2 molecules have an average lifespan of 100 years in the atmosphere and (b) that the amount of carbon emissions per unit of GDP declines 1.3 percent a year, both the CO_2 build-up and the warming projections become far less ominous. Instead of Cline's assumed eight-fold increase in carbon dioxide, there would be only about a one-and-a-half-fold increase. And the temperature increase resulting from this carbon buildup falls from between 10°C and 13°C to just 2°C. Even allowing for a generous margin of error, it would seem that Cline's projections are terribly pessimistic.

* * *

Assessing carbon abatement measures requires the comparison of costs and benefits over very long periods of time. This raises an important question: How is a benefit enjoyed in many years' time to be compared with a benefit enjoyed immediately? Most people would be unwilling to exchange $1.00 for, say, only $1.02 in one year's time—even if the $1.02 were indexed for inflation.

The need to discount the future at some rate of interest implies that the benefits in two or three centuries' time of abating GHG emissions now would have to be astronomic to justify significant current sacrifices. In fact, for almost any discount rate at all, what happens in the twenty-third century is of almost no importance. For example, if future costs and benefits are discounted at 2 percent a year—which is well below what most people would expect to earn on their investments, even net of tax and inflation—$1 of cost or benefit in 200 years' time would have a present value today of only 1.9 cents. In other words, if the damage done by global warming in 200 years' time were to be $1,000 billion, it would not be worthwhile taking steps to avoid it if the cost of doing so today would be greater than $19 billion. If a more conventional discount rate were used—say, 6 percent—it would not be worthwhile taking steps to avoid $1,000 billion of damage in 200 years' time if the cost of doing so today exceeded only $8.7 million.

People discount the future for two types of reasons. First, many people simply prefer to consume resources now rather than in the future. This "time preference" generally arises from any of three motives, namely (a) the risk that one might not survive to reap the future rewards for sacrifice of consumption today; (b) an expectation that future consumption levels will be higher (combined with the usual assumption of diminishing marginal utility of consumption), and (c) "pure" time preference—e.g., sheer impatience, or lack of imagination.

But even an individual who had no *basic* time preference whatsoever—who had no worry that her investment might not pay off, who did not expect to be richer, and was not impatient—would still not lend $1 now for $1 next year (leaving aside personal motivations, such as helping out a friend). The reason for this is that she would know that any old fool can get a better rate of return on the market. She would lend, therefore, up to the point where *at the margin* the rate of return she could get on her savings and investments would be equal to the relative valuation she places on consumption today as against consumption tomorrow. The same principle applies—with a few adjustments—to society.

In other words, the use of a discount rate in allocating investments today between alternative uses does not reflect any tendency by economists to attach less value, per se, to future *welfare*. On the contrary, a unit of *welfare* in 200 years' time is given the same value as a unit of welfare today. But, if technological progress and economic growth continue, a unit of *consumption* in 200 years' time will give a smaller unit of welfare than it does today. Taking account of the discount rate when choosing between projects is a technique designed to maximize welfare over the whole time period regarded as relevant. To invest in some environmental project that yields only, say, a 1 percent rate of return, when there are alternative projects around that will yield, say, 5 percent, would leave future generations much worse off than they could otherwise have been.

The simple answer, therefore, to the criticism that, by discounting, one is being unfair to future generations is this: If, Heaven forbid, there were some leap in medical science so that we all now expected to live for 300 years, *we would still use the discount rate in our savings and investment decisions.* So, as a result of our doing so today (when we do not expect to survive for centuries), future generations are left no worse off than we would be if it were us who were to be alive in 200 years' time, not them. Hence, it is absurd to argue that we are somehow or other being unfair to them.

In short, the widespread environmentalist attack on the validity of time preference is a vast red herring. What matters is the rate of technological progress and economic growth that one can expect to take place. As we have argued, there are good reasons for expecting this to be as rapid in the future as in the past. Of course, if it is expected to slow down to zero, or become negative—which is not beyond the bounds of possibility—one should adopt a zero or negative discount rate for later years. But a case should be laid out for such a prediction. The "immorality" of time preference has nothing to do with it.

* * *

Global warming may be a problem, but it is no cause for undue alarm or drastic action. There is plenty of time to improve our understanding of the science and scrap policies that encourage economically inefficient uses of fossil fuels. It does not justify diverting vast amounts of time, energy, and funds from more urgent environmental problems, particularly those in developing countries. Nor does it justify a massive diversion of resources from high-yield projects in the private sector. We are not on the edge of an abyss and the human race is not facing destruction from the accumulation of greenhouse gases. There is far less danger of the human race being wiped out on account of the conflict between Man and the Environment than on account of the conflict between Man and Man (or Woman and Woman). Global warming is far more glamorous and telegenic, of course, than the need for better toilets and drains in the Third World. But if we truly care about the welfare of our fellow world citizens, it is these kinds of environmental issues upon which we must focus our attention.

POSTSCRIPT

Should Society Be Concerned About Global Warming?

In 1992 the United Nations Conference on Environment and Development in Rio de Janeiro was held. High on the agenda was the issue of global warming, but despite widespread concern and calls for reductions in carbon dioxide releases, the United States refused to consider rigid deadlines or set quotas. The Bush administration felt that the uncertainties were too great and that the economic costs of cutting back on carbon dioxide emissions might well be greater than the costs of letting the climate warm.

However, James Kasting of Pennsylvania State University and James Walker of the University of Michigan warn that if one looks a little further into the future than the next century, the prospects look much more frightening. By 2100, they say, the amount of carbon dioxide in the atmosphere will reach double its preindustrial level. By the 2200s it could be 7.6 times the preindustrial level. With draconian restrictions, it could be held to only 4 times the preindustrial level. Correspondingly, they predict, global warming in the twenty-first century will be worse than anyone is currently forecasting.

Are there any practical alternatives? In October 1993 the Clinton administration announced a "Climate Change Action Plan" that called for stabilizing carbon dioxide releases by such measures as planting trees (which remove carbon dioxide from the air) and promoting energy efficiency. Unfortunately, population growth and the need to use land for growing food render this solution unlikely.

In a recent experiment, researchers spread high-iron fertilizer across several square miles of the Pacific Ocean to see whether or not it could stimulate the growth of algae and the absorption of carbon dioxide from the air. The process worked, but it would probably be too expensive to apply as a worldwide anti-greenhouse measure.

Gelbspan is by no means alone in his concerns that the 1990s have seen a worldwide pattern of extreme fluctuations in the weather. Already the world's insurance industry is growing very concerned because its losses due to storm and flood damage have been increasing rapidly. See Christopher Flavin, "Storm Warnings: Climate Change Hits the Insurance Industry," *World Watch* (November/December 1994). And according to Christopher Flavin and Odil Tunali, in "Getting Warmer: Looking for a Way Out of the Climate Impasse," *World Watch* (March/April 1995), governments are not acting on the problem. In September 1995 the Intergovernmental Panel on Climate Change (IPCC) reported the consensus view that global warming is real, and Thomas Karl of the National Climatic Data Center in Asheville, North Carolina, said, "There's a 90 to 95% chance that we're not being fooled."

However, even the IPCC admits that the data are inadequate to determine with certainty that human activities are to blame for changes in climate and weather. It can be very difficult to discern a clear trend in a system that varies erratically from year to year and from place to place, such as climate. Yet research is making it very clear that looking for such trends is important. Studies of ice laid down millennia ago in Greenland and in glaciers in South America and China are showing that climate can warm or cool dramatically in very short times and that such changes happen frequently. See Richard Monastersky, "The Case of the Global Jitters," *Science News* (March 2, 1996). The concern here is that even though human-induced climate change may seem gradual, it may suddenly become much more abrupt and leave society very little time to adjust.

On the other hand, there are intriguing new data connecting variations in the amount of energy emitted by the sun to variations in the Earth's climate. As reported by Richard A. Kerr, in "A New Dawn for Sun-Climate Links?" *Science* (March 8, 1996), "An effort to reconstruct changes in the sun's brightness over the last 400 years has yielded [a pattern that implies] that the sun could have been responsible for as much as half of the warming of the past century." Scientists are still arguing over the data and their interpretation, but the point remains: Human-released greenhouse gases may not be entirely to blame for global warming. Society may still need to be concerned about global warming and its consequences, but that concern need not have quite so large a component of guilt.

On the Internet, information on global warming can be found at: http://www.noaa.gov.

ISSUE 8

Is Ozone Depletion a Genuine Threat?

YES: Mary H. Cooper, from "Ozone Depletion," *CQ Researcher* (April 3, 1992)

NO: James P. Hogan, from "Ozone Politics: They Call This Science?" *Omni* (June 1993)

ISSUE SUMMARY

YES: Mary H. Cooper, a staff writer for *CQ Researcher,* asserts that scientific findings in recent years indicate that the ozone layer is being depleted and that such depletion threatens the health of Earth's living organisms.

NO: James P. Hogan, a science fiction writer, maintains that reports of the ozone being destroyed by chlorofluorocarbons are politically motivated scare stories unsupported by any valid scientific evidence.

The debate about ozone depletion may offer a good example of how attempts to make life better may actually do great harm. The controversy can be traced back to early improvements on the refrigerator. The fluid in the cooling coils of early refrigerators was ammonia, which is both highly irritating and very toxic. Chlorofluorocarbons (CFCs) replaced ammonia in the 1930s because they were nontoxic, nonirritating, nonflammable, inexpensive, noncorrosive, and stable (that is, they did not have to be replaced periodically). They were ideal for the purpose, and later on they proved to be ideal for other purposes as well. Consequently, CFC production grew, and by 1974 over 800,000 metric tons of CFCs were being produced per year.

Around this time, however, Sherwood Rowland and Mario Molina, chemists at the University of California at Irvine, realized that those safe, stable chlorofluorocarbon molecules were stable enough to rise all the way into the stratosphere before they broke down. When the molecules did break down, the chemists said, they would release their chlorine component precisely where it could destroy stratospheric ozone. Two years later, the first solid evidence of CFC-induced damage to the ozone layer was reported. As a result, in 1978 the U.S. Environmental Protection Agency and Food and Drug Administration banned the use of CFCs in aerosol spray cans. In 1985 a roughly circular zone of greatly diminished ozone concentration— commonly called the "ozone hole"—was discovered over Antarctica. Since then, several key events have occurred that have firmly established ozone depletion as a worldwide concern: In 1987 the United States and 23 other countries signed the Montreal Protocol (promising to cut CFC use drastically); in 1991 the United Nations Environment Programme (UNEP) issued a report concluding that ozone depletion was a worldwide phenomenon; and in 1992 scientists from the National Aeronautics and Space Administration (NASA) reported alarmingly high levels of ozone-destroying chlorine monoxide in the stratosphere over the Northern Hemisphere, confirming the conclusions of the UNEP.

Why is news of the depleted ozone alarming? It has been known for many years that stratospheric ozone absorbs much of the ultraviolet (UV) light that comes to Earth from the sun (or "solar ultraviolet"). The small amount that reaches Earth's surface stimulates the production of vitamin D in human skin, but it also causes sunburn, skin cancer, and cataracts, as well as other problems. An increase in solar UV at ground level would therefore pose a serious health threat to human beings. It would also threaten other living organisms, including crop plants.

As yet, there is no proof that ozone depletion is already causing health problems, but according to everything that scientists know or can calculate, it will. Furthermore, since CFCs can remain in the air for years, many believe that society cannot wait for the signs of damage to become incontrovertible before taking action because by then it will be too late to keep the damage from growing still worse for years.

Although the facts strongly suggest a connection between CFCs and the depletion of stratospheric ozone, science cannot prove beyond a doubt that CFCs are destroying the ozone. Despite the evidence, not everyone accepts as true the threat of CFCs and ozone depletion. Critics have denounced the "ozone scare" as a politically motivated scam, a conspiracy to provide monopoly control to companies that have patents on refrigerant alternatives to CFCs, a way to gain public funding for unnecessary research, and so on.

In the following selections, Mary H. Cooper provides a clear account of the discovery and nature of ozone depletion, and she asserts that the hazards of CFCs are real. James P. Hogan argues that any conclusions about the destruction of the ozone by CFCs are based on sloppy scientific procedures and misinterpretations of data, and he maintains that public fears about the ozone are perpetuated for political reasons.

YES

Mary H. Cooper

OZONE DEPLETION

Scientists at the National Aeronautics and Space Administration (NASA) hadn't planned to hold a news conference on February 3 [1992]. But, they decided at the last minute, their preliminary findings about Earth's upper atmosphere were too important to sit on. Earth's protective ozone layer,[1] they announced, was losing ozone much faster than anyone had predicted, exposing humans to higher amounts of harmful radiation.

Even more ominous, they said, it seemed likely that a highly depleted section of the ozone layer, known as a "hole," would develop over the Arctic, exposing populated areas of the Northern Hemisphere. A similar hole had first been observed over Antarctica in 1985.

The scientists based their startling announcement on new data collected over northern New England, eastern Canada and much of Europe and Asia. What their airborne instruments—carried aloft by a satellite and two high-flying planes—detected was the highest concentration of ozone-destroying chlorine monoxide ever measured in the atmosphere.

Chlorine monoxide is a derivative of an important family of synthetic chemicals that are known as chlorofluorocarbons (CFCs). They have enjoyed wide use for decades as coolants in refrigerators and air conditioners, propellants in aerosol spray cans, blowing agents in the manufacture of plastic and rubber foam products and as solvents in the production of electronic equipment.

Once released into the atmosphere, CFCs drift upward until they reach the ozone layer, which begins in the stratosphere. As long as they remain in their original molecular form, CFCs are harmless. But intense ultraviolet radiation can break the CFC molecule apart, producing chlorine monoxide and setting off a series of reactions that destroy ozone.

High levels of chlorine monoxide are alarming enough by themselves. But NASA's scientists found evidence of even more worrisome atmospheric problems: high levels of bromine monoxide. A byproduct of halons, man-made chemicals used in fire extinguishers, bromine monoxide is even more destructive than chlorine monoxide.

Michael Kurylo, NASA's program manager for the study, estimated that the two chemicals could destroy 1 to 2 percent of the ozone layer daily during

From Mary H. Cooper, "Ozone Depletion," *CQ Researcher,* vol. 2, no. 13 (April 3, 1992). Copyright © 1992 by Congressional Quarterly, Inc. Reprinted by permission. Some notes omitted.

brief periods of late winter. At that rate, as much as 40 percent of the ozone over populous areas of the Northern Hemisphere could be depleted by early spring, when ozone destruction ends each year. The resulting hole, scientists said, could be almost as serious as the one over Antarctica, where ozone depletion has been known to reach 50 percent.

In addition to high levels of ozone-destroying chlorine monoxide and bromine monoxide, the NASA team found reduced levels of nitrogen oxides, which protect ozone from the other two gases by converting them into harmless compounds before they have time to destroy ozone. The loss of nitrogen oxides, which scientists attribute to high levels of volcanic ash ejected into the stratosphere last summer during the eruption of Mount Pinatubo in the Philippines, diminishes the atmosphere's natural ability to recover from ozone depletion.

"The latest scientific findings indicate pretty clearly that the atmosphere all over the place, and not just in the polar regions, is nearly devoid of some of the constituents that protect ozone against depletion," says Michael Oppenheimer, senior scientist at the Environmental Defense Fund in New York City.

...[R]ecent findings are serious enough that several countries, including the United States, have taken new steps to slow ozone depletion. In 1987, for example, the main producers and consumers of CFCs and halons signed the Montreal Protocol, which mandated phasing out these destructive chemicals by the year 2000, or sooner. The phaseout was subsequently accelerated in 1990, and several signatories to the protocol have since committed themselves to beating the deadline....

How Dangerous Is Ozone Depletion?

Ozone-destroying chemicals are extremely stable, so they last in the atmosphere for many decades. That means that even if production of all CFCs and halons stopped today, the chemicals already in the atmosphere would go on destroying ozone well into the 21st century. And because large quantities of these chemicals are contained in existing air conditioners and refrigerators, from which they continue to escape through malfunction or intentional venting, it may be a century before the ozone layer has built itself back up.

Just how devastating widespread ozone depletion would be is not known. But a 1975 government study on the environmental effects of an all-out nuclear war—which scientists say would destroy much of the ozone layer—provided a chilling glimpse of the aftermath. Ozone depletion of 50 percent, the study postulated, "would cause [skin] blistering after one hour of exposure. This leads to the conclusion that outside daytime work in the Northern Hemisphere would require complete covering by protective clothing.... It would be very difficult to grow many (if any) food crops, and livestock would have to graze at dusk if there were any grass to eat."

The study speculated that a 25 to 30 percent depletion of stratospheric ozone —which NASA's findings indicate already may have occurred over parts of the Northern Hemisphere—would make it "difficult to imagine" how survivors could carry out postwar recovery operations.

Since the ozone hole opened over Antarctica in 1985, scientists have been assessing the impact of increased ultraviolet (UV) radiation on phytoplankton, the micro-organisms that make up the essential first link in the food chain that maintains all animal life in warm southern waters, including whales. Preliminary findings show that phytoplankton populations have dropped by up to 12 percent in areas where surface UV radiation has increased under the Antarctic ozone hole.

This is the first evidence outside the laboratory that links ozone depletion to damage of living organisms on Earth.

Excessive UV radiation is also thought to disrupt photosynthesis, the process by which green plants use the sun's radiant energy to produce carbohydrates. Ozone depletion could thus cause reduced yields in crops such as soybeans and rice, crops that are essential to feeding large parts of the Third World.

Ultraviolet radiation has long been known to cause health problems in animals, including cataracts in humans— the leading cause of blindness. The United Nations Environment Programme (UNEP), which was set up in 1972 to foster international cooperation in protecting the environment, predicts that ozone depletion will cause an additional 1.6 million cases per year.

There are also preliminary reports of widespread blindness among rabbits, sheep, horses and cattle in southern Chile, where high UV radiation exposure resulted from the ozone hole over Antarctica.

UNEP also foresees an annual increase of 300,000 cases of skin cancer, by the year 2000, particularly in Argentina and Australia, which have come under increased UV radiation. UNEP also estimates that a 10 percent depletion of the ozone layer would cause up to 26 percent more basal and squamous-cell skin cancers. The agency cites new evidence that UV radiation may also contribute to cancers of the lip and salivary glands.

Other studies project that a 10 percent increase in UV penetration would cause up to a 9 percent increase in the incidence of the more deadly malignant melanoma among light-skinned people, the group that is most vulnerable to this virulent form of cancer.

Ultraviolet radiation may also undermine the immune system's ability to ward off infectious diseases. This, says Margaret L. Kripke, an immunologist at the University of Texas' M. D. Anderson Cancer Center in Houston, is the biggest unknown health effect of UV radiation. Animal experiments have indicated that UV radiation may reduce lymphocytes' ability to destroy certain microorganisms that enter the body through the skin, such as Leishmania, malaria, schistosoma and the leprosy bacillus.

Although it is not known whether UV radiation actually reduces human resistance to these agents, Kripke testified last fall, "infectious diseases constitute an enormous public health problem worldwide, and any factor that reduces immune defenses... is likely to have a devastating impact on human health."

Kripke's research was particularly ominous for sun worshipers. She found that commercial sunscreen preparations, which protect against sunburn and other damage to the skin from UV radiation, don't block the immunosuppressive effects of UV radiation. Similarly, skin pigmentation, which protects darker-skinned people from skin cancers that are prevalent among Caucasians, doesn't seem to protect the immune system from UV damage....

FIRST SIGNS OF TROUBLE

Even as industry was finding new uses for CFCs in the early 1970s, scientists were beginning to link them to ozone destruction. In 1974, Ralph Cicerone, then at the University of Michigan, and his colleague, Richard S. Stolarski, investigated the possible effects on stratospheric ozone of chlorine released by NASA rockets. They concluded that a single atom of chlorine would destroy many thousands of ozone molecules.

However, because the number of rockets passing through the ozone layer was small, and no other sources of chlorine at that altitude had been identified, their findings did not cause widespread alarm.

Findings reported later that year, however, showed that rocket engines were not the only source of chlorine in the stratosphere. Sherwood Rowland and Mario Molina at the University of California at Irvine decided to study CFCs after they are released into the atmosphere. They found that CFCs are so durable that they do not break down under the forces of solar radiation and precipitation in the lower atmosphere, but continue to float around in their original state for many years, eventually drifting upward into the stratosphere.

"What we did was to ask a question that hadn't been asked before: What is going to happen to the CFCs?" Rowland recalls. "The conclusion we came to was that nothing would happen quickly, but on the time scale of many decades CFCs would go away into the stratosphere and release chlorine atoms and then that the chlorine atoms would attack the ozone.... We concluded that there was danger to the ozone layer and... that we should quit putting CFCs into the atmosphere."

Not surprisingly, Rowland and Molina faced hostile reactions from the producers of CFCs when they published their results in 1974. "The public was probably more likely to believe it than the chemistry community," Rowland says. "Within the chemistry community then and still now there is a feeling that most environmental problems are really just public relations problems, that they are not real problems."

Rowland says the chemicals manufacturers set up the Committee on Atmospheric Science to discredit the two researchers' findings. Indeed, he adds that many critics dismissed their conclusions as "kooky. One of my favorites was an aerosol-propellant company that claimed [our results were] disinformation put out by the KGB."

But their data held up. In 1976, after a nationwide research effort involving NASA and the National Oceanic and Atmospheric Administration (NOAA), the National Academy of Sciences confirmed that CFC gases released into the atmosphere from spray cans were in fact damaging the ozone layer.

Two years later, after consumer boycotts had reduced the market for spray cans by almost two-thirds, the United States banned the use of CFCs as aerosol propellants in spray cans for most uses.

OZONE HOLE DISCOVERED

Although other industrial nations continued to produce and use CFCs for aerosol sprays and other purposes, the international scientific community continued the search for data on ozone depletion launched by Rowland and Molina. During the early 1980s, most research was confined to computer models of the atmosphere. Then, in 1985, British scientists discovered that ozone depletion had become so severe over a vast area of Antarctica that it amounted to a virtual "hole" in the ozone layer.

Still, resistance to the ozone-depletion theory remained so strong that the British team was refused additional government funding to continue their research. Ironically, they obtained backing instead from the U.S. Chemical Manufacturers Association, whose members had the most to lose from confirmation of Rowland and Molina's theory. Because of mounting pressure at home to find substitutes for CFCs, however, the American chemical industry wanted to resolve the issue once and for all before abandoning CFCs.

Meanwhile, Rowland and other scientists were learning more about ozone depletion and why the phenomenon was so strong over the Antarctic.

They discovered that CFCs are concentrated over the South Pole because of strong circular winds known as the "polar vortex," which sweep unimpeded over the flat, barren continent of Antarctica. The vortex gathers the destructive gases from the surrounding atmosphere into a wide funnel over Antarctica, where they remain isolated during the dark, frigid winter months.

Equally important, they found that as CFCs break down, the resulting chlorine monoxide clings to the ice crystals that form clouds in the stratosphere. These ice crystals provide the surfaces needed for the catalytic reaction in which chlorine breaks down ozone.

With the return of sunlight to Antarctica during September and October, the beginning of spring in the Southern Hemisphere, solar radiation acts as a catalyst enabling the chlorine monoxide produced by CFCs to destroy the surrounding ozone layer.

As the days lengthen, the air over Antarctica warms up, breaking up both the stratospheric ice clouds and the polar vortex. The destruction of ozone slows as the chlorine atoms are once again bound into harmless chlorine nitrate and hydrogen chloride molecules, and the hole disappears as the vortex dissipates, allowing ozone from the surrounding regions to fill the void.

The final confirmation of Rowland and Molina's theory linking CFCs to ozone depletion came in 1987, when NASA undertook a series of aerial tests over Antarctica. From inside the ozone hole, the NASA instruments detected high concentrations of chlorine monoxide.

Montreal Protocol Signed

International reaction to the proof that CFCs were destroying the ozone layer was swift. On Sept. 16, 1987, just nine months after formal negotiations began, 24 nations signed the Montreal Protocol on Substances That Deplete the Ozone Layer. The agreement garnered an unprecedented degree of international support for such a sweeping program to protect the environment: The ratifying nations accounted for 99 percent of the world's production of CFCs and 90 percent of their consumption.

The Montreal Protocol called for freezing halon emissions at 1986 levels by 1992; for halving CFC emissions by 1998; and halving CFC production and importation by 1999. To compensate for their low levels of production of ozone-depleting chemicals, developing nations were given an additional 10 years to meet these deadlines. By Jan. 1, 1989, the protocol had been ratified by enough countries to go into effect.

Richard Elliot Benedick, a Foreign Service officer who led the U.S. delegation in negotiating the Montreal Protocol, identifies several reasons for the treaty's overwhelming success. First, international cooperation among scientists allowed for the rapid discovery of CFCs' role in ozone depletion. Public opinion, which was then beginning to focus on environmental issues throughout the industrial world, was also quick to press governments to act. Negotiations were supported by the UNEP.

Benedick also credits the United States for its leading role in gaining support for the treaty. The United States was the first producer of ozone-depleting chemicals to restrict their production, he points out in his account of the negotiations surrounding the protocol. In addition, Congress passed ozone-protection legislation as early as 1977, long before the governments of Western Europe responded at all.

The United States also was primarily responsible for the 1985 Vienna Convention for the Protection of the Ozone Layer, an agreement among the major CFC producers to collect additional data that led up to the Montreal Protocol.

"The U.S. government reflected its concerns over the fate of the ozone layer through stimulating and supporting both American and international scientific research," Benedick wrote. "Then, convinced of the dangers, it undertook extensive diplomatic and scientific initiatives to promote an ozone protection plan to other countries, many of which were initially hostile or indifferent to the idea."

The drafters of the Montreal Protocol also assured its success by making the agreement flexible. As such, it could be rapidly amended to reflect subsequent changes in environmental conditions or new findings. And new findings were soon to test the agreement's flexibility.

The ozone hole over Antarctica continued to appear each September and October after its initial discovery in 1985. In 1988, scientists were encouraged to find that the hole was not as big as before. But the following year, the ozone hole reappeared, covering more than 15 million square miles.

Arctic Expedition Launched

The same year, NASA and NOAA launched an airborne expedition to the Arctic to investigate whether conditions were ripe near the North Pole for another ozone hole. Because the Arctic terrain is not as flat as that of Antarctica—and because temperatures at the North Pole do not fall as low as they do at the South Pole—the polar vortex was found to be weaker in the north. But the scientists did find higher than expected concentrations of chlorine compounds and concluded that an ozone hole could easily develop.

Because more people live at far northern latitudes than in southern Chile, Argentina, Australia and New Zealand, which border the area exposed to UV radiation in the Southern Hemisphere, an ozone hole over the Arctic would pose far greater risks to human health.

Other research revealed a new potential source of ozone depletion in areas far from the polar regions. American chemists Susan Solomon and Dave Hoffman found that sulfate particles spewed into the stratosphere by strong volcanic eruptions could act in much the same way as ice crystals in polar stratospheric clouds by providing surfaces on which chlorine and bromine compounds can destroy ozone more efficiently than when they are floating free.

Studying the impact of volcanic ash in the aftermath of the 1982 eruption of El Chichon in Mexico, Solomon and

HOW OZONE-DEPLETING AGENTS ATTACK THE OZONE LAYER

Beginning in the stratosphere at an altitude of about 15 miles and extending up into the mesosphere, the 25-mile-wide ozone layer protects Earth by blocking out most of the sun's harmful ultraviolet light. Breakdown of ozone by chlorofluorocarbons and other chemicals allows harmful radiation to reach Earth.

1. Oxygen molecules in the stratosphere are transformed into ozone by solar ultraviolet (UV) radiation, which splits the oxygen molecule and releases highly reactive oxygen atoms. The free oxygen atoms then bind to oxygen molecules to form ozone molecules, which also are broken up by UV radiation. This continuous creation and destruction of oxygen and ozone occurs normally in the stratosphere.
2. Once certain chemicals, chiefly chlorofluorocarbons (CFCs), reach the ozone layer, UV radiation bombards the CFC molecule, breaking off an atom of chlorine.
3. The free chlorine atom attacks an ozone molecule, breaking off one of ozone's three oxygen atoms to form one chlorine monoxide molecule and leaving one oxygen molecule.
4. When the chlorine monoxide molecule encounters a free oxygen atom, produced during the natural mixing of oxygen and ozone, the oxygen atom breaks up the chlorine monoxide molecule and binds to its oxygen atom, forming a new oxygen molecule and leaving behind a free chlorine atom.
5. The newly freed chlorine atom can continue to destroy ozone molecules for many years. Oxygen molecules continue to break apart and form ozone, but this natural replenishing process is slowed in the presence of chlorine monoxide.
6. Because oxygen, unlike ozone, does not reflect UV radiation, the sun's potentially harmful UV rays penetrate the depleted areas of the ozone layer and reach Earth's surface.

Hoffman found that ozone concentrations over the middle latitudes were significantly depleted. They concluded that ozone depletion was likely following other major volcanic eruptions.

Although their research was limited to El Chichon, Solomon, a NOAA chemist in Boulder, Colo., says, "We found that similar processes could also take place on the liquid sulfuric acid and water particles that form following major volcanic eruptions."

The implications of Solomon and Hoffman's research are clear. While ice clouds form only over the polar regions, volcanic ash can travel anywhere. If volcanic ash does facilitate ozone depletion even in the absence of ice crystals, an ozone hole could open over any region on Earth.

In the summer of 1990, NASA reported that, globally, the ozone layer had been depleted by 2 to 3 percent over the previous two decades. It was also reported that the ozone layer had already begun to thin over the United States and other populated areas in the middle latitudes.

At the same time, the chemicals industry was quickly bringing into production substitutes for CFCs that are less damaging to the ozone layer. While not completely benign, these hydrochlorofluorocarbons, or HCFCs, were hailed as temporary substitutes for CFCs in many applications, particularly as coolants. Most important, the HCFCs and other substitute chemicals facilitated the rapid phaseout of CFCs.

Montreal Protocol nations were quick to respond to the news that ozone depletion was intensifying. In June 1990, in London, they amended the agreement to accelerate the phaseout of ozone-depleting chemicals. Under the new guidelines, all production and importation of CFCs and halons must stop by the year 2000. Other ozone-depleting agents, such as carbon tetrachloride and methyl chloroform, were added to the list of chemicals to be phased out of production. Developing countries still have an additional 10 years to meet the deadline. As a result of the new deadlines, chlorine pollution was expected by 2075 to fall below levels recorded prior to the first appearance of the ozone hole.

The amendments also addressed the special problems faced by developing nations. Although they produce few ozone-depleting chemicals, India, China and other countries have counted on introducing cheap refrigeration and air conditioning as part of their plans for modernization. They succeeded in convincing the industrial world to set up a fund to help them pay for the more expensive substitutes they will be forced to purchase, as well as information and equipment to help them produce environmentally sound refrigerators and air conditioners themselves.

Also in 1990, Congress passed the far-reaching Clean Air Act Amendments, which call for the complete phaseout of CFCs, halons and carbon tetrachloride by 2000, of methyl chloroform by 2002 and HCFCs by 2030. The law made the United States the first nation to legislate a ban on these chemicals. To reduce emissions of existing stores of ozone-depleting agents, the law called for regulations to require recycling of refrigerants and air-conditioning coolants. Finally, the new law mandated faster elimination of ozone-depleting substances if warranted by new scientific findings of damage to the ozone layer.

VAST AREA AT RISK

No sooner had the ink dried on the revisions to the Montreal Protocol than new information pointed to an even more dire situation. In October 1990, scientists found the lowest ozone levels ever recorded over Antarctica and discovered that the hole had stretched into southern Chile including Punta Arenas, a city of 100,000. There was also further evidence that parts of Australia had been exposed to high levels of UV radiation when bits of the ozone hole broke away as the polar vortex weakened and drifted northward from Antarctica.

On Oct. 22, the UNEP and the World Meteorological Organization announced that ozone depletion had begun to occur at the middle and high latitudes of both the Northern and the Southern Hemispheres in spring, summer and winter.

"Ozone depletion in the middle and high latitudes means that it covers almost all of North America, Europe, the Soviet Union, Australia, New Zealand and a sizable part of Latin America," said UNEP Director Mostafa K. Tolba. "The only area with no indication of change, that is, no visible reduction of ozone, is the tropical belt around the Earth."

European researchers, building on Solomon and Hoffman's volcano-ash findings, are now predicting that last year's eruption of Mount Pinatubo threatens to erode the ozone layer to dangerous levels over much of Europe this spring. Researchers participating in the 17-nation European Arctic Stratospheric Ozone Experiment based in northern Sweden have yet to complete their experiments. But they issued a recommendation in early February that governments in Northern Europe should take more urgent steps to protect the ozone layer.

The most recent signs of severe ozone loss were detected by NASA's Upper Atmosphere Research Satellite (UARS), launched last September [1991] to monitor the ozone layer and measure substances that destroy ozone. On Feb. 3, two months before the current study was scheduled for completion, NASA announced that the satellite had detected high levels of chlorine monoxide over Scandinavia and northern Eurasia, an area that includes London, Moscow and Amsterdam. The levels were comparable to concentrations found in the ozone hole over Antarctica.

NASA predicted that an ozone hole could open over the Northern Hemisphere this spring if chlorine monoxide levels remain high enough. Final results of the study are due in mid-April.

The bad news was not limited to the far north. NASA's satellite observations also showed ozone depletion over the tropics, which the agency suggested was due to plumes of ash from Mount Pinatubo. In addition, the satellite detected areas of low ozone across the western United States. These findings were confirmed by separate measurements taken in Boulder, Colo.

Confirming the satellite data were new findings from the NASA-led Airborne Arctic Stratospheric Expedition, which monitors ozone depletion from two specially equipped aircraft: the ER-2, a converted U-2 spy plane that gathers data at 70,000 feet, and the DC-8-72, a "flying lab" that operates at 41,000 feet. The expedition reported Feb. 3 that it had found even higher levels of chlorine monoxide than the satellite had over eastern Canada and northern New England. The readings—at 1.5 parts per billion by volume—surpass anything ever measured in either polar region.

"These findings have increased our concern that significant ozone loss will occur during any given winter over the Arctic in the next 10 years," scientists announced. "This is based on significant new data with improved instrumentation obtained with broader geographic and seasonal coverage and the knowledge that past release of CFCs will increase chlorine substantially in the stratosphere in the decade to come."

NOTES

1. The ozone layer is a 25-mile-wide band above the Earth with a high but uneven concentration of ozone gas. Starting at an altitude of about 15 miles, it shields humans and other organisms from the most harmful effects of the sun's ultraviolet (UV) radiation.

NO

James P. Hogan

OZONE POLITICS:
THEY CALL THIS SCIENCE?

Every age has its peculiar folly: some scheme, project, or fantasy into which it plunges, spurred on by the love of gain, the necessity of excitement, or the mere force of imitation.

—Charles Mackay
Extraordinary Popular Delusions and the Madness of Crowds, 1841

Earlier centuries saw witch-hunting hysteria, the Crusades, gold stampedes, and the South Sea Bubble. Periodically, societies are seized by collective delusions that take on lives of their own, where all facts are swept aside that fail to conform to the expectations of what has become a self-sustaining reality. Today we have the environmentalist mania reaching a crescendo over ozone.

Manmade chlorofluorocarbons, or CFCs, we're told, are eating away the ozone layer that shields us from ultraviolet radiation, and if we don't stop using them now deaths from skin cancer in the United States alone will rise by hundreds of thousands in the next half century. As a result, 80 nations are about to railroad through legislation to ban one of most beneficial substances ever discovered at a cost the public doesn't seem to comprehend but that will be staggering. It could mean having to replace today's refrigeration and air-conditioning equipment with more expensive types running on substitutes that are toxic, corrosive, flammable if sparked, less efficient, and generally reminiscent of the things people heaved sighs of relief to get rid of in the 1930s. And the domestic side will be only a small part. The food industry that we take for granted depends on refrigerated warehouses, trucks, and ships. So do supplies of drugs, medicines, and blood. Whole regions of the sunbelt states have prospered during the last 40 years because of the better living and working environments made possible by air conditioning. And to developing nations that rely completely on modern food-preservation methods, the effects will be devastating.

Now, I'd have to agree that the alternative of seeing the planet seared by lethal levels of radiation would make a pretty good justification for whatever drastic action is necessary to prevent it. The only problem is, there isn't one

From James P. Hogan, "Ozone Politics: They Call This Science?" *Omni*, vol. 15, no. 8 (June 1993). Copyright © 1993 by Omni Publications International, Ltd. Reprinted by permission of the author.

piece of solid, scientifically validated evidence to support the contention. The decisions being made are political, driven by media-friendly pressure groups wielding a power over public perceptions that is totally out of proportion to any scientific competence they possess. But when you ask the people who do have the competence to know—scientists who have specialized in the study of atmosphere and climate for years—a very different story emerges.

What they're saying, essentially, is that the whole notion of the ozone layer as something fixed and finite, to be eroded away at a faster or slower rate like shoe leather, is all wrong to begin with—it's simply not a depletable resource; that even if it were, the process by which CFCs are supposed to deplete it is highly speculative and has never been observed to take place; and even if it did, the effect would be trivial compared to what happens naturally. In short, there's no good reason for believing that human activity is having any significant effect at all.

To see why, let's start with the basics and take seashores as an analogy. Waves breaking along the coastline continually generate a belt of surf. The surf decomposes again, back into the ocean from where it came. The two processes are linked: Big waves on stormy days create more surf; the more surf there is to decay, the higher the rate at which it does so. The result is a balance between the rates of creation and destruction. Calmer days will see a general thinning of the surf line and possibly "holes" in more sheltered spots —but obviously the surf isn't something that runs out. Its supply is inexhaustible as long as oceans and shores exist.

In the same kind of way, ozone is all the time being created in the upper atmosphere—by sunshine, out of oxygen. A normal molecule of oxygen gas consists of two oxygen atoms joined together. High-energy ultraviolet radiation, known as UV-C, can split one of these molecules apart (a process known as photodissociation) into two free oxygen atoms. These can then attach to another molecule to form a three-atom species, which is ozone—produced mainly in the tropics above a 30-kilometer altitude where the ultraviolet flux is strongest. The ozone sinks and moves poleward to accumulate in lower-level reservoirs extending from 17 to 30 kilometers—the so-called ozone "layer."

Ozone is destroyed by chemical recombination back into normal oxygen— by reaction with nitrogen dioxide (produced in part by high-altitude cosmic rays), through ultraviolet dissociation by the same UV-C that creates ozone, and also by a less energetic band known as UV-B, which isn't absorbed in the higher regions. Every dissociation of an oxygen or ozone molecule absorbs an incoming UV-B photon, and that may be what gives this part of the atmosphere its ultraviolet screening ability.

Its height and thickness are not constant, but adjust automatically to accommodate variations in the incoming ultra-violet flux. When UV is stronger, it penetrates deeper before being absorbed; with weaker UV, penetration is less. Even if all the ozone were to suddenly vanish, there would still be 17 to 30 kilometers of hitherto untouched oxygen-rich atmosphere below, which would become available as a resource for new ozone creation, and the entire screening mechanism would promptly regenerate. As Robert Pease, professor emeritus of physical climatology at the University of California at Riverside, says, "Ozone in the atmosphere is not in finite supply." In other words, as in the case of surf with oceans and shores, it is inexhaustible for as long as sunshine and air continue to exist.

If ozone were depleting, UV intensity at the earth's surface would be increasing. In fact, actual measurements show that it has been decreasing—by as much as 8 percent in some places over the last decade.

Ordinarily, a scientific hypothesis that failed in its most elementary prediction would be dumped right there. But as Dr. Dixy Lee Ray—former governor of Washington state, chairman of the Atomic Energy Commission, and a scientist with the U.S. Bureau of Oceans and the University of Washington—put it: "There are fads in science. Scientists are capable of developing their own strange fixations, just like anyone else." Even though the physics makes it difficult to see how, the notion of something manmade destroying the ozone layer has always fascinated an apocalyptic few who have been seeking possible candidates for more than 40 years. According to Hugh Ellsaesser, guest scientist at the Atmospheric and Geophysical Sciences Division of the Lawrence Livermore National Laboratory, "There has been a small but concerted program to build the possibility of man destroying the ozone layer into a dire threat requiring governmental controls since the time of CIAP [Climatic Impact Assessment Program on the supersonic transport (SST), conducted in the early 1970s]."

In the 1950s, it was A-bomb testing; in the 1960s, the SST; in the 1970s, spacecraft launches and various chemicals from pesticides to fertilizers. All of these claimed threats to the destruction of the ozone layer were later discredited, and for a while, the controversy died out. Then, in 1985 and 1986, banner headlines blared that a huge ozone hole had been discovered in the Antarctic. This, it was proclaimed, confirmed the latest version of the threat.

In 1974, two chemists, Rowland and Molina at the University of California at Irvine, hypothesized that ozone might be attacked by CFCs—which had come into widespread use during the previous 20 years. Basically, they suggested that the same chemical inertness that makes CFCs noncorrosive, nontoxic, and ideal as a refrigerant would enable them to diffuse intact to the upper atmosphere. There, they would be dissociated by high-energy ultraviolet and release free atoms of chlorine. Chlorine will combine with one of the three oxygen atoms of an ozone molecule to produce chlorine monoxide and a normal two-molecule oxygen atom, thereby destroying the ozone molecule. The model becomes more insidious by postulating an additional chain of catalytic reactions via which the chlorine monoxide can be recycled back into free chlorine, hence evoking the specter of a single chlorine atom running amok in the stratosphere, gobbling up ozone molecules like Pac-Man.

Scary, vivid, sensational; perfect for activists seeking a cause, politicians in need of visibility; just what the media revel in. Unfortunately, however, it doesn't fit with a few vital facts. And if you claim to be talking about science, that's kind of important.

First, CFCs don't rise in significant amounts to where they need to be for UV-C photons to break them up. Because ozone absorbs heat directly from the sun's rays, the stratosphere exhibits a reverse temperature structure, or thermal "inversion"—it gets warmer with altitude rather than cooler. As Robert Pease points out, "This barrier greatly inhibits vertical air movements and the interchange of gases across the tropopause [the boundary between the lower atmosphere and the stratosphere], including CFCs. In the stratosphere, CFC gases decline rapidly and drop to only two percent of surface values by thirty kilometers of altitude. At the same time, less than two percent of the UV-C penetrates this deeply." Hence the number of CFC splittings is vastly lower than the original hypothesis assumes—for the same reason there aren't many marriages between Eskimos and Australian Aborigines: They don't mix very much.

For the UV photons that do make it, there are about 136 million oxygen molecules for them to collide with for every CFC—and every such reaction will create ozone, not destroy it. So even if we allow the big CFC molecule three times the chance of a small oxygen molecule of being hit, then 45 million ozone molecules will still be created for every CFC molecule that's broken up. Hardly a convincing disaster scenario, is it?

Ah, but what about the catalytic effect, whereby one chlorine atom can eat up thousands of ozone molecules? Doesn't that change the picture?

Not really. The catalysis argument depends on encounters between chlorine monoxide and free oxygen atoms. But the chances are much higher that a wandering free oxygen atom will find a molecule of normal oxygen rather than one of chlorine monoxide. So once again, probability favors ozone creation over ozone destruction.

At least 192 chemical reactions occur between substances in the upper stratosphere along with 48 different identifiable photochemical processes all linked through complex feedback mechanisms that are only partly understood. Selecting a few reactions brought about in a laboratory and claiming that this is what happens in the stratosphere (where it has never been measured) might be a way of getting to a predetermined conclusion. But it isn't science.

But surely it's been demonstrated! Hasn't a thousand times more chlorine been measured over the Antarctic than models say ought to be there?

Yes. High concentrations of chlorine—or to be exact, chlorine monoxide. But all chlorine atoms look alike. There is absolutely nothing to link the chlorine found over the Antarctic with CFCs from the other end of the world. What the purveyors of that story omitted to mention was that the measuring station at McMurdo Sound is located 15 kilometers downwind from Mount Erebus, an active volcano venting 100 to 200 tons of chlorine every day, and that in 1983 it averaged 1,000 tons per day. Mightn't that just have more to do with it than refrigerators in New York or air conditioners in Atlanta?

World CFC production is currently about 1.1 million tons annually—750,000 tons of which is chlorine. Twenty times as much comes from the passive outgassing of volcanoes. This can rise by a factor of ten with a single large eruption—for example that of Tambora in 1815, which pumped a minimum of 211 million tons straight into the atmosphere. Where are the records of all the cataclysmic effects that should presumably have followed from the consequent ozone depletion?

And on an even greater scale, 300 million tons of chlorine are contained in spray blown off the oceans every year. A single thunderstorm in the Amazon region can transport 200 million tons of air per hour into the atmosphere, containing 3 million tons of water vapor. On average 44,000 thunderstorms occur daily, mostly in the tropics. Even if we concede to the depletion theory and allow this mechanism to transport CFCs also, compared to what gets there naturally, the whiff of chlorine produced by all of human industry (and we're only talking about the leakage from it) is a snowflake in a blizzard.

Despite all that, isn't it still true that a hole has appeared in the last ten years and is getting bigger? What about that, then?

In 1985, a sharp, unpredicted decline was reported in the mean depth of ozone over Halley Bay, Antarctica. Although the phenomenon was limited to altitudes between 12 and 22 kilometers and the interior of a seasonal circulation of the polar jet stream known as the "polar vortex," it was all that the ozone-doomsday pushers needed. Without waiting for any scientific evaluation or consensus, they decided that this was the confirmation that the Rowland-Molina conjecture had been waiting for. The ominous term "ozone hole" was coined by a media machine well rehearsed in environmentalist politics, and anything the scientific community had to say has been drowned out.

Missing from the press and TV accounts, for instance, is that an unexpectedly low value in the Antarctic winter-spring ozone level was reported by the British scientist Gordon Dobson in 1956 —when CFCs were barely in use. In a 40-year history of ozone research written in 1968, he notes: "One of the most interesting results... which came out of the IGY [International Geophysical Year] was the discovery of the peculiar annual variation of ozone at Halley Bay." His first thought was that the result might have been due to faulty equipment or operator error. But when such possibilities were eliminated and the same thing happened the following year, he concluded: "It was clear that the winter vortex over the South Pole was maintained late into the spring and that this kept the ozone values low. When it suddenly broke up in November, both the ozone values and the stratosphere temperatures suddenly rose." A year after that, in 1958, a similar drop was reported by French scientists at the Antarctic observatory at Dumont d'Urville—larger than that causing all the hysteria today.

These measurements were on the edge of observational capability, especially in an environment such as the Antarctic, and most scientists regarded them with caution. After the 1985 "discovery," NASA reanalyzed its satellite data and found that it had been routinely throwing out low Antarctic ozone readings as "unreliable."

The real cause is slowly being unraveled, and while some correlation is evident with volcanic eruptions and sunspot cycles, the dominant factor appears to be the extreme Antarctic winter conditions, as Dobson originally suspected. The poleward transportation of ozone from its primary creation zones over the tropics does not penetrate into the polar vortex, where chemical depletion can't be replaced because of the lack of sunshine. Note that this is a localized minimum relative to the surrounding high-latitude reservoir regions, where global ozone is thickest. As Hugh Ellsaesser observes, "The ozone hole... leads only to spring values of ultraviolet flux over Antarctica . . . a factor of two less than those experienced every summer in North Dakota."

But isn't it getting bigger every year? And aren't the latest readings showing depletion elsewhere, too?

In April, 1991, EPA Administrator William Reilly announced that the ozone layer over North America was thinning twice as fast as expected and produced the figures for soaring deaths from skin cancer. This was based on readings from NASA's Nimbus-7 satellite. I talked to Dr. S. Fred Singer of the Washington-based Science and Environmental Policy Project, who developed the principle of UV backscatter that the ozone monitoring instrument aboard Nimbus-7 employs. "You simply cannot tell from one sunspot cycle," was his comment. "The data are too noisy. Scientists need at least one more cycle of satellite observations before they can establish a trend." In other words the trend exists in the eye of the determined beholder, not in any facts he beholds.

February 1992 saw a repeat performance when a NASA research aircraft detected high values of chlorine monoxide in the northern stratosphere. Not of CFCs; nor was there any evidence that ozone itself was actually being depleted, nor any mention that the Pinatubo volcano was active at the time. Yet almost as if on cue, the U.S. Senate passed an amendment only two days later calling for an accelerated phaseout of CFCs. (It's interesting to note that NASA's budget was under review at the time. After getting its increase, NASA has since conceded that perhaps the fears were premature.)

But apart from all that, yes, world mean-total ozone declined about 5 percent from 1979 to 1986. So what? From 1962 to 1979 it increased by 5 1/2 percent. And since 1986, it has been increasing again (although that part's left out of the story the public gets). On shorter time scales, it changes naturally all the time and from place to place, hence surface ultraviolet intensity is not constant and never was. It varies with latitude—for instance, how far north or south from the equator you are—with the seasons, and with solar activity. And it does so in amounts that are far greater than those causing all the fuss.

The whole doomsday case boils down to claiming that if something isn't done to curb CFCs, ultraviolet radiation will increase by 10 percent over the next 20 years. But from the poles to the equator, it increases naturally by a whopping factor of 50, or 5,000 percent, anyway! —equivalent to 1 percent for every six miles. Or to put it another way, a family moving from New York to Philadelphia would experience the same increase as is predicted by the worst-case depletion scenarios. Alternatively, they could live 1,500 feet higher in elevation—say, by moving to their summer cabin in the Catskills.

Superposed on this is a minimum 25-percent swing from summer to winter, and on top of that, a 10- to 12-year pattern that follows the sunspot cycle. Finally, there are irregular fluctuations caused by the effects of volcanic eruptions, electrical storms, and the like on atmospheric chemistry. Expecting to find some "natural" level that shouldn't be deviated from in all this is like trying to define sea level in a typhoon.

Skin cancer is increasing, nevertheless. Something must be causing it.

An increasing rate of UV-induced skin cancer means that more people are receiving more exposure than they ought to. It doesn't follow that the intensity of ultraviolet is increasing as it would if ozone were being depleted. (In fact, it's decreasing, as we saw earlier.) Other considerations explain the facts far better, such as that sun worship has become a fad among light-skinned people only in the last couple of generations, or the migrations in comparatively recent times of peoples into habitats for which they aren't adapted: for instance, the white population of Australia. (Native Australians have experienced no skin-cancer increase.)

Deaths from drowning increase as you get nearer the equator—not because the water becomes more lethal but because human behavior changes: Not many people go swimming in the Arctic. Nevertheless, when it comes to skin cancer, the National Academy of Sciences [NAS] has decided that only variation of UV matters. And from the measured ozone thinning from poles to equator and the change in zenith angle of the sun they determined that a 1-percent decrease in ozone equates to a 2-percent rise in skin cancer.

How you make a disaster scenario out of this, according to Ellsaesser, is to ignore the decline in surface UV actually measured over the last 15 years, ignore the reversal that shows ozone to have been increasing again since 1986, and extend the 1979–1986 slope as if it were going to continue for the next 40 years. Then, take the above formula as established fact and apply it to the entire U.S. population. Witness: According to the NAS report (1975), approximately 600,000 new cases of skin cancer occur annually. So, by the above, a 1-percent ozone decrease gives 12,000 more skin cancers. Projecting the 5-percent ozone

swing from the early 1980s through the next four decades gives 25 percent, hence a 50-percent rise in skin cancer, which works out at 300,000 new cases in the year 2030 A.D., or 7.5 million over the full period. Since the mortality rate is around 2.5 percent, this gives the EPA's "200,000 extra deaths in the United States alone." Voilà: Instant catastrophe.

As if this weren't flaky enough, it's possible that the lethal variety of skin cancer has little to do with UV exposure, anyway. The cancers that are caused by radiation are recognizable by their correlation with latitude and length of exposure to the sun and are relatively easily treated. The malignant melanoma form, which does kill, affects places like the soles of the feet as well as exposed areas, and there is more of it in Sweden than in Spain.

So, what's going on? What are publicly funded institutions that claim to be speaking science doing, waving readings known to be worthless (garbage in, gospel out?), faking data, pushing a cancer scare that contradicts fact, and force-feeding the public a line that basic physics says doesn't make sense? The only thing that comes through at all clearly is a determination to eliminate CFCs at any cost, whatever the facts, regardless of what scientists say.

Would it come as a complete surprise to learn that some very influential concerns stand to make a lot of money out of this? The patents on CFCs have recently run out, so anybody can now manufacture them without having to pay royalties. Sixty percent of the world CFC market is controlled by four companies who are already losing revenues and market share to rapidly growing chemicals industries in the Third World, notably Brazil, South Korea, and Taiwan. Some hold the patents on the only substitutes in sight, which will restore monopoly privileges once again if CFCs are outlawed. Mere coincidence?

Ultraviolet light has many beneficial effects as well as detrimental. For all any one knows, the increase that's being talked about could result in more overall good than harm. But research proposals to explore that side of things are turned down, while doomsayers line up for grants running into hundreds of millions. The race is on between chemicals manufacturers to come up with a better CFC substitute while equipment suppliers will be busy for years. Politicians are posturing as champions of the world, and the media are having a ball.

As Bob Holzknecht, a Florida engineer in the CFC industry for 20 years observes, "Nobody's interested in reality. Everyone who knows anything stands to gain. The public will end up paying through the nose, as always, but the public is unorganized and uninformed."

Good science will be the victim, too, of course. But science has a way of winning in the end. Today's superstitions can spread a million times faster than anything dreamed of by the doom prophets in days of old. But the same technologies which make that possible can also prove equally effective in putting them speedily to rest.

POSTSCRIPT

Is Ozone Depletion a Genuine Threat?

The critics of the "ozone scare" have made very little headway against the evidence. In November 1992 the Montreal Protocol was strengthened, and the deadline for ending production of CFCs was moved up by as much as nine years. By December 92 nations had ratified the treaty.

In March 1993 researchers reported a drop in Northern Hemisphere ozone concentrations that was worse than the one that kicked off the 1992 alarm discussed by Cooper. In April NASA researchers reported record thinning of the ozone layer worldwide. By autumn researchers had added that the 1993 ozone hole over the Antarctic was fully 15 percent worse than the one that had appeared the year before.

Some critics have suggested that the decline in ozone is a perfectly natural response to chlorine injected into the atmosphere (as hydrochloric acid) by volcanic eruptions or that volcanic chlorine could be making the problem worse than it would otherwise be. Separate studies done in May and August 1993, however, indicated that CFCs are the cause of the problem and that volcanic activity would have very little effect on the ozone.

In 1995 F. Sherwood Rowland and Mario J. Molina, with Paul Crutzen, shared the Nobel Prize in Chemistry for discovering the hazards that CFCs pose to the ozone layer. The Nobel committee said that their work contributed to "our salvation from a global environmental problem that could have catastrophic consequences." At the same time, computer models suggested that the ozone hole was not likely to grow any worse—that indeed the problem was on the mend, and over the next 50 years the stratosphere would return to normal.

However, some people still refuse to cooperate with the ban on CFCs. In March 1996 the U.S. Customs Service said that smuggling of CFCs, especially Freon (the chief coolant for air conditioners), is now second only to illegal drugs as a smuggling problem. If the CFC black market continues to grow, it could undo all the good done by the Montreal Protocol, and instead of getting better over the next 50 years, ozone depletion may only get worse.

For more reports on ozone depletion, see Richard S. Stolarski, "The Antarctic Ozone Hole," *Scientific American* (January 1988) and Owen B. Toon and Richard P. Turco, "Polar Stratospheric Clouds and Ozone Depletion," *Scientific American* (June 1991).

Two articles by critics of the "ozone scare" are Gary Taubes, "The Ozone Backlash," *Science* (June 11, 1993) and Ronald Bailey, "The Hole Story: The Science Behind the Scare," *Reason* (June 1992).

On the Internet, visit: http://www.epa.gov/docs/ozone/index.html.

PART 3

The Cutting Edge of Technology

Many interesting controversies arise in connection with technologies that are so new that they often sound more like science fiction than fact. Some examples are technologies that allow the exploration of both outer space and the ocean depths, devices that search for extraterrestrial life, and advances in computer intelligences. Such advances offer capabilities undreamed of in earlier ages, and they raise genuine, important questions about what it is to be a human being, the limits on human freedom in a technological age, and the place of humanity in the broader universe. They also raise questions of how society should respond: Should we accept the new devices and abilities offered by scientists and engineers? Or should we reject them?

- Should the Goals of the U.S. Space Program Include Manned Exploration of Space?

- Is It Worthwhile to Continue the Search for Extraterrestrial Life?

- Will It Be Possible to Build a Computer That Can Think?

ISSUE 9

Should the Goals of the U.S. Space Program Include Manned Exploration of Space?

YES: Doug Beason, from "America's Blueprint for Mars: The Report of the Synthesis Group," *Analog Science Fiction and Fact* (Mid-December 1992)

NO: John Merchant, from "A New Direction in Space," *IEEE Technology and Society Magazine* (Winter 1994)

ISSUE SUMMARY

YES: Associate professor of physics Doug Beason argues that a U.S. government program oriented to the manned space exploration of Mars would provide an invigorating, economy-stimulating focus for the nation.

NO: John Merchant, a retired staff engineer at Loral Infrared and Imaging Systems, argues that it will be much cheaper to develop electronic senses and remotely operated machines that humans can use to explore other worlds.

The dream of conquering space has a long history. The pioneers of rocketry —the Russian Konstantin Tsiolkovsky (1857–1935) and the American Robert H. Goddard (1882–1945)—both dreamed of exploring other worlds, although neither lived long enough to see the first artificial satellite, the Soviet Sputnik, go up in 1957. That success sparked a race between America and the Soviet Union to be the first to achieve each step in the progression of space exploration. The next steps were to put dogs (the Soviet Laika was the first), monkeys, chimps, and finally human beings into orbit. Communications, weather, and spy satellites were then designed and launched. And on July 20, 1969, the U.S. Apollo program landed the first men on the moon (see Buzz Aldrin and Malcolm McConnell, *Men from Earth*, Bantam Books, 1989).

There were a few more Apollo moon landings, but not many. The United States had achieved its main political goal of beating the Soviets to the moon and, in the minds of the government, demonstrated American superiority. Thereafter, the United States was content to send automated spacecraft (operated by robots) off to observe Venus, Mars, and the rings of Saturn; to land on Mars and study its soil; and even to carry recordings of Earth's sights and sounds past the distant edge of the solar system, perhaps to be retrieved by intelligent life from other worlds. (Those recordings are attached to the Voyager spacecraft, launched in 1977; if you wish a copy, it was advertised in February 1994 as a combination of CD, CD-ROM, and book, *Murmurs of Earth: The Voyager Interstellar Record*, available from Time-Warner Interactive Group, 2210 Olive Avenue, Burbank, CA 91506.)

Humans have not left near-Earth orbit for two decades, even though the technology of space travel has continued to develop. The Soviets even have a small space station in orbit now. The American equivalent, Skylab, fell to Earth in 1979 and has not been replaced. However, the National Aeronautics and Space Administration (NASA) does have the space shuttle, which is able to lift crews of a few men and women into space for a few days at a time, where they perform experiments, launch satellites, and in the next few years may build a new space station.

Why has human space exploration gone no further? One reason is that robots are now extremely capable; indeed, James A. Van Allen called them more appropriate for the task than humans in "Space Science, Space Technology and the Space Station," *Scientific American* (January 1986). Although some robot spacecraft have failed partially or completely, there have been many grand successes that have added enormously to mankind's knowledge of Earth and other planets.

Another reason for the reduction in human space travel seems to be the fear that astronauts will die in space. This point was emphasized by the explosion of the space shuttle *Challenger* upon takeoff in January 1986, which killed seven astronauts and froze the entire shuttle program for over two and a half years. Still another reason is money: Lifting robotic explorers into space is expensive, but lifting people into space—along with all the food, water, air, and other supplies necessary to keep them alive for the duration of a mission —is much more expensive. And there are many people in government and elsewhere who believe that there are numerous better ways to spend the money on Earth.

Physicist Doug Beason was a member of the Synthesis Group of the White House Science Office during the Bush administration. The group was given the task of finding the best way to go to Mars, and it concluded that the benefits of such a mission would be much greater than simply getting to Mars; additional benefits would include job creation, investment in science and technology, and stimulated innovation. In the following selections, Beason outlines the requirements for the manned exploration of Mars and argues that although manned space exploration may have high costs, it also has many benefits for society on Earth. Because manned space projects are very expensive and society has needs here at home, many people argue that we should not embark upon them. Robots work fine in space, say critics, and they are much cheaper. Engineer John Merchant argues that there is a third choice that takes advantage of modern computer technology: instead of people, he advocates sending their eyes, ears, and hands to space in electronic form.

YES

Doug Beason

AMERICA'S BLUEPRINT FOR MARS: THE REPORT OF THE SYNTHESIS GROUP

On July 20, 1989, on the steps of the National Air and Space Museum, President George Bush gave a speech commemorating the 20th anniversary of the landing of the first men on the Moon. In this speech he outlined an exhilarating national goal—for humans to return to the Moon, this time to stay, and then to go to Mars *and beyond*. This marked the first time since John F. Kennedy's speech that America was challenged to "go where no man has gone before."

For all intents and purposes, the nation had pulled out of exploring space at the end of the Apollo era. Human presence was limited to a mere few hundred kilometers from the surface of the Earth.

However, if properly instituted, this new challenge could define a renaissance for exploring the Universe.

In response to Bush's speech, NASA [National Aeronautics and Space Administration] conducted a "90 Day Study" that laid the groundwork for achieving the president's goal. The next step was taken by Vice President Quayle, as head of the National Space Council. Determined not to continue business as usual, he directed NASA to establish the Outreach Program to "cast nets widely" for new approaches to accomplish SEI, the Space Exploration Initiative. The Outreach Program was initiated as a nationwide hunt for the best ideas on how to send humans to Mars, cheaper, faster, smarter.

Astronaut Tom Stafford—*Gemini* pilot, *Apollo* X commander (where he brought the lunar module to within kilometers of the lunar surface) and pilot of the *Apollo/Soyuz* mission—was asked by the vice president to establish a *Synthesis Group*, responsible for pulling the Outreach program together. Stafford assembled a group of 46 experts hailing from all walks of life—academia, industry and government—after receiving nominations for his group from industry heads, cabinet officials, and professional societies. He also included 23 senior members consisting of internationally acknowledged space leaders, ranging from a former secretary of the Air Force, to the designer of the *Mercury, Gemini* and *Apollo* spacecraft. Once convened, the Synthesis Group was tasked to achieve three goals: to analyze and

From Doug Beason, "America's Blueprint for Mars: The Report of the Synthesis Group," *Analog Science Fiction and Fact*, vol. 112, no. 15 (Mid-December 1992). Copyright © 1992 by Doug Beason. Reprinted by permission.

synthesize the thousands of Outreach responses, to recommend two or more significantly different architectures for the Space Exploration Initiative, and to identify technological priorities and early milestones to land humans on Mars.

The Synthesis Group report has been widely distributed, briefed to Congress, and its ramifications are still being debated throughout academia, industry, and government. The report provides a vision of America's future in the exploration of space. This article will concentrate on the rationale of why specific recommendations were made and how they will affect America's space program.

The crux of the Space Exploration Initiative is to pursue the peaceful application of high technology. With a goal of reaching Mars, this will inspire and invigorate generations to come. And when combined with technical spin-offs, the increase in scientific knowledge will add to reestablishing national leadership.... [T]he Synthesis Group has... drawn up blueprints for invigorating the nation, just as *Apollo* did in the sixties.

But before the results of the Synthesis Group are presented, two questions brought by critics should be addressed: why bother exploring space, and why now?

The obvious answer is that SEI provides a focus not only for our space efforts, but for the nation as a whole. It allows us to invest in our nation's scientific and technological base, creating new job opportunities and markets; arguing to go to space for "Teflon and Tang" simply won't hack it anymore.

More directly, SEI provides the chance to reorient our GNP [gross national product] from being fueled by the military-industrial complex to being based on that of a space-faring nation. This is especially critical during these post-Cold War days, where America needs a stimulating national goal on which to base its economy.

SEI has the opportunity to facilitate the commercialization of space and promote space-based industries, products, and services. In fact, one of the architectures developed by the Synthesis Group concentrates on using space resources for just these purposes.

Further, SEI allows for advancing technological innovation. This means spurring new technologies with terrestrial and commercial applications. This in turn will inspire interest in science and engineering.

The consequence of investing in space is to radically increase our knowledge of the Universe. This will help us better understand the origin of the Universe, planets and perhaps life itself.

These are all good reasons for establishing a space exploration policy. But still the question remains, why should America do this now? Why can't we wait until times are "better," economically as well as socially? After all, it's pretty hard to justify sending a few people to Mars when there are plenty of people hurting right here at home.

Part of the reason has already been given—SEI is a fundamental way to ensure that those better times will come. It's more than just sending people to another planet. Rather than simply dumping money into the hands of bureaucrats, "experts" in redistributing wealth, it provides for a systematic way to rebuild America's infrastructure. In the 1940s, after World War II, America invested in the future of its past adversaries, Germany and Japan, through vehicles such as the Marshall Plan and MacArthur accords. Some may say that looking back, this was not such a bright idea, but there is no doubt of the success these programs have had in rebuilding those nations' infrastructure.

America is in a similar situation today. But this time we have the chance to invest in *ourselves*, to rebuild the very backbone that defines our nation's economic strength.

And there are other compelling reasons.

The SEI is more than an exploration program; it embodies the essence of a new social paradigm and it is therefore constructed without limits. This is different from saying that "no end is in sight." Rather than having a closed goal of only getting humans to Mars and ending the program there, SEI uses education as a basic priority to bring out the very best in our nation, and to hold the future open for our children. It is forward-looking and will focus technologies to allow this social effort to succeed. (Compare this to what happened to the *Apollo* program: once we got to the Moon, the public lost interest and the space program went downhill.)

The SEI provides a focus to the entire space program. Just as *Apollo* succeeded in the 1960s, SEI can unify our future goals in space.

The Moon and Mars are the first elements of an exploration program. The Moon provides a natural platform for astronomy, planetary science, and even as a resource for materials and energy. Since it's only 240,000 miles away from Earth, it's a logical first step for getting to Mars. With a surface area of 14.6 million square miles—roughly that of Africa—it provides a unique test bed for checking out equipment and procedures while being only three days away.

In addition to the fact that Mars might someday be a habitable colony, the opportunities to explore this pristine planet can reveal myriad facts about Earth—through geologic evolution, how the atmosphere and climate has changed over time, and even by searching for fossil life. This would be perhaps the most far reaching discovery of all: if true life is found to have existed on Mars, the societal implication back on Earth will have enormous ramifications.

The mere task of getting to Mars is much harder than simply fielding a test bed on the Moon and then rocketing out to the fourth planet. The differences between the Moon and Mars are vast. Everything from the presence of an atmosphere to radio delay times of up to 40 minutes will bring unique challenges. As such, any architecture for SEI must be diverse, robust, and flexible.

To define the architectures, the Synthesis Group established the concept of *Waypoints*—specific objectives to be achieved on the surface of the Moon or Mars. The architectures were then comprised of a linear combination of these Waypoints. This allowed the group to configure a set of architectures that gives policy makers a wide choice in how they accomplish SEI's goals. . . .

Architecture 1: Mars Exploration

This architecture is the classic "flags and footprints" mission. It achieves the basic SEI goal of landing humans on Mars by 2014. In addition, its main strengths include exploring Mars and accomplishing good science. In this and the following architectures, the human missions are preceeded by a cargo mission. The philosophy of splitting up the cargo and human missions is called a "split sprint" concept. That is, the cargo is sent on an energy efficient (minimum energy) Hohmann transfer orbit, taking as long as 1,000 days to reach Mars. Since there are no humans on board, there is no reason to minimize transit time. Once the cargo ship has successfully been inserted into an orbit around Mars, then a fast, or "sprint" mission with humans may be launched to rendezvous with the cargo ship. The human mission is thus relieved from carrying the enormous amount of fuel and supplies needed for a Martian descent....

Expeditionary missions will precede any permanent outpost on Mars. Timelines for this architecture are to land the first 5 person mission on the Moon in 2005 for a stay of 14 Earth days....

Architecture 2: Science Emphasis for Moon and Mars

This architecture takes full advantage of the Moon and Mars to increase our knowledge of the Universe. It consists of a balanced science program and emphasizes exploration.

Pressurized lunar rovers, especially fitted for long duration missions of up to two weeks, can roam 50 kilometers from base, increasing to 100 kilometers on later missions. Mini-telerobotic prospectors, perhaps piloted with virtual presence technology, can greatly add to the exploration. On the lunar surface, these prospectors may even be commanded from Earth. The 2.5 second round trip light delay is not enough to preclude direct interaction with Earth researchers. On the other hand, on Mars the light delay will run from 10 to 40 *minutes* each way, depending on the relative positions of the planets. This will result in a radical change of command and control philosophy. No longer will the astronauts be required to clear every activity with mission control. Emergencies won't wait for light delays.

As an example of the science program, an optical interferometer on the Moon with arms kilometers in length may be able to achieve resolutions on the order of a microarcsecond—over a hundred thousand times greater than what the Hubble telescope was designed to resolve. With resolutions this small, it is not only possible to detect Earth-sized planets orbiting nearby star systems, but to make interferometric studies of those planets' atmospheres (for example, we can tell if the atmosphere holds oxygen and other life-bearing constituents).

Compared to the Earth there is a *million times* less seismic activity on the Moon. The Moon is thus a near perfect place to put sensitive astronomical equipment such as the optical interferometer.

... All in all, if SEI develops as an ongoing program, the science return could be (sorry!) astronomical.

Timelines for this architecture are to land the first 5 person mission on the Moon in 2003 for a stay of 14 Earth days. Several additional lunar missions with increasingly complex astronomical equipment are planned with longer stays, until a training mission for the Mars flight occurs in 2008. A 600-day Mars mission, the first of several, is planned for 2014.

Architecture 3: Moon to Stay and Mars Exploration

Along with sending humans to Mars, this architecture fulfills the president's goal of establishing a permanent, albeit initially small, human presence on the Moon. More importantly, this is the architecture that will expand mankind's presence in the Universe. It's the first step in setting up a self-sufficient colony.

As with the other architectures, the lunar colony will use the Moon as a test bed for exploring Mars, putting into operation as many Mars systems as possible. In addition, it will accomplish a small amount of science and exploration on the lunar surface.

The main thrust of Architecture 3 is still to explore Mars by making a concerted effort to study geological features, search for fossil life, and to make a detailed study of Mars. But the most exciting aspect of this architecture is that if humans are ever going to go to the stars, if they are ever going to take that first step in colonizing the planets, *this* is the way to go. This doesn't mean that the other architectures won't result in colonies—rather, this is the architecture that explicitly states that as a goal.

Timelines for this architecture are to land the first 5 person mission on the Moon in 2004 and set up a man-tended site for a period of 14 Earth days. Additional lunar missions are planned, increasing the number of inhabitants to 18 with a yearly rotation of 6 crew members. As in the other architectures, a training mission for the Mars flight is planned with a 600-day Mars mission in 2014.

Architecture 4: Space Resource Utilization
This architecture emphasizes the maximum, early use of extraterrestrial resources to support exploration. The ultimate goal is to explore the Moon and Mars while solving such problems on Earth as the greenhouse effect, depletion of the ozone layer, and the dwindling supply of finite (and "dirty") energy sources. This architecture will allow us to meet our energy problems head-on.

The Moon could provide energy for the Earth in the form of helium-3— a fusion energy source created in the Sun, swept away by the solar wind and absorbed into the lunar regolith

(dirt).... [A]llowing time to gear up for full-scale helium-3 mining, this fits in well with the Department of Energy's forecast of having a working commercial fusion reactor by 2025. An estimated 25 metric tons of helium-3 per year is needed to supply the entire world's energy demand.

In addition to mining helium-3, solar cells manufactured on the lunar surface for use in space would be cheaper than lifting the cells off Earth. This results from the need to overcome Earth's gravity well and lift the solar cells into low-Earth-orbit. Lunar regolith could also provide volatiles for propellant, oxygen, water, and even building material for use on the Moon or in space.

The initial plan for this architecture is to demonstrate that it's feasible to process regolith and extract volatiles....

Timelines for this architecture are to land the first 5 person mission on the Moon in 2003 for a stay of 14 Earth days. Additional lunar missions are planned, increasing to 180 day stays in which a demonstration mining plant is working on the lunar surface. A 600 day Mars mission is planned for 2016, allowing time to accomplish the lunar mining goals....

CONCLUSIONS

Since the Synthesis Group report has been released, NASA has appointed Dr. Mike Griffin, formerly Deputy Director for Technology of the Strategic Defense Initiative and a long-time space researcher, to head up the Exploration Office. Dr. Griffin has assembled an impressive team of space experts and is aggressively pursuing a program based on the recommendations of the Synthesis Group. Further, the president has established a multi-agency organization to accomplish the SEI. The Departments of Energy and Defense are joining NASA in pursuing this national goal.

The president has stated that the long-term goals for space exploration are the Space Exploration Initiative. The nation is truly at a threshold—and not a crossroads. A crossroads implies that there exist more than one choice that the nation can make if it is going to flourish; a *threshold* correctly suggests that *there is no other choice.*

The Synthesis Group's vision for the 21st century includes a strong relation between science, technology, and manned and unmanned exploration. This vision compliments NASA's current Mission to Planet Earth and bases its success upon excellence in education. The Synthesis Group believes this initiative should be the centerpiece of the nation's space program.

More importantly, they believe that the nation can't afford *not* to do it. As the group so often stated during their year-long tenure: "We must make the decision to either lead, follow, or get out of the way."

The bottom line is that if we're going to survive, we *must* go down this path.

NO

John Merchant

A NEW DIRECTION IN SPACE

From the very beginning of the Space Age, a fundamental issue has been whether space exploration should be conducted by manned missions or by unmanned missions. In a so-called unmanned mission, only inanimate systems are transported into space. In a manned mission, human beings are on board the spacecraft.

Manned missions are very much more expensive because of the difficulty of maintaining human life in the implacably hostile environment of space. Many in the scientific community complain that the very expensive manned missions drain resources from unmanned scientific missions. For a variety of reasons, manned missions have attracted political support in spite of their very high cost. This support is eroding, however, and may not now be sufficient to achieve goals such as the human exploration of Mars. As a result, "America's manned space program is at a crossroads."

A third option may now be available: an unmanned mission providing virtually the same subjective and objective effect as a manned mission, but with the much lower cost of an unmanned mission. The ongoing revolution in digital processing technology may now make it possible to develop the means for a human to be effectively there, without going there, over interplanetary distances. Unlike conventional robotic rover missions, this third option would be, both subjectively and objectively, virtually equivalent to a manned mission.

Manned space exploration is currently based upon transportation technology that physically moves the human body to the space environment to be explored. This is a technology that has little or no terrestrial application. The progress of manned space exploration has been slow, and is likely to continue that way, because of the prohibitive cost and the danger to human life of the current technology. It is conceivable that manned space exploration, based upon the current technology, might even be abandoned at some point. The new (third) option for manned-equivalent space exploration is based upon semi-autonomous control technology. Investment in this technology is likely to pay off with critically important industrial applications on Earth in the coming decades, no matter what may happen in space. Manned-equivalent

From John Merchant, "A New Direction in Space," IEEE Technology and Society Magazine (Winter 1994), vol. 13, no. 4, pp. 22–29. Copyright © 1994 by IEEE. Reprinted by permission of IEEE and John Merchant. References and some notes omitted.

space exploration by this new approach will be much less expensive, and much more likely to prosper and to produce knowledge and commercial opportunities in space....

THE REMOTE PROJECTION OF HUMAN ACTION

In normal human action, an operator interacts directly with the local environment in which the operator is located. The operator senses that environment with sense organs and then effects changes in it by the direct neuromuscular effort of arms, hands, fingers, legs, etc,. The operator is 100% coupled to the local environment. Our entire species experience has been that the only way of effecting human action is by the direct location of the body. To allow humans to explore space, the technological response has therefore been to provide the means, however expensive, of transporting the human body into space. However, human action is an information process. Information can be transmitted, or projected, over great distances. Thus, at least in principle, as in a thought experiment, human action can be effected at a remote location, without locating the body there, by the remote projection of human action.

Remote projection allows an operator to effect human action on a remote environment exactly as if the operator's body were there. In our thought experiment, the operator interfaces directly with a Local Projection Unit (LPU), which is located, with the operator, in the local environment. The LPU is connected via a data link to a Remote Projection Unit (RPU) located in the remote environment. Physical sensors on the RPU derive exactly the same sensory information that the operator would sense if the operator's body

were actually located in the remote environment. This information is relayed back to the LPU and presented to the operator's sense organs so that the operator experiences exactly the same subjective sensation as if the operator's body were in the remote environment. Likewise, the neuromuscular effort exerted by the operator in response to this sensory information is measured by transducers in the LPU, relayed to the RPU, and then applied to mechanical transducers in the RPU to cause the same mechanical effort to be exerted on the remote environment as if the operator's body were indeed located there.[1] In this idealized thought experiment the operator is 100% coupled to the remote environment.

Conventional remote control falls between normal human action and the remote projection of human action. The operator remains strongly coupled to the local environment and is only weakly coupled to the remote environment. Only a small part of human action is projected to the remote environment. For example, in remote control of an underwater robot (Remotely Operated Vehicle or ROV) the operator's visual field is almost entirely covered by the local scene of the cabin in the mother ship where the operator is located (strong coupling to the local environment), whereas the operator can see only a small TV image of the remote scene (weak coupling to the remote environment). Likewise, the ROV operator can exert full neuromuscular effort on the local environment on the ship but has only a crude capability, via the robot's manipulator arms, to exert neuromuscular effort on the remote underwater environment.

The remote projection of human action does not violate physical law and is, therefore, a valid thought experiment.

(It is assumed, for the moment, that the distance over which human action is projected is small enough [e.g., less than 1,000 miles] so that the round trip transmission delay involved [0.005 sec over 1,000 miles] is negligible relative to the human physiological response time [about 0.1 sec]. Practical implementation, and the extension to very much longer distances, will be considered later.)

By the remote projection of human action an operator can effect human action on a remote environment, exactly as if the operator's body were there. The subjective sensation would be the same as being there. Objectively, the ability to effect change would be the same as being there. For all practical purposes, the operator is there. But the operator's body is not.

What exactly does it mean to "be there"? For inanimate objects there is no doubt about what it means. A car can unambiguously be said to be in the parking lot when it is physically located in that parking lot. However, for a person, there are two entirely different meanings, corresponding to which of the two entirely different types of human interaction apply—physical interaction or human action. For physical interaction, which supports the physical existence of the body by exchange of physical entities, to be there necessarily means to locate the body there. But this is not the case for the information process, defined as human action. Suppose a person is carrying out human action in an environment in such a way as to be indistinguishable from the way it would be carried out if that person's body were present in that environment. This would be virtually equivalent to that person being present in that environment. (The physical interaction of the person with the environment is irrelevant in the present context.)

If, indeed, this could be done over interplanetary distances, then transporting the human body into space—at enormous expense and risk—would make absolutely no sense. But this is true only if the great leap can be made from conventional remote control to a practical implementation of the remote projection of human action of such fidelity as to be virtually equivalent to going there.

It will be seen that the ongoing revolution in digital processing technology may make it possible to implement the remote projection of human action to this standard over interplanetary distances. It may be possible, for example, to operate a space station in Earth orbit, to set up a lunar base, or to explore Mars, without humans ever leaving the Earth.

This is the proposed new direction in space. It will be described here in the context of a mission to Mars, but is applicable to any mission of space exploration for which a manned mission might otherwise be considered.

SPECIFICATION

Can what was described in principle actually be done in practice? In one very limited, but extremely important, way it already has been done—by the telephone.

The sense of hearing and the neuromuscular action of speech comprise a very important, self-contained, subset of human action by which much of the communication between human beings is effected. Words spoken by another person are received by the sense of hearing. This information is processed by the brain to derive an appropriate response. The vocal cords are then exercised by neuromuscular effort to send this response back by speech.

Relative to the full set of human action, the telephone is conventional remote control. However, relative to the self-contained action subset of hearing and speech the telephone implements the remote projection of human action over terrestrial distances—with great economic advantage over going there.

To project human action into space it is not necessary to project the full range of human sensory and neuromuscular functions but only those that an astronaut would be able to, and would need to, deploy while exploring and developing space.

The visual sense is fundamental for exploration, whether on Earth or in space. Accordingly, if an operator on Earth is to explore Mars (for example) by the remote projection of human action, then that operator should be provided with remote vision of Mars virtually equivalent to the vision of Mars that would be experienced by an astronaut actually on Mars. The remote display of the Martian scene should therefore cover the operator's entire field of view no matter in which direction the operator's head is pointed. The operator should be able to instantly derive the dynamic visual effect of looking around and moving over the surface of Mars at will, going in for close-up views of detail of special interest. The subjective sensation of viewing the Martian scene remotely should in all respects be virtually the same as going there, moving around, and viewing the scene directly.

In order for the remote projection of human action to be a valid alternative to going there, the operator on Earth should also be provided with a capability for exerting remote neuromuscular effort on Mars virtually equivalent to that of an astronaut on Mars. That is, the operator on Earth should be able, in effect, to move around on Mars, pick up and examine Martian artifacts, operate scientific equipment, operate construction equipment, assemble structures, etc. The operator should also be able to repair equipment on Mars. In particular, when operating remotely via one RPU, the operator should be able to repair another RPU.

It is not necessary that these tasks be performed as fast as they could be by the direct action of an astronaut. Unlike exploration by a manned mission, exploration by the remote projection of human action could be almost continuously active over an essentially indefinite period with a number of RPUs operating simultaneously. An overall mission-effectivity at least equal to that of a manned mission could therefore be achieved even if the average rate of task performance of each RPU was significantly (e.g., up to ten times) lower than by the direct action of an astronaut.

These are the basic sensory and neuromuscular requirements of a system to project human action into space. A very challenging aspect of this specification is that it must be satisfied over very long operating ranges. For a space station in Earth orbit, the operating range would be of the order of 10,000 miles, for exploration of the moon 250,000 miles, and for exploration of Mars 100 million miles.

The transmission delay introduced by these long round-trip distances has a devastating effect on conventional remote control. Suppose that an operator on Earth were trying to aim a TV camera on Mars. If the operator commanded the camera to pan over to a new direction it would take about half an hour before the TV picture relayed back from Mars would change in response to this command. If the operator started to pick up a rock on Mars with a remotely controlled mechanical hand it would be half an hour before the operator saw the mechanical hand begin to move in the TV picture relayed back from Mars. The hand-eye coordination needed to grasp and pick up objects would be virtually impossible.

Another challenging aspect of the specification is that a remote vision capability far in excess of conventional TV is required. Even a single standard TV channel would strain the capacity of the Mars-Earth data link.

In the next section it will be shown how the new technology of semi-autonomous systems, AI, and image processing might be applied to satisfy these challenging technical requirements. The processing power needed to apply these sophisticated techniques may now be available as a result of the digital processing revolution.

IMPLEMENTATION

To project human action to Mars (for example) a Remote Projection Unit (RPU) is located on Mars and connected, via an interplanetary data link, to a Local Projection Unit (LPU) located on Earth. A human operator on Earth is interfaced to the LPU to allow the operator to effect human action on Mars.

The RPU is equipped with one or more video cameras, means of locomotion, a navigation device giving its current position in local Martian coordinates, and a digital processor. The LPU has a powerful digital processor and a spherical dome display screen consisting of approximately 100 high-resolution

display panels. This screen provides the operator, at the center of the dome, with a [spherical] visual display.

New technology is applied to provide the specified functions of *remote vision* and *remote neuromuscular effort* on Mars. As a result of the ongoing digital processing revolution, the processing power needed to implement these sophisticated functions may now be available.

Remote Vision
As the RPU moves around on Mars, a TV camera mounted on the RPU will generate a continuous sequence of 30 video frames per second of the Martian scene. Single frames are selected from this camera at a very low frame rate (e.g. one frame every three seconds) and transmitted back to Earth. (At this low frame rate, only a small part [e.g. 0.1 Mbps] of the channel capacity of the data link will be used.) As these frames are received on Earth they are [used to construct a] ... 3-D model of the Martian scene [that] is stored in the LPU. It is continuously extended and updated as new video frames are received. As soon as enough of the model becomes available, it is processed in real time by the LPU processor to generate whatever view of the Martian scene the operator has currently selected. Images of RPUs and other human-made objects will be automatically inserted into this view based upon current estimates of their position and orientation on Mars. This high-resolution view of the Martian scene, covering the operator's entire visual field at all times, is displayed on the operator's ... spherical display screen. The operator sees nothing of the local environment. If the operator's head should be turned to look to the side, or even all the way around to

look backwards, the display will always present to the operator the corresponding view of the Martian scene.

The displayed view is computed, 30 times a second, according to the viewing point and viewing direction on Mars as currently selected by manual action of the operator. The operator is able to command continuous motion of this viewing point along any path. The corresponding sequence of images generated by the LPU instantly provides the operator with the same dynamic visual effect, over the operator's entire visual field, as if the operator were actually walking, driving, or even flying around the Martian scene. The operator therefore experiences virtually the same total subjective visual sensation as an astronaut would, actually there on Mars.

The derivation of a 3-D model... and then the generation of selected views from this model, has been demonstrated in video releases from NASA to the TV networks after an encounter of a spacecraft with a planet or moon.... [It will] not only make it possible to overcome the effect of transmission delay on the operation of the remote vision system, it [will] also make much better use of the limited capacity of the data link between Mars and Earth. Instead of continuously transmitting the highly redundant sequence of video frames at 30 frames/sec from the camera, new scene structure information is transmitted only when needed to update the current 3-D model in the LPU, and then at a very low frame rate.

This remote vision system requires a powerful digital processor in the LPU to perform the stereo matching and also to generate the very-wide-angle, high-resolution output imagery at 30 frames per second. About 100 high-resolution flat-panel displays (FPDs) would be needed to present this imagery to the operator. To limit the processing load, the operator's head direction can be measured and the resolution of the computed imagery reduced in the peripheral areas of the operator's visual field. In particular, no picture information at all need be computed over the [half-sphere] immediately behind the operator.

By terrestrial standards this remote vision system is expensive, but not relative to space systems and operations. Although complex and highly sophisticated, no technological breakthrough is needed.

In actual operation a number of RPUs would be deployed at one location on Mars, together with scientific instruments and support equipment for the mission of exploration and development. A central control unit equipped with a powerful processor would control all of the RPUs. Roving RPUs would be used to generate the video frames to be transmitted to Earth. These frames would be buffered and processed in the LPU, on Earth, to derive the 3-D structure of the region. As the operator in the LPU explored the scene currently being displayed, the operator's areas of interest would be noted and relayed back to the central control unit on Mars. The control unit would then redirect the roving RPUs to generate more detailed views of these particular areas so that a correspondingly more detailed 3-D model of them could be computed by the LPU.

On moving into a new scene area it might take several hours for the roving RPUs to gather video imagery of that area and transmit it back to Earth, and for the 3-D model of that Martian scene to be computed by the LPU processor. If the operator should designate a particular region as being of special interest, there would be a similar delay before a close-up 3-D model of that region became available on Earth. These delays would be accommodated by appropriate scheduling of the operator's work. While close-up views of one region were being developed by one RPU, the operator could direct other RPUs to perform other tasks such as operation of scientific equipment, gathering of samples, etc.

Remote Neuromuscular Effort

Because of the approximately 30-minute transmission delay, the operator on Earth cannot exert neuromuscular effort on Mars by direct, micro-managing, remote control of the RPU. Instead, functioning as a supervisor, the operator will generate a sequence of high-level instructions, transmit them to the RPU, and then leave it to the RPU to carry them out. For example, the operator might designate a point on the operator's display of the Martian scene and instruct the RPU to move to that point, pick up a particular rock, and then bring that rock to a scientific test station for analysis. This packet of high-level directives would be transmitted to Mars and then executed autonomously by the RPU during the transmission-delay period. The operator, like a good supervisor, would leave it to the RPU to do the work, checking only afterwards that the instructions had been properly carried out.

The RPU uses its on-board navigational sensors and TV cameras to sense its position relative to the terrain. Range information is derived by laser ranging and/or stereo matching (in the RPU) of views of the terrain immediately ahead. All of this information is used by the RPU to help it move, autonomously, from point to point as commanded by the operator.

The RPU uses its manipulator arms to perform the manual action tasks that have been commanded by the operator. Laser ranging and/or stereo matching (by the RPU processor) of the images from TV cameras on the RPU will provide whatever 3-D information may be required for "hand-eye" coordination in the autonomous execution of these tasks.

The RPU on Mars must be able to operate autonomously for a period of the order of the transmission delay. The operator will send a detailed, time-sequenced, list of tasks to be performed during this period. These tasks will be defined according to the operator's goals and by the remote visual sensing by the operator of the Martian environment. Because the environment in which the RPU will operate is highly predictable, all of these tasks will generally be as appropriate when they are received on Mars as when they were formulated on Earth some time earlier. In other words, the RPU needs only enough intelligence to perform each individual task with a high probability of success, determine when it has been completed, or determine when the task cannot be completed. Thus, although the RPU must operate autonomously during the transmission delay period, the bulk of the intelligence applied during that time is the human intelligence of the operator on Earth who formulates the task list.

The new subsumption (robot control) architecture developed by Brooks, in which there is a tight coupling of sensing to action rather than the top-down approach of traditional artificial intelligence, may be particularly appropriate to provide the limited task-based intelligence needed by the RPU.

For navigation, the task-list from the operator will specify the route to be followed as a series of arcs along the Martian surface defined in Martian spatial coordinates. A number of systems (robots) have been developed that demonstrate autonomous movement over rough terrain.

In addition to navigation, the RPU must be able to use its manipulator arms to autonomously assemble, operate, and repair human-made systems as commanded by the operator. In many cases the operator will issue a list of task macros for these mechanical tasks. The detailed task list for each macro will be pre-defined as part of the design of these human-made systems. To facilitate task execution, the human-made components will be specially designed, marked, and color-coded for automatic recognition and ranging by image processing, and for handling by mechanical hands.

Highly sophisticated mechanical arms and hands (manipulators) have been demonstrated that, for example, can hold an egg and crush a can. Autonomous control of manipulators to perform mechanical tasks has been demonstrated.

The RPU will also collect samples from the Martian surface for detailed visual examination or analysis by scientific instruments. The operator will designate on the visual display of the Martian scene in the LPU the samples to be collected as well as the route to be taken by the RPU to get to them. Once again, only a limited intelligence in the RPU is needed to move along a designated path, grasp and pick up the designated object, and retrieve it if it should be dropped.

Just as terrestrial systems are human-engineered for easy operation and maintenance by humans, all of the scientific equipment, construction equipment, forklifts, and other support equipment deployed on Mars would be "RPU-engineered" to facilitate operation by RPUs. For example, control and operation of this equipment would be exerted by the RPUs by wireless (radio) control, not by knobs, levers, and switches. Diagnostic information for servicing would likewise be derived mainly by wireless interface, rather than by test probes. The support equipment would be marked and mechanically designed to facilitate assembly and maintenance by means of tools and techniques specially designed to exploit the positive features of a manipulator arm rather than those of the human hand.

Once Remote Projection Units (RPUs) were deployed on Mars, or other space locations, they would remain in operation there indefinitely, repairing each other as necessary. On Earth, there would be continuous access to these space locations for exploration and commercial development.

Processing Power

The processing power that can be implemented in human-made systems, virtually zero just a few decades ago, is now approaching that of sophisticated physiological systems. Raw processor speed has increased dramatically, and this increase is still continuing. New device technologies, for example based upon quantum effects or the use of photons instead of electrons, may provide additional dramatic increases in speed. Massively parallel computing is another, potentially very important, route to increased computational power.

From the powerful computers commonplace in all aspects of daily life to virtual reality and the projected information superhighway, the digital processing revolution—a great watershed event in the history of human development—is already transforming life here on Earth. This new technology may now make it possible to implement the functions of remote vision and remote neuromuscular effort—that is, to project human action over interplanetary distances.

CONCLUSION

The benefits of the development and application of the remote projection of human action for space exploration are seen as:

1. The same mission result is achieved as would be derived from a manned space mission, but at much lower cost. This is because only inanimate systems, not human bodies, are transported into the alien environment of space.

2. No danger to human life.

3. Exploration and development of a space environment could be conducted indefinitely, since there is no requirement to return human bodies to Earth.

4. Because of items 1, 2, and 3, commercial operations in space would be more likely to develop.

5. Exploration could be conducted by anybody—not just by astronauts.

6. In the next century the semi-autonomous robotic, vision, and computer technologies upon which the remote projection of human action is based will likely find very important industrial application for enhanced productivity. There are already a number of terrestrial applications for telerobots.[2]

7. The development of the remote projection of human action would preserve and utilize the talents of scientists and engineers, and the resources of industry, now becoming available as military R&D [research and development] programs wind down.

The basis of the technology required to project human action into space already exists: high-resolution display panels, manipulator arms, autonomous execution of elementary tasks, generation of 3-D models of the object scene from moving video and from stereo pairs, powerful digital processors, etc. Can all of this technology be extended, developed and assembled to provide, within an acceptable cost and schedule, virtual equivalence to going there?

Initial design studies should be undertaken to assess feasibility. Among the many issues to be considered are the algorithms for remote vision and remote neuromuscular effort, the processing power (gigaflops) and electrical power (watts) needed at the remote space location, the processing power needed in the LPU to drive the display, and the display system itself. Non-real-time, and real-time, laboratory demonstrations of the critical functions of remote vision and remote neuromuscular effort would follow the initial design study. Finally, a full terrestrial demonstration of the remote projection of human action over interplanetary distances would be undertaken. The interplanetary transmission delay would be simulated by passing the high-level, and thus very low bandwidth, operator commands through a digital delay line.

This step-by-step program would establish the feasibility, quantify the cost, and demonstrate performance of the remote projection of human action into space. Technical risk would be low since each step would be taken only when justified by prior results.

The information-processing revolution is a watershed event in human history. Looking forward from the vantage of this great technological divide, development of the remote projection of human action over interplanetary distances may already, or will likely soon, be possible. Then, the impasse of prohibitive cost that has bedeviled the manned space program from its inception would be broken.

NOTES

1. This combination of RPU, LPU, and data link is known as a teleoperator if it functions as a direct mindless extension of the operator's senses and motor effectors, or as a telerobot if it has sufficient intelligence so that the operator's role is supervisory.

2. Undersea oil operations, undersea science, nuclear power plants and radioactive "hot cells," toxic waste cleanup, construction, agriculture, mining, warehousing and mail delivery, firefighting and lifesaving, policing, military operations, assistive devices for the disabled, telediagnosis, telesurgery.

POSTSCRIPT

Should the Goals of the U.S. Space Program Include Manned Exploration of Space?

Parts of Beason's original report, which were edited out for brevity, included a call for the development of a Heavy Lift Launch Vehicle (HLLV) to reduce the cost and difficulty of getting materials into orbit. Such a cargo vehicle has been discussed for years as a supplement to the space shuttle, with a great deal of emphasis on its value for constructing space stations as well as interplanetary spaceships. Although the dream continues—see Stanley Schmidt and Robert Zubrin, eds., *Islands in the Sky: Bold New Ideas for Colonizing Space* (John Wiley, 1996)—an HLLV has never been approved, and it seems very unlikely that NASA will be able to find funds for any major new launch system that would replace or supplement the space shuttle as well as make a mission to Mars possible.

In the fall of 1993 a new technology was introduced in the United States—the Delta Clipper DC-X, which boasted vertical-takeoff-and-landing capabilities and total reusability. Immediately after its successful test flight, however, the Defense Department canceled its funding. Fortunately for the program, as reported in the February 7, 1994, issue of *Aviation Week and Space Technology*, NASA was able to find $1 million to pay for some further testing.

If this new spaceship is able to continue development successfully, it may help change the outlook of the space program a few years from now. However, funding shortages seem likely to continue, largely because problems on Earth (environmental and other) seem to need money more urgently than do space exploration projects. Major new missions—manned or unmanned—are likely to become rare events. See Christopher Anderson, "The Coming Crunch for Space Science," *Science* (February 18, 1994). Certainly the prospects for a renewal of manned space exploration, much less a trip to Mars, seem very dim.

The reason for NASA's shrinking budget is that efforts to reduce the federal deficit have forced government agencies to trim back programs to free up funds for new programs. The resulting funding cuts are eliminating numerous once-planned missions and seriously hampering efforts to analyze data from spacecraft already in space. Money that is available is flowing toward programs such as Mission to Planet Earth, which focuses on Earth and its environmental problems, not toward programs that propose to study the distant reaches of the solar system.

The space station may also suffer. In April 1994 the station's cost was quoted as $28 billion, and the projected cost savings from Russian participation in the project were cut in half, prompting some to fear that the space station—and even the space shuttle—could be scrapped. See James R. Asker, "NASA's Budget Woes Will Threaten Station," *Aviation Week and Space Technology* (March 14, 1994).

It is worth noting that manned space exploration is not the only kind of manned exploration in trouble. Marine scientists are currently arguing over whether the best way to explore the ocean floor is with manned submersibles such as *Alvin*, which has served well for three decades and earned considerable fame with the public for making photographs of the sunken *Titanic* possible (see *National Geographic*, December 1985, December 1986, and October 1987), or with robots such as *Jason*, which photographed the wreck of the *Lusitania* (see *National Geographic*, April 1994). Arguments against manned exploration, here as in space, include both safety and expense. See John Travis, "Deep-Sea Debate Pits Alvin Against Jason," *Science* (March 12, 1993).

At the moment, Merchant's vision offers one of the few rays of hope available to space enthusiasts. It is well worth noting that human operation of a far-distant space vehicle has already proven its worth with the 1994 Clementine mission to the moon and that the sort of full sense replacement Merchant discusses is being rapidly developed under the name "virtual reality." His vision may be much nearer than we think.

The Internet address for NASA and the space program is http://www.hq.nasa.gov/

ISSUE 10

Is It Worthwhile to Continue the Search for Extraterrestrial Life?

YES: Frank Drake and Dava Sobel, from *Is Anyone Out There? The Scientific Search for Extraterrestrial Intelligence* (Delacorte Press, 1992)

NO: Richard G. Teske, from "Is This the E.T. to Whom I Am Speaking?" *Discover* (May 1993)

ISSUE SUMMARY

YES: Professor of astronomy Frank Drake and science writer Dava Sobel argue that the search for radio signals from extraterrestrial civilizations has only just begun and that scientists must continue to search because contact will eventually occur.

NO: Professor of astronomy Richard G. Teske asserts that Earth's history is so unique that it is highly unlikely that there are any beings outside of the planet with the technological capability to send signals that scientists on Earth can receive.

In the 1960s and early 1970s the business of listening to the radio whispers of the stars and hoping to pick up signals emanating from some alien civilization was still new. Few scientists held visions equal to Frank Drake, one of the pioneers of the search for extraterrestrial intelligence (SETI) field. Drake and scientists like him utilize radio telescopes—large, dish-like radio receiver–antenna combinations—to scan radio frequencies (channels) for signal patterns that would indicate that the signal was transmitted by an intelligent being. In his early days, Drake worked with relatively small and weak telescopes out of listening posts that he had established in Green Bank, West Virginia, and Arecibo, Puerto Rico. (See Carl Sagan and Frank Drake, "The Search for Extraterrestrial Intelligence," *Scientific American,* May 1975.)

There have been more than 50 searches for extraterrestrial radio signals since 1960. The earliest ones were very limited. Later searches have been more ambitious, culminating in the 10-year program known as the High Resolution Microwave Survey (HRMS). The HRMS, which began on Columbus Day of 1992, uses several radio telescopes and massive computers to scan 15 million radio frequencies per second. This has been the most massive SETI to date and the one with the greatest hope of success.

At the outset, many people thought—and many still think—that SETI has about as much scientific relevance as searches for Loch Ness Monsters and

Abominable Snowmen. However, to Drake and his colleagues, it seemed inevitable that with so many stars in the sky, there must be other worlds with life upon them, and some of that life must be intelligent and have a suitable technology and the desire to search for alien life too.

Writing about SETI in the September–October 1991 issue of *The Humanist*, physicist Shawn Carlson compares visiting the National Shrine of the Immaculate Conception in Washington, D.C., to looking up at the stars and "wondering if, in all [the] vastness [of the starry sky], there is anybody out there looking in our direction.... [A]re there planets like ours peopled with creatures like us staring into their skies and wondering about the possibilities of life on other worlds, perhaps even trying to contact it?" That is, SETI arouses in its devotees an almost religious sense of mystery and awe, a craving for contact with the *other*. Success would open up a universe of possibilities, add immensely to human knowledge, and perhaps even provide solutions to problems that our interstellar neighbors have already defeated.

SETI also arouses strong objections, partly because it challenges human uniqueness. Many scientists have objected that life-bearing worlds such as Earth must be exceedingly rare because the conditions that make them suitable for life as we know it—composition and temperature—are so narrowly defined. Others have objected that there is no reason whatsoever to expect that evolution would produce intelligence more than once or that, if it did, the species would be similar enough to humans to allow communication. Still others say that even if intelligent life is common, technology may not be so common, or technology may occupy such a brief period in the life of an intelligent species that there is virtually no chance that it would coincide with Earth scientists' current search. Whatever their reasons, SETI detractors agree that listening for extraterrestrial signals is a waste of time and money.

In the selections that follow, Drake and science writer Dava Sobel discuss Drake's first search for messages from distant stars (Project Ozma). Today's technology, the authors note, has made it possible to duplicate all of Ozma's work in a fraction of a second, making it that much more probable that Earth will soon make contact with extraterrestrials. Richard G. Teske, a professor of astronomy at the University of Michigan, represents the pessimistic view, arguing that the evolutionary processes of Earth that have supplied humans with the raw materials of technology are too unlikely to have been repeated elsewhere.

YES   Frank Drake and Dava Sobel

NO GREATER DISCOVERY

My scientific colleagues raise their eyebrows when I speculate on the appearance of extraterrestrials. But about 99.9 percent of them agree wholeheartedly that other intelligent life-forms do exist—and furthermore that there may be large populations of them throughout our galaxy and beyond.

Personally, I find nothing more tantalizing than the thought that radio messages from alien civilizations in space are passing through our offices and homes, right now, like a whisper we can't quite hear. In fact, we have the technology to detect such signals *today*, if only we knew where to point our radio telescopes, and the right frequency for listening.

I have been scanning the stars in search of extraterrestrial intelligence (an activity now abbreviated as SETI, and pronounced *SET-ee*) for more than thirty years. I engineered the first such effort in 1959, at the National Radio Astronomy Observatory in Green Bank, West Virginia. I named it "Project Ozma," after a land far away, difficult to reach, and populated by strange and exotic beings. I used what would now be considered crude equipment to listen for signals from two nearby, Sunlike stars. It took two months to complete the job. With the marvelous technological advances we have made in the intervening years, we could repeat the whole of Project Ozma today in a fraction of a second. We could scan for signals from a *million* stars or more at a time, at distances of at least a *thousand* light-years from Earth. . . .

Until the late 1980s, the fact that we had not yet found another civilization, despite continued global efforts and better equipment, simply meant we had not looked long enough or hard enough. No knowledgeable person was disappointed by our inability to detect alien intelligence, as this in no way proved that extraterrestrials did not exist. Rather, our failure simply confirmed that our efforts were puny in relation to the enormity of the task —somewhat like hunting for a needle in a cosmic haystack of inconceivable size. The way we were going about it, with our small-scale attempts, was like looking for the needle by strolling past the haystack every now and then. We weren't embarked on a search that had any real chance of success.

Then many people began to grasp the nature and scope of the challenge, the consequent investment required to succeed, and the importance of success

From Frank Drake and Dava Sobel, *Is Anyone Out There? The Scientific Search for Extraterrestrial Intelligence* (Delacorte Press, 1992). Copyright © 1992 by Frank Drake and Dava Sobel. Reprinted by permission of Dell Books, a division of Bantam Doubleday Dell Publishing Group, Inc. Notes omitted.

to all humanity. They pushed relentlessly for a serious search. And won. The National Aeronautics and Space Administration (NASA) committed $100 million to a formal SETI mission spanning the decade of the 1990s, making the work a priority for the space agency and guaranteeing that coveted telescope time will be devoted to the search.

Now, after all our efforts over the past three decades, I am standing with my colleagues at last on the brink of discovery.... I see a pressing need to prepare thinking adults for the outcome of the present search activity—the imminent detection of signals from an extraterrestrial civilization. This discovery, which I fully expect to witness before the year 2000, will profoundly change the world....

I want to show that we need not be afraid of interstellar contact, for unlike the primitive civilizations on Earth that were overpowered by more advanced technological societies, we cannot be exploited or enslaved. The extraterrestrials aren't going to come and eat us; they are too far away to pose a threat. Even back-and-forth conversation with them is highly unlikely, since radio signals, traveling at the speed of light, take *years* to reach the nearest stars, and many *millennia* to get to the farthest ones, where advanced civilizations may reside. But one-way communication is a different story. Just as our radio and television transmissions leak out into space, carrying the news of our existence far and wide, so similar information from the planets of other stars has no doubt been quietly arriving at Earth for perhaps billions of years. Even more exciting is the likelihood of *intentional* messages beamed to Earth for our particular benefit. As we know from our own

efforts at composing for a pangalactic audience, reams of information about a planet's culture, history, and technology —the entire thirty-seven-volume set, if you will, of the "Encyclopedia Galactica" —could be transmitted (and received) easily and cheaply.

As a scientist, I'm driven by curiosity, of course. I want to know what's out there. But as a human being, I persevere in this pursuit because SETI promises answers to our most profound questions about who we are and where we stand in the universe. SETI is at once the most technical of scientific subjects, and also the most human. Every tactical problem in the search endeavor rests on some age-old philosophical conundrum: *Where did we come from? Are we unique? What does it mean to he a human being? ...*

* * *

[W]e have only just begun to search.

So many individuals I meet seem to think that we have already searched the sky completely and continuously over the past thirty years. The deed is done, they assume. And since we found nothing out there, to search further is to beat a dead horse. But in fact, the combinations of frequencies and places to look have hardly been touched.

In my historical analysis; the search for extraterrestrial intelligence divides itself into four eras. The first dates back at least three thousand years, to the time when people started contemplating the universe....

I trace the start of the second era to the coming of the Copernican Revolution in the sixteenth century. That was when astronomers such as Kepler and Galileo, who used a real telescope, recognized that some of the other objects in the Solar System were planets similar to the

Earth. Scientific observations could now support the philosophical argument in favor of other life in the cosmos—and perhaps even within the Solar System....

The third era began in 1959–60, when scientists first employed quantitative measures to compute the strength of possible signs of life crossing interstellar space. In other words, we made precise calculations of the detectability of alien signals, and acted on them. Projects —beginning with [Cornell physics professors Philip] Morrison and [Giuseppe] Cocconi's proposal to search for radio waves and my strategy for Project Ozma —sprang from a greater knowledge of the universe and a real sense of the numbers involved. For the first time, SETI embodied philosophical, qualitative, *and* quantitative elements. Scientists conducted some sixty "third era" extraterrestrial searches in the 1960s, 1970s, and 1980s. Most of these, however, were low-budget productions, done with leftover funds in borrowed time on equipment built for other purposes.

The fourth era, which starts now, is not only quantitative, it is also, finally, *thorough*. The projects of the 1990s represent the most exhaustive probing to date of the cosmic haystack. Here I am referring especially to the NASA SETI project....

My involvement in SETI activities has actually increased over the years, because SETI itself has grown so much. It occupies more people than ever before, and demands more of their time. Jill Tarter, for example, is the first astronomer to work full-time as a SETI scientist. When she isn't fully engaged in her role as project scientist, the senior scientific position in the NASA SETI project, she is in Washington, explaining the project to congressional representatives. Paul

Horowitz runs a close second in activity. Despite his teaching duties at Harvard, Paul has had one search or another in progress since 1977. In some years he devotes nearly 100 percent of his time to these efforts—masterminding a new project and then personally soldering the thousands of joints that hold the equipment together....

I finally got my turn to meet Paul in 1977, when he was already a full professor of physics at Harvard....

A short time later,... Paul accepted a 1981–82 NASA Ames fellowship, which enabled him to work on SETI at the Ames Research Center and at Stanford University. He joined the Ames-Stanford group trying to create a SETI machine that could analyze a huge number of separate channels—128,000 of them, more than anyone had ever been able to monitor simultaneously....

The sheer number of channels in this multichannel analyzer was a big advance in itself, but Paul also made the components portable, so they could be packed up in three small boxes and hand-carried to any observatory, anywhere in the world. The system, which he dubbed "Suitcase SETI," traveled first to Arecibo [Ionospheric Observatory in northern Puerto Rico, home of the largest radio telescope ever built]. After examining 250 stars with it, Paul took it back to Harvard in 1983. He hooked it up to the same telescope I had partially built and calibrated in my student days —the one I had used to observe the Pleiades for my doctoral thesis. Suitcase SETI's rambling days were over at that point. Portable though it was, it never ventured out of Harvard's Oak Ridge Observatory again, A new name, Project Sentinel, recognized the fact that Paul's multichannel analyzer was now connected to a dedicated telescope, with funding from The Planetary Society to run a permanent SETI facility.

In time, Sentinel begat "META-SETI" —the Megachannel ExtraTerrestrial Assay—which boosted the number of channels from 128,000 to more than 8 million.... Paul needed the extra channels, he said, to respond to a new concept put forward by Phil Morrison, who had reminded him in a letter that everything in the universe is in motion....

Intelligent radio signals from distant civilizations could [therefore] be expected to arrive shifted in frequency, just as the starlight from distant suns is shifted toward the red or the blue end of the optical spectrum by stellar motions. There was no way to predict which way a signal's frequency would shift without knowing how its home star was moving. Thus a message transmitted on the hydrogen frequency could wind up far above or far below that frequency by the time it reached a radio telescope on Earth.

With META, Paul could scrutinize myriad frequencies in the vicinity of the hydrogen line and sift through them, narrow bandwidth by narrow bandwidth, on millions of channels at once to detect the displaced signals.

In 1991 Paul set up a second META, also financed by The Planetary Society, called META II, in the Southern Hemisphere, at the Instituto Argentino de Radioastronomia in Villa Elisa, Argentina. This allowed Argentinian astronomers led by Raul Colombo to observe the portion of the southern sky that's not visible from Cambridge. META II opened up very important new regions of the Milky Way as well as a clear line of sight to the two galaxies that are the Milky Way's nearest neighbors: the Magellanic Clouds. Now, with META and META

II thriving, Paul is already dreaming of BETA. This would be a new system ("It'll be *betta* than META," he promises), with one hundred million channels.

Paul has obviously done more searching, with more sensitivity, than anybody who preceded him, so it shouldn't be too surprising to learn that he's actually heard things through his systems. Indeed, Paul has records of about sixty signals that are all excellent candidates for being the real thing. But Paul's searches run themselves, automatically. By the time he recognizes the candidates in the recorded data, hours or days later, it's too late to check them. Looking for them later proves fruitless, as they are no longer where they were. No doubt the civilizations are still there—if that's what made the signal—but they've stopped talking, at least for the moment.... If only Paul's strategy included a human operator who could double-check the signals on the spot! However, Paul has severe budget constraints, and I know that he can't afford to pay someone to sit there through the long nights and wait.

The new NASA SETI Microwave Observing Project will change all that, because I'll be sitting there myself. Or Jill will, or some other radio astronomer who will be able to react immediately to chase down a candidate signal the moment it appears. This project, which has been in various stages of planning and development since 1978, is just now beginning its methodical hunt. Because of its great power and sensitivity, it outstrips all previous search activities combined. Three days' operation can accomplish more than was done in the preceding three decades. Indeed, it gives me a strange chill to acknowledge that it takes this new setup only one one-hundredth of a second to duplicate what

Project Ozma did in its full two hundred hours....

What does NASA SETI have that no other search had? The short answer is "everything." It has everything that early searches had, and everything we could think of that had never been done before.

Like Ozma, NASA SETI scrutinizes a group of relatively close, Sun-like stars for signs of intelligent life. But where Ozma had only two targets, NASA SETI has one thousand. This much more extensive "targeted search," however, is still only half the mission. The other half is an "all-sky survey" that repeatedly scans the whole grand volume of outer space for alien signals from any star, anywhere. Our dual search strategy deals with two alternate possibilities for our cosmic neighbors: Either the easiest aliens to detect are right nearby (targeted search), or they are very far away but very bright (all-sky survey and targeted search).

Like the Ohio State project, NASA SETI is an ongoing endeavor that will run for years. But unlike the low-cost efforts that preceded it, this project fought for and won a total of more than $100 million in federal funding. While other searches started up and faded out without so much as a nod from NASA, this one enjoys the same position as a mission to send a small spacecraft to another planet. Mission status means that SETI is supported all through NASA management, right up to the topmost level.

Like META and META II, NASA SETI spans the globe and the heavens. It utilizes at least five telescopes—at Arecibo, Green Bank, the Observatoire de Nançy in France, the Goldstone Tracking Station in California, and an identical NASA tracking station at Tidbinbilla, Australia.

It is the first truly global cooperative effort to search for interstellar signals.

Unlike... Suitcase SETI, NASA SETI is no backseat or part-time visitor. It constitutes the largest single program running at Arecibo and will soon dominate a fully dedicated telescope at Green Bank. It employs more than one hundred people, including a rotating team of radio astronomers who stand ready to respond to candidate signals in real time.

Most American searches until now have sought narrow-band signals on magic frequencies, such as the hydrogen line. We call them "magic" because they seem to have some real rationale for being logical channels of communication. Part of their magic is that they occupy quiet regions of the electromagnetic spectrum. What's more, the hydrogen line, considered the most magical frequency of all, is such a fertile field for making general discoveries in radio astronomy that scientists of all civilizations probably keep close tabs on it. Thus, a signal on that particular frequency should have the greatest chance of being detected. The hydrogen line is the frequency Morrison and Cocconi suggested in their original paper, and the actual frequency searched in Project Ozma....

Magic frequencies have special appeal, but even human beings disagree as to which ones are best.... The point is, any search based on a magic frequency assumes first of all that extraterrestrials are broadcasting on a chosen frequency, and furthermore that we can know what that frequency is.

The NASA SETI project makes no such assumptions. It scans most of the frequencies in the waterhole that penetrate the Earth's atmosphere. This means we'll have a much greater chance than ever before to detect a message, whether the aliens choose a frequency for convenience' sake or some numerology of their own. Our new equipment frees us from the need to select just one or two frequencies from among the vast field of possibilities....

META set a world's record with 8 million channels, but NASA SETI has 28 million. At the core of its hardware is a device called a multichannel spectrum analyzer (MCSA in NASA's beloved alphabet soup), which divides the incoming radio noise into 14 million narrowband channels. The MCSA also combines the signals from several adjacent channels to create another 14 million broader bandwidths, just in case the extraterrestrials use them.

The MCSA relies on ultra-advanced software to make sense out of the millions of data points pouring in every second. Software analyzes the data, looking for patterns that reveal intelligence—and that could not possibly be intercepted as fast or as well by human intelligence. The human operator, whose presence is so important to me, steps in *after* computers sound the alarm that a candidate signal has just been detected....

In the course of gushing about the great power of NASA SETI compared to any and all of its predecessors, I've dropped several huge numbers, referring to everything from frequencies and sensitivities to dollars and cents. That said, do I really need one more quantitative comparison to make my point? Would it really clarify things further to say that NASA SETI is a ten-millionfold improvement over past efforts? Maybe not. Maybe the more important thing to say now is that the magnitude of our current efforts creates so much promise that we find ourselves contemplating what we should do when we actually receive signal evidence of extraterrestrial life. When and how do we inform the people of Earth?

John Billingham [a former aerospace physician with England's Royal Air Force] has probably given more thought to this delicious dilemma than anyone else. Working with other members of the SETI committee of the International Academy of Astronautics (IAA), he has drawn up a "Declaration of Principles Concerning Activities Following the Detection of Extraterrestrial Intelligence." It lists all the steps to be taken to verify the authenticity of a signal and inform the proper authorities that extraterrestrial word has been heard.

This document has been approved or endorsed by every major, international, professional space society, including the IAA, the International Institute of Space Law, the Committee on Space Research, Commission 51 of the International Astronomical Union, and Commission J of the Union Radio Scientifique Internationale. In essence, Billingham's protocol says, *Make sure you've got something; then tell EVERYBODY.*

I've spoken at some length about how one goes about checking a candidate signal for authenticity—how to establish extraterrestrial origin, and how the special hallmarks of artificiality can distinguish a signal as being of intelligent design. But to announce to the world at large that you've made the greatest discovery in the history of astronomy—perhaps in history, period—takes an even wider margin of certainty.

On the NASA SETI project, you probably can't ask another observatory to help you verify your findings. If the long-awaited signal is intercepted at Arecibo, and it is weak, which is the most likely possibility, then no other observatory in the world could make the desired verification. This is because Arecibo has the greatest collecting area of any telescope, as well as the Gregorian feed and other specialized equipment. Even the other participants in NASA SETI, in France and Australia, will not match Arecibo's wide range of frequency coverage. And if the signal did fall within their frequency range, they might lack the sensitivity to hear it. Arecibo is so much more sensitive than the others—ever so much more capable of picking a faint, fragile *"We are here!"* out of a welter of cosmic noise.

In lieu of interobservatory checks and balances, the people at Arecibo (I hope I'm one of them when this happens) will have to spend several days checking and rechecking their data, locating the signal, if possible, a second, third, and fourth time rather than risk setting off a false alarm. After several days, however, repeated observations would build up a chink-free wall of evidence that would justify going public. . . .

Hard upon detection of an intelligent signal, there follows the delicate matter of a reply to the civilization that sent it. I've thought a lot, of course, about what to say in that happy situation. I have waited a lifetime for the opportunity, and the waiting has not diminished my confidence or my enthusiasm. I can't be specific about it, though, because when you really think about it, the only answer to the question "What do you say?" is "It depends."

It depends on the nature of the signal and what it's telling us. It depends on the world's reaction. It depends on the distance the message traveled, because we couldn't establish true dialogue with civilizations far removed from us— only lengthy monologues, crossing each other eternally in the interstellar mail. It depends on whether we can understand it. Certainly no stock reply, prepared in advance and stashed in someone's file cabinet, could match more than one of the infinite possibilities for the message's content. Certainly any reply should be crafted on a worldwide basis, and only after lengthy deliberation by knowledgeable individuals.

I have a recurring dream in which we receive our much-anticipated intelligent signal from across the Galaxy. The signal is unambiguous. It repeats over and over, allowing us to get a fix on its source, some twenty thousand light-years away. The signal is . . . apparently dense with information content. It is so full of noise, however, that we can't extract any information from it. And so we know only that another civilization exists. We cannot decipher the message itself.

If this dream becomes real, such documented detection of alien signals will, of course, be big news in itself. It will be a call to action, too, beckoning us to do whatever is required—build a much larger radio-telescope system, for example—to obtain information about that civilization, to learn whatever secrets the extraterrestrials will share with us.

Indeed, our response to a message from an alien civilization may thus be a response to the *situation* instead of an actual reply to the senders. We will tell the world at large what has happened, and that we're taking the next step by building better equipment to understand the message we've received. How I would love to have to go to Congress with a budget request for that project. I don't imagine I'd encounter much opposition. . . .

I do not wonder *whether* this will happen. My only question is *When?*

The silence we have heard so far is not in any way significant. We still have not looked long enough or hard enough. We've not explored a large enough chunk of the cosmic haystack. I could speculate that "they" are watching us to see if we are worth talking to. Or perhaps the ethic exists among them that rules, "There is no free lunch in the Galaxy." If we want to join the community of advanced civilizations, we must work as hard as they must. Perhaps they will send a signal that can be detected only if we put as much effort into receiving it as they put into transmitting it. NASA SETI is the beginning of the first truly meaningful effort to demonstrate the sincerity of our intentions.

Thus, the lesson we have learned from all our previous searching is that the greatest discovery is not a simple one to make. If there were once cockeyed optimists in the SETI endeavor, there aren't any now. In a way, I am glad. The priceless benefits of knowledge and experience that will accrue from interstellar contact should not come too easily. To appreciate them, we should expect to devote a substantial portion of our resources, our assets, our intellectual vigor, and our patience. We should be willing to sweat and crawl and wait.

The goal is not beyond us. It is within our grasp.

NO
Richard G. Teske

IS THIS THE E.T. TO WHOM
I AM SPEAKING?

Those who have seen the movie *E.T.* will remember that as the little extraterrestrial lies near death amid the bedlam of a makeshift medical center, an amazed scientist rushes in exclaiming, "He's got DNA! He's got DNA!" Why "he"? Why "DNA"? We know almost nothing about how alien life might begin and evolve. We are totally ignorant about whether sex is essential for the creation of a race of advanced beings. We are unable to say for sure if DNA or a similar complex genetic material is a requirement for intelligence. Despite this ignorance—or because of it—radio astronomers involved in NASA's Search for Extraterrestrial Intelligence (SETI) are now listening intently for broadcasts from the stars. They listen in hopes of hearing the signal of another civilization. Hope, in this case, springs from something called the principle of humility: Surely, among the billions of stellar systems in the billions of galaxies that fill our universe, Earth's ability to support intelligent life isn't unique. The universe is too vast, and we're not that special—something else is probably out there. It's just a matter of our finding it, or of its finding us.

I don't agree. I think it's unlikely that an intelligent being from outer space will communicate with us. And I think this not because of any insight into life's origins, molecular structure, and evolution but because of some very basic issues of technology.

I start with an assumption: any extraterrestrial that we might hear has to use metal. Radio antennas and rockets are fabricated of massive metal structures because of that material's strength, electrical conductivity, and other properties. The science and technology that have to lie behind the making of such hardware imply a culture possessing vast industrial talents. In turn this demands planetary natural resources aplenty, especially metallic ores—the raw materials for the technical infrastructure.

We now have a good idea how the useful ores of our own planet were made. Surprisingly, this information indicates that planets with mineral riches may be as hard to find as the forty-niners' mother lode. Even more surprisingly, it means the odds are *against* E.T.'s having the resources to build an

From Richard G. Teske, "Is This the E.T. to Whom I Am Speaking?" *Discover* (May 1993). Copyright © 1993 by The Walt Disney Company. Reprinted by permission.

interstellar phone, no matter how favorably you calculate the odds of the alien's existence.

Let's take a close look at those odds. Alien existence is usually estimated with a famous equation first suggested by astronomer Frank Drake. The calculation begins with a guess at the number of planets in the galaxy: There are some 400 billion stars in the Milky Way, and astronomers believe that planets are fairly common, perhaps orbiting around one star in 10. That's 40 billion stars with planets. If each star has 10 planets (similar to our solar system), that's 400 billion planets.

After that, certain probabilities that go into the equation are roughed out using the humility principle. There are various opinions about how high or low those probabilities should be set; I'll use values that fall somewhere on the optimistic side. To estimate the number of potentially habitable planets, we can say that because in our solar system only Earth and perhaps Mars have ever qualified as fit places to live, the likelihood of habitable planets existing in other planetary systems is roughly 2 in 10—say, 80 billion planets. What are the odds that one of these habitable planets will actually develop life? Again using the local evidence of Earth and Mars, we can set this value at 1/2. So the result is 40 billion planets with life.

How many shelter *intelligent* life? There's really no way to determine this. Some people arbitrarily set the odds at 1/100. But if we want to be as generous as possible, we can argue that the one planet we know of with life also has intelligent creatures, and thus we can set the probability at 1. That leaves us with anywhere from 400 million to 40 billion planets teeming with intelligent life.

But how many of those are capable of the highly technical achievement of radio communication between the stars? We now need to estimate the probability that intelligent creatures can create the necessary technology and decide to make use of it. SETI advocates often set the value between 1/10 and 1/5, again using the local evidence and the principle of humility. They point out that on Earth there have been a number of independently developed civilizations. But only one—modern Western European—has indeed created a high level of technology. Depending on just how they count the number of past civilizations, SETI supporters reason that one out of five or seven or maybe ten other planetary civilizations will develop the tools of interstellar contact. At any rate, we are left with between 40 million and 8 billion communicating civilizations.

This number can be, and usually is, reduced far further—sometimes down to mere thousands—even by SETI's most dedicated proponents. They factor in such things as the average life of a planet and the life of any single civilization on it —after all, what we are interested in is the possibility of communicating with other intelligent beings *right now,* and it does us little good if some alien signal is going to miss our attempts to detect it by millions of years.

But we don't have to focus on these last steps. Let's consider only the assumption above, that one out of five or ten civilizations will be able to develop the technology necessary for interstellar communication. It is precisely here that recent strides in understanding the origins of Earth's natural wealth require a different, and more pessimistic, calculation. Let us, as the SETI advocates do, look at the local evidence. When a planet like Earth forms, most of the high-density materials such as iron and nickel sink to the center of the molten sphere. But some of this material is left behind in the mantle, where it is widely scattered in small amounts. If something hadn't happened on Earth to bring it to the surface and concentrate it in significant quantities, metallic material would have remained unavailable to the creatures who inherited the planet, no matter how intelligent they became.

What happened was this: Starting about 3.8 billion years ago, according to geologists, lavas rich in iron and magnesium erupted cataclysmically from the seafloor. Chemical reactions of the magma with materials dissolved by the seawater resulted in deposition of metal-enriched sediments. Later the sediments were remelted and modified by rumbling, ongoing volcanism, which further enriched and concentrated metal ores deposited on the sea bottom.

On our planet this sea bottom moves. Its crustal plates unroll from midocean ridges like huge conveyor belts. Floating upon them are thick, lighter, nearly permanent continents, rafting back and forth. The conveyor belts of ocean bottom eventually dive under the edges of the buoyant continents at areas called subduction zones. As this crust slides beneath the continents, it sinks down into the mantle, where metal-rich sediments are heated and rise to the surface, becoming part of mountain ranges. The heat generated by this activity also promotes volcanoes, and the erupting lavas further concentrate the metals.

The existence and near permanence of continents is an important ingredient in making metal ores available to us. Had the earliest sea-bottom ore deposits been carried beneath the continents and lost altogether, there would be fewer resources for us to recover. Instead, and to our great good fortune, some primitive oceanic deposits were incorporated into the long-surviving continents, where further chemical and physical modification and concentration could take place. There the ores were stored over billion-year intervals.

Circulation of water in Earth's crust is essential in making ores, too. On the continents as well as beneath the seafloor, water gurgles into the rocks through cracks and fractures that may let it percolate miles deep. The groundwater or seawater contains dissolved salts, acids, or bases that promote chemical reactions between rock and fluid. Metals are dissolved and transported to other regions, often quite far away, where further chemical reactions release them, precipitating the metallic materials and thus creating ores. For example, midcontinental ore deposits in the Mississippi Valley were brought there by groundwater circulating from the ancient Appalachian Mountains almost half a continent away.

A planet's atmosphere also plays an important role in metal accumulation. According to geologist George Brimhall of the University of California at Berkeley, the gases interact with crustal rocks, creating a chemical environment that has a decisive effect on the kinds of metals that can be dissolved and concentrated. For example, when free oxygen is absent, iron separates from other substances easily, and so the iron particles can settle together on the ocean bottom, creating large iron deposits. In the presence of free oxygen, however, iron combines stubbornly with it, becomes insoluble, and stays locked up as dispersed iron in the rocks.

* * *

Remarkably, our atmosphere has provided both kinds of environment, each for about half Earth's lifetime. The most recent of the known major iron ore deposits are roughly 1.6 to 1.9 billion years old, suggesting that that period was the transition time, and prior to it Earth's atmosphere had little or no free oxygen. Why did such a transition occur? Most scientists believe our oxygen atmosphere is the product of biological activity, that the transition took place when one-celled ancestors of green plants learned the lesson of photosynthesis and began taking in carbon dioxide and releasing oxygen.

Although the arrival of free oxygen ended a long period of transport and deposition of iron, it led to a period of greater mobility for many other metals that, unlike iron, dissolve more easily when oxygen abounds. The transition thus paved the way for deposition of new kinds of ores such as uranium, copper, lead, and zinc. Concentration of these materials—used today for fission bombs, pennies, and water pipes—continued to be driven at a snail's pace by the thrust and collision of moving crustal plates, while ongoing circulation of crustal waters continued to be essential in emplacing Earth's bounty.

Of course, making these ores is only part of what's needed. They don't do us any good if we can't get at them. They have to be close to the surface. Therefore their availability often depends upon their being uncovered by erosion and weathering. Yet if erosion goes too far, the ores may be modified and dispersed— and wasted. It's a truly delicate balance.

So much for our planet. A brief tour through the solar system gives us an idea of just how rare each of these processes is, and how much rarer still is their combination. For this examination, let's look at just the four planets of the inner solar system, plus our moon. The other planets have followed different paths of development since their assembly, and I believe that if our own history is any guide, they are unlikely to have significant ore deposits. In any case, we simply don't yet know enough about them to judge.

Mercury and the moon never accumulated dense atmospheres nor abundant surface waters, and they show no signs of the moving crustal plates that drive the machinery of ore deposition on Earth. On Venus there seem to be a few small continentlike areas, and it is probable that these rest upon a soft, hot interior like that of Earth. But scientists think the crust is too thick and stiff for plate movements. Water was lost very early because it stayed up in the atmosphere, where the sun's rays could slice apart vast numbers of water molecules and quickly let free hydrogen escape to space in massive amounts. Some of the atmospheric water may also have been lost when it reacted with the crust, with the oxygen combining with rocks and the light hydrogen escaping. Either way, the absence of sufficient water to transport dissolved metals, together with the absence of moving crustal plates, means there's little chance that the goddess of beauty can be a goddess of metallic wealth.

Mars shows no widespread evidence of moving crustal plates, either. Because of its smaller size, Mars had less inner heat than Earth and so had volcanism that was wimpy by comparison. As a result, less water and fewer gases emerged from its crust and interior. Moreover, release of the gases petered out at an early time, so that as hydrogen was lost in space the water from which it came was not replaced. Spacecraft imagery of Mars' surface shows undeniable evidence that water was once present, but the pictures of floodplains and gullies also indicate that aquatic circulation was violent and short-lived, with floods and torrents that ended during the planet's middle age. This is not the kind of continuing process that produced our planet's plenitude.

None of this activity—plate movements on Mars and Venus, continents on Venus, early Martian water—exhibits the musical humming of Earth's planetary engine. The crucial issue is whether the processes of ore deposition are orchestrated elsewhere by nature as harmoniously as here at home. It's possible these different factors are somehow physically linked like Siamese quadruplets, so that if you have one you'll also have others. I believe, however, the evidence from Venus and Mars indicates that these factors are indeed independent. Yet they all need to operate together and in the right way. In the solar system only Earth is so blessed, suggesting that delicate balances may be but rarely achieved.

Remember that factor in the Drake equation that expresses the probability that intelligent beings will develop the technology and taste for interstellar communication? Recall that it's often given a value of 1/10 or 1/5, based on Earth's civilizations. But the evidence of the solar system yields a much lower number.

* * *

How many planets have the attributes necessary for metal-based technology? (The processes that give rise to this are independent of habitability, so it is fair for us to consider the four inner planets plus our moon, and not just habitable Earth and Mars.) On only 1 in 5 of these objects (Earth) do long-lasting crustal plate movements occur. On 1 in 5 of them do we find an ongoing hydrologic cycle. On just 1 in 5 of them did the atmosphere gain enough free oxygen for a long enough time so that deposition of a great range of metal ores could take place. And on 1 in 5 do we have large and long-lasting areas of buoyant continents to store resources in. If I am correct in viewing these as independent processes, we would calculate their joint probability by multiplying the individual probabilities: $1/5 \times 1/5 \times 1/5 \times 1/5 = 1/625$.

But the sample in the solar system surely does not include all possible planetary examples. Suppose we knew of five more objects unlike Earth. With them included among the present five and in the spirit of unlinked processes, we would calculate a joint probability of $1/10 \times 1/10 \times 1/10 \times 1/10 = 1/10,000$. Notice the predicted probability diminishes rapidly as more examples of impotent planets are included. I think we still haven't seen all possible kinds of planets and that the value of the probability can go lower still.

Am I being too harsh, too pessimistic? If we were to find more examples of potent planets, of course, the odds would go the other way. But I actually think I'm being overly *generous*. In our arithmetic we have not yet assessed such "delicate balances" as how long an atmosphere needs to have free oxygen, and how much it needs, to create industrial-strength ore deposits of all kinds. We haven't examined the fine balance between deposition and erosion, nor estimated how many nearly permanent, floating continents are desirable. My guess is that if we knew enough about these matters right now, we would come up with an extraordinarily low value for that key number in the Drake equation.

It is safe to predict that life indeed does exist elsewhere. It's probably safe to predict that some of that life is intelligent. But the rare and delicate balance of geology and chemistry that led to technology on Earth leads me to predict that there may be few or no technologically competent civilizations in the galaxy other than ourselves. I wish SETI all the success in the world, or in any world, for contact would be a truly exciting, absolutely marvelous discovery. But there may not be any calls from E.T. to listen for after all.

POSTSCRIPT

Is It Worthwhile to Continue the Search for Extraterrestrial Life?

The modern, high-tech version of SETI, the High Resolution Microwave Survey (HRMS), almost never came to pass. As Donald Tarter of the International Space University, in "Treading on the Edge: Practicing Safe Science With SETI," *Skeptical Inquirer* (Spring 1993), writes, "SETI's recent history has been one of fighting for scientific respect and then fighting for funding.... SETI has been so frequently ridiculed and singled out as [a program that could be eliminated by budget-cutting congressional members] that officially SETI no longer exists." He then notes that, shortly before NASA began its current search for extraterrestrial intelligence, the name was changed to HRMS.

However, the name change did not solve the problem. A year after HRMS was born, the budget was cut. By October 12, 1993, the $1 million a month needed to sustain it had been eliminated from the budget by a House-Senate conference committee. In support of the cut, Senator Richard H. Bryan (D-Nevada) said, "The Great Martian Chase may finally come to an end. As of today, millions have been spent and we have yet to bag a single little green fellow. Not a single martian has said 'take me to your leader,' and not a single flying saucer has applied for FAA approval." See Seth Shostak, "The New Search for Intelligent Life," *Mercury* (September–October 1993).

It was not the sort of arguments raised by critics such as Teske that defeated HRMS; it was image. SETI smacked too much of science fiction and Hollywood. It might not be terribly expensive—the cost of a single space shuttle flight could pay SETI's bills for several years—but whatever it cost seemed to the budget cutters pure waste when compared to the many other programs and problems requiring funds.

Politicians were not the only ones who reacted in this way. Harvard University biologist Ernst Mayr reacted to a review of Drake and Sobel's book *Is Anyone Out There?* by saying, "I find it astounding... that such a highly dubious endeavor is supported by NASA in this time of appalling federal debt" (*Science*, March 12, 1993, pp. 1522–1523).

Yet SETI was not dead. Many scientists—including nonastronomers such as David M. Raup of the University of Chicago's Department of Geophysical Sciences and Committee on Evolutionary Biology—disagree with those who believe that humans are probably alone in the universe and who say that the search for intelligent extraterrestrials is not worth the effort. So do many nonscientists. The private SETI Institute has been able to garner $7.5 million in donations so far, chiefly from prominent business leaders in California's computer industry. "They're in it for the adventure. They have vision," said Seth Shostak, a SETI Institute scientist (*Science*, January 28, 1994).

In 1995 that vision permitted the observation of 209 sun-like stars (see *Science*, February 23, 1996), and backers have promised money for another five years of searching. Frank Drake, the SETI Institute's president, says that the institute hopes to raise an endowment sufficient to maintain the search for many more years.

The Planetary Society (which is open to public membership) is also running a pair of sky searches—the SERENDIP SETI Sky Survey and the META II search. There is also BETA (the Billion Channel Extraterrestrial Assay), which is using a Harvard-Smithsonian radio telescope and a high-capacity signal analyzer built with donated computer chips to mount a broad survey under the directorship of Harvard physicist Paul Horowitz (see *Science*, March 24, 1995, and *Time*, February 5, 1996).

Suspicious signals are still turning up, as they did during Drake's earlier work, but so far all seem to be of terrestrial origin. Is there any reason for continued hope? Astronomers have recently observed planets around distant stars, with signs that some may have water. So there are hints that conditions elsewhere may be suitable for life. Professor Paul Davies, in "The Harmony of the Spheres," *Time* (February 5, 1996), writes, "The discovery of life beyond Earth would transform not only our science but also our religions, our belief systems and our entire world view ... [our sense of] who we are and what our place is in the grand sweep of the cosmos."

Students who wish to find more information on the Internet will find this site a useful starting point: http://www.seti-inst.edu/.

ISSUE 11

Will It Be Possible to Build a Computer That Can Think?

YES: Hans Moravec, from "The Universal Robot," in *Vision-21: Interdisciplinary Science and Engineering in the Era of Cyberspace* (National Aeronautics and Space Administration, 1993)

NO: John R. Searle, from "Is the Brain's Mind a Computer Program?" *Scientific American* (January 1990)

ISSUE SUMMARY

YES: Research scientist Hans Moravec describes the necessary steps in what he considers to be the inevitable development of computers that match and even exceed human intelligence.

NO: Professor of philosophy John R. Searle argues that a crucial difference between artificial (machine) intelligence and human intelligence—that humans attach meaning to the symbols they manipulate while computers cannot—makes it impossible to create a computer that can think.

The first primitive digital computers were instantly dubbed "thinking machines" because they were able to perform functions—initially only arithmetic—that had always been considered part of the uniquely human ability to think. Some critics of the "thinking machine" label, however, objected that arithmetic is so much simpler than, say, poetry or philosophy (after all, it is only a matter of following a few simple rules) that computers were not thinking at all. Thinking, they said, is for humans only. In fact, if a machine can do it, then it cannot possibly be real thinking.

In 1950 Alan Turing (1912–1954), an English mathematician and logician, devised a test to determine whether or not a machine was intelligent. Turing's test entailed whether or not one could converse with a person and a computer (through a teletype so that neither could be seen nor could the human be heard) and, after a suitable period, tell which was which. If the computer could pass for an intelligent conversationalist, Turing felt, then it would have to be considered intelligent.

Over the next two decades, computer scientists learned how to program their machines to play games such as chess, solve mathematical theorems, parse sentences (break them down into their grammatical components), and perform a number of other tasks that had once been thought doable by thinking humans only. In most cases the machines were not as good at these tasks as humans, but many artificial intelligence (AI) researchers believed that it was only a matter of time before the machines matched and even exceeded their creators.

The closest any machine has come to passing the Turing test may have been in the early 1970s, when Kenneth Mark Colby, then a Stanford University psychiatrist and computer scientist, programmed a computer to imitate the conversational style of paranoid humans. This was much easier than programming a computer to imitate a nonparanoid human's conversational style because paranoid individuals tend to be very rigid and predictable in their responses. When Colby had psychiatrists interview the programmed computer and a human paranoid (through a teletype, per Turing's criteria), only half could correctly distinguish between computer and human. That is, the computer did indeed come close to passing the Turing test. On the other hand, it was not trying to pass as an average human being, whose thought processes are far freer and more flexible than those of a paranoid person.

Will a computer ever be able to imitate a normal human being? And if it can, will that mean it is really "thinking" or really "intelligent"? Many computer scientists believe that it is still just a matter of time before a computer passes the Turing test with flying colors and that that machine will be truly intelligent. Indeed, many even say that the human mind is nothing more than a program that runs on a biological machine.

Others argue that machines cannot have emotions or appreciate beauty and that computers cannot be self-aware or conscious, no matter how intelligent they may seem to an interrogator. They therefore can never be intelligent in a human way.

Hans Moravec, director of the Mobile Robot Laboratory at Carnegie Mellon University's Robotics Institute, strongly believes that true artificial intelligence can be achieved. It will require computers that are much more powerful than any that exist today, he predicts, and the process of achieving intelligence will involve a series of evolutionary stages.

In contrast, John R. Searle, professor of philosophy at the University of California, Berkeley, argues that although humans *can* be regarded as biological machines, there are essential differences between natural and artificial intelligence. Furthermore, he objects to the idea that the human mind is nothing more than a computer program.

YES

Hans Moravec

THE UNIVERSAL ROBOT

Abstract. Our artifacts are getting smarter, and a loose parallel with the evolution of animal intelligence suggests one future course for them. Computerless industrial machinery exhibits the behavioral flexibility of single-celled organisms. Today's best computer-controlled robots are like the simpler invertebrates. A thousand-fold increase in computer power in the next decade should make possible machines with reptile-like sensory and motor competence. Properly configured, such robots could do in the physical world what personal computers now do in the world of data—act on our behalf as literal-minded slaves. Growing computer power over the next half-century will allow this reptile stage to be surpassed, in stages producing robots that learn like mammals, model their world like primates and eventually reason like humans. Depending on your point of view, humanity will then have produced a worthy successor, or transcended some of its inherited limitations and so transformed itself into something quite new.

INTRODUCTION: STATE OF THE ART

Instincts which predispose the nature and quantity of work we enjoy probably evolved during the 100,000 years our ancestors lived as hunter-gatherers. Less than 10,000 years ago the agricultural revolution made life more stable, and richer in goods and information. But, paradoxically, it requires more human labor to support an agricultural society than a primitive one, and the work is of a different, "unnatural" kind, out of step with the old instincts. The effort to avoid this work has resulted in domestication of animals, slavery and the industrial revolution. But many jobs must still be done by hand, engendering for hundreds of years the fantasy of an intelligent but soulless being that can tirelessly dispatch the drudgery. Only in this century have electronic sensors and computers given machines the ability to sense their world and to think about it, and so offered a way to fulfill the wish.

From National Aeronautics and Space Administration. Office of Management. Scientific and Technical Information Program. *Vision-21: Interdisciplinary Science and Engineering in the Era of Cyberspace.* (NASA Conference Publication 10129; 1993). References omitted.

As in fables, the unexpected side effects of robot slaves are likely to dominate the resulting story. Most significantly, these perfect slaves will continue to develop, and will not long remain soulless. As they increase in competence they will have occasion to make more and more autonomous decisions, and so will slowly develop a volition and purposes of their own. At the same time they will become indispensable. Our minds were evolved to store the skills and memories of a stone-age life, not the enormous complexity that has developed in the last ten thousand years. We've kept up, after a fashion, through a series of social inventions—social stratification and division of labor, memory aids like poetry and schooling, written records, stored outside the body, and recently machines that can do some of our thinking entirely without us. The portion of absolutely essential human activity that takes place outside of human bodies and minds has been steadily increasing. Hard working intelligent machines may complete the trend.

Serious attempts to build thinking machines began after the second world war. One line of research, called Cybernetics, used simple electronic circuitry to mimic small nervous systems, and produced machines that could learn to recognize simple patterns, and turtle-like robots that found their way to lighted recharging hutches. An entirely different approach, named Artificial Intelligence (AI), attempted to duplicate rational human thought in the large computers that appeared after the war. By 1965, these computers ran programs that proved theorems in logic and geometry, solved calculus problems and played good games of checkers. In the early 1970s, AI research groups at MIT (the Massachusetts Institute of Technology) and Stanford University attached television cameras and robot arms to their computers, so their "thinking" programs could begin to collect their information directly from the real world.

What a shock! While the pure reasoning programs did their jobs about as well and about as fast as college freshmen, the best robot control programs took hours to find and pick up a few blocks on a table. Often these robots failed completely, giving a performance much worse than a six month old child. This disparity between programs that reason and programs that perceive and act in the real world holds to this day. In recent years Carnegie Mellon University produced two desk-sized computers that can play chess at grandmaster level, within the top 100 players in the world, when given their moves on a keyboard. But present-day robotics could produce only a complex and unreliable machine for finding and moving normal chess pieces.

In hindsight it seems that, in an absolute sense, reasoning is much easier than perceiving and acting—a position not hard to rationalize in evolutionary terms. The survival of human beings (and their ancestors) has depended for hundreds of millions of years on seeing and moving in the physical world, and in that competition large parts of their brains have become efficiently organized for the task. But we didn't appreciate this monumental skill because it is shared by every human being and most animals—it is commonplace. On the other hand, rational thinking, as in chess, is a newly acquired skill, perhaps less than one hundred thousand years old. The parts of our brain devoted to it are not well organized, and, in an absolute sense, we're not very good at it. But until recently we had no competition to show us up.

By comparing the edge and motion detecting circuitry in the four layers of nerve cells in the retina, the best understood major circuit in the human nervous system, with similar processes developed for "computer vision" systems that allow robots in research and industry to see, I've estimated that it would take a billion computations per second (the power of a world-leading Cray 2 supercomputer) to produce the same results at the same speed as a human retina. By extrapolation, to emulate a whole brain takes ten trillion arithmetic operations per second, or ten thousand Crays worth. This is for operations our nervous systems do extremely efficiently and well.

Arithmetic provides an example at the other extreme. In 1989 a new computer was tested for a few months with a program that computed the number pi to more than one billion decimal places. By contrast, the largest unaided manual computation of pi was 707 digits by William Shanks in 1873. It took him several years, and because of a mistake every digit past the 527th was wrong! In arithmetic, today's average computers are one million times more powerful than human beings. In very narrow areas of rational thought (like playing chess or proving theorems) they are about the same. And in perception and control of movement in the complex real world, and related areas of common-sense knowledge and intuitive and visual problem solving, today's average computers are a million times less capable.

The deficit is evident even in pure problem solving AI programs. To this day, AI programs exhibit no shred of common sense—a medical diagnosis program, for instance, may prescribe an an-

tibiotic when presented a broken bicycle because it lacks a model of people, diseases or bicycles. Yet these programs, on existing computers, would be overwhelmed were they to be bloated with the details of everyday life, since each new fact can interact with the others in an astronomical "combinatorial explosion." [A ten year project called Cyc at the Microelectronics and Computer Consortium in Austin, Texas, is attempting to build just such a common-sense data base. They estimate the final result will contain over one hundred million logic sentences about everyday objects and actions.]

Machines have a lot of catching up to do. On the other hand, for most of the century, machine calculation has been improving a thousandfold every twenty years, and there are basic developments in research labs that can sustain this for at least several decades more. In less than fifty years computer hardware should be powerful enough to match, and exceed, even the well-developed parts of human intelligence. But what about the software that would be required to give these powerful machines the ability to perceive, intuit and think as well as humans? The Cybernetic approach that attempts to directly imitate nervous systems is very slow, partly because examining a working brain in detail is a very tedious process. New instruments may change that in the future. The AI approach has successfully imitated some aspects of rational thought, but that seems to be only about one millionth of the problem. I feel that the fastest progress on the hardest problems will come from a third approach, the newer field of robotics, the construction of systems that must see and move in the physical world. Robotics research is imitating the evolution of animal minds, adding capabilities to machines a few at a time, so that the resulting sequence of machine behaviors resembles the capabilities of animals with increasingly complex nervous systems. This effort to build intelligence from the bottom up is helped by biological peeks at the "back of the book"—at the neuronal, structural, and behavioral features of animals and humans.

The best robots today are controlled by computers which are just powerful enough to simulate the nervous system of an insect, cost as much as houses, and so find only a few profitable niches in society (among them, spray painting and spot welding cars and assembling electronics). But those few applications are encouraging research that is slowly providing a base for a huge future growth. Robot evolution in the direction of full intelligence will greatly accelerate, I believe, in about a decade when the mass-produced general purpose, universal robot becomes possible. These machines will do in the physical world what personal computers do in the world of data—act on our behalf as literal-minded slaves.

THE DUMB ROBOT (ca. 2000–2010)

To be useful in many tasks, the first generation of universal robots should navigate efficiently over flat ground and reliably and safely over rough terrain and stairs, be able to manipulate most objects, and to find them in the nearby world. There are beginnings of solutions today. In the 1980s Hitachi of Japan developed a mobility system of five steerable wheels, each on its own telescoping stalk that allows it to accommodate to rises and dips in uneven terrain, and to climb stairs, by raising one wheel at a time while

standing stably on the other four. My laboratory at Carnegie Mellon University in Pittsburgh has developed a navigation method that enables a robot equipped with sonar range measuring devices and television cameras to build probabilistic maps of its surroundings to determine its location and plan routes. An elegant three-fingered mechanical hand at the Massachusetts Institute of Technology can hold and orient bolts and eggs and manipulate a string in a humanlike fashion. A system called 3DPO from SRI International in Menlo Park, California, can find a desired part in a jumble seen by a special range-finding camera. The slow operation of these systems suggests one other element needed for the universal robot, namely a computer about one thousand times as powerful as those found on desks and in robots today. Such machines, able to do one billion computations per second, would provide robots approximately the brain power of a reptile, and the personality of a washing machine.

Universal robots will find their first uses in factories, where they will be cheaper and more versatile than the older generation of robots they replace. Eventually they will become cheap enough for some households, extending the reach of personal computers from a few tasks in the data world to many in the physical world. . . .

LEARNING (2010–2020)

Useful though they will be, the first generation of universal robots will be rigid slaves to simple programs. If the machine bangs its elbow while chopping beef in your kitchen making Stroganoff, you will have to find another place for the robot to do its work, or beg the software manufacturer for a fix. Second generation robots with more powerful computers will be able to host a more flexible kind of program able to adjust itself by a kind of conditioned learning. First generation programs will consist primarily of sequences of the type "Do step A, then B, then C. . . ." The programs for the second generation will read "Do step A1 or A2 or A3... then B1 or B2 or B3... then C1 or C2 or C3. . . ." In the Beef Stroganoff example, A1 might be to chop with the right hand of the robot, while A2 is to use the left hand. Each alternative in the program has a "weight," a number that indicates the desirability of using it rather than one of the other branches. The machine also contains a "pain" system, a series of programs that look out for problems, such as collisions, and respond by reducing the weights of recently invoked branches, and a "pleasure" system that increases the relevant weights when good conditions, such as well charged batteries or a task efficiently completed, are detected. As the robot bangs its elbow repeatedly in your kitchen, it gradually learns to use its other hand (as well as adapting to its surroundings in a thousand other ways). A program with many alternatives at each step, whose pain and pleasure systems are arranged to produce a pleasure signal on hearing the word "good" and a pain message on hearing "bad" could be slowly trained to do new tasks, like a small mammal. A particular suite of pain- and pleasure-producing programs interacting with a robot's individual environment would subtly shape its behavior and give it a distinct character.

IMAGERY (2020–2030)

Adaptive robots will find jobs everywhere, and the hardware and software industry that supports them could become the largest on earth. But teaching them new tasks, whether by writing programs or through punishment and reward, will be very tedious. This deficiency will lead to a portentous innovation, a software world-modeler (requiring another big increase in computer power), that allows the robot to simulate its immediate surroundings and its own actions within them, and thus to think about its tasks before acting. Before making Beef Stroganoff in your kitchen, the new robot would simulate the task many times. Each time its simulated elbow bangs the simulated cabinet, the software would update the learning weights just as if the collision had physically happened. After many such mental run-throughs the robot would be well trained, so that when it finally cooks for real, it does it correctly. The simulation can be used in many other ways. After a job, the robot can run though its previous actions, and try variations on them to improve future performance. A robot might even be configured to invent some of its own programs by means of a simpler program that can detect how nearly a sequence of robot actions achieves a desired task. This training program would, in repeated simulations, provide the "good" and "bad" indications needed to condition a general learning program like the one of the previous section.

It will take a large community of patient researchers to build good simulators. A robot entering a new room must include vast amounts of not directly perceived prior knowledge in its simulation, such as the expected shapes and probable contents of kitchen counters and the effect of (and force needed for) turning faucet knobs. It needs instinctive motor-perceptual knowledge about the world that took millions of years of evolution to install in us, that tells us instinctively when a height is dangerous, how hard to throw a stone, or if the animal facing us is a threat. Robots that incorporate it may be as smart as monkeys.

REASONING (2030–2040)

In the decades while the "bottom-up" evolution of robots is transferring the perceptual and motor faculties of human beings into machinery, the conventional Artificial Intelligence industry will be perfecting the mechanization of reasoning. Since today's programs already match human beings in some areas, those of 40 years from now, running on computers a million times as fast as today's, should be quite superhuman. Today's reasoning programs work from small amounts of clear and correct information prepared by human beings. Data from robot sensors such as cameras is much too voluminous and too noisy for them to use. But a good robot simulator will contain neatly organized data about the robot and its world. For instance, if a knife is on a countertop, or if the robot is holding a cup. A robot with a simulator can be married to a reasoning program to produce a machine with most of the abilities of a human being. The combination will create beings that in some ways resemble us, but in others are like nothing the world has seen before.

FIRST GENERATION TECHNICALITIES

Both industrial robot manipulators and the research effort to build "smart" robots are twenty five years old. Universal robots will require at least another decade of development, but some of their ele-ments can be guessed from the experience so far. One consideration is weight. Mobile robots built to work in human sized spaces today weigh too many hundreds of pounds. This dangerously large mass has three major components: batteries, actuators and structure. Lead-acid batteries able to drive a mobile robot for a day contribute about one third of the weight. But nickel-cadmium aircraft batteries weigh half as much, and newer lithium batteries can be half again as light. Electric motors are efficient and precisely controllable, but standard motors are heavy and require equally heavy reducing gears. Ultrastrong permanent magnets can halve the weight and generate high torque without gears. Robot structure has been primarily aluminum. Its weight contribution can be cut by a factor of four by substituting composite materials containing superstrength fibers of graphite, aramid or the new material Spectra. These innovations could be combined to make a robot with roughly the size, weight, strength and endurance of a human.

The first generation robot will probably move on wheels. Legged robots have advantages on complicated terrain, but they consume too much power. A simple wheeled robot would be confined to areas of flat ground, but if each wheel had a controlled suspension with about a meter of travel, the robot could slowly lift its wheels as needed to negotiate rough ground and stairs. The manipulation system will consist of two or more arms ending in dexterous manipulators. There are several designs in the research labs today, but the most elegant is probably that of the so-called Stanford-JPL hand (mentioned above, now found at MIT), which has three fingers each with three controlled joints.

The robot's travels would be greatly aided if it could continuously pinpoint its location, perhaps by noting the delay from a handful of small synchronized transmitters distributed in its environment. This approach is used in some terrestrial and satellite navigation systems. The robot will also require a sense of its immediate surroundings, to find doors, detect obstacles and track objects in its workspace. Research laboratories, including my own, have experimented with techniques that do this with data from television cameras, scanning lasers, sonar transducers, infrared proximity sensors and contact sensors. A more precise sensory system will be needed to find particular work objects in clutter. The most successful methods to date start with three dimensional data from special cameras and laser arrangements that directly measure distance as well as lateral position. The robot will thus probably contain a wide angle sensor for general spatial awareness, and a precise, narrow angle, three dimensional imaging system to find particular objects it will grasp.

Research experience to date suggests that to navigate, visually locate objects, and plan and control arm motions, the first universal robots will require a billion operations per second of computer power. The 1980s have witnessed a number of well publicized fads that claim to be solutions to the artificial intelligence or robot control problem. Expert systems, the Prolog logical inference language, neural nets, fuzzy logic and massive parallelism have all had their spot in the limelight. The common element that I note in these pronouncements is the sudden enthusiasm of groups of researchers experienced in some area of computer science for applying their methods to the robotics problems of perceiving and act-

ing in the physical world. Invariably each approach produces some simple showcase demonstrations, then bogs down on real problems. This pattern is no surprise to those with a background in the twenty five year research robotics effort.

Making a machine to see, hear or act reliably in the raw physical world is much, much more difficult than naive intuition leads us to believe....

MIND CHILDREN (2050+)

The fourth robot generation and its successors, with human perceptual and motor abilities and superior reasoning powers, could replace human beings in every essential task. In principle, our society could continue to operate increasingly well without us, with machines running the companies and doing the research as well as performing the productive work. Since machines can be designed to work well in outer space, production could move to the greater resources of the solar system, leaving behind a nature preserve subsidized from space. Meek humans would inherit the earth, but rapidly evolving machines would expand into the rest of the universe.

This development can be viewed as a very natural one. Human beings have two forms of heredity, one the traditional biological kind, passed on strands of DNA, the other cultural, passed from mind to mind by example, language, books and recently machines. At present the two are inextricably linked, but the cultural part is evolving very rapidly, and gradually assuming functions once the province of our biology. In terms of information content, our cultural side is already by far the larger part of us. The fully intelligent robot marks the point where our cultural side can exist on its own, free of biological limits. Intelligent machines, which are evolving among us, learning our skills, sharing our goals, and being shaped by our values, can be viewed as our children, the children of our minds. With them our biological heritage is not lost. It will be safely stored in libraries at least; however its importance will be greatly diminished.

What about life back on the preserve? For some of us the thought of being grandly upstaged by our artificial progeny will be disappointing, and life may seem pointless if we are fated to spend it staring stupidly at our ultra-intelligent progeny as they try to describe their ever more spectacular discoveries in baby-talk that we can understand. Is there any way individual humans might join the adventure?

You've just been wheeled into the operating room. A robot brain surgeon is in attendance, a computer waits nearby. Your skull, but not your brain, is anesthetized. You are fully conscious. The robot surgeon opens your brain case and places a hand on the brain's surface. This unusual hand bristles with microscopic machinery, and a cable connects it to the computer at your side. Instruments in the hand scan the first few millimeters of brain surface. These measurements, and a comprehensive understanding of human neural architecture, allow the surgeon to write a program that models the behavior of the uppermost layer of the scanned brain tissue. This program is installed in a small portion of the waiting computer and activated. Electrodes in the hand supply the simulation with the appropriate inputs from your brain, and can inject signals from the simulation. You and the surgeon compare the signals it produces with the original ones. They flash by very fast, but any discrepancies

are highlighted on a display screen. The surgeon fine-tunes the simulation until the correspondence is nearly perfect. As soon as you are satisfied, the simulation output is activated. The brain layer is now impotent—it receives inputs and reacts as before but its output is ignored. Microscopic manipulators on the hand's surface excise this superfluous tissue and pass them to an aspirator, where they are drawn away.

The surgeon's hand sinks a fraction of a millimeter deeper into your brain, instantly compensating its measurements and signals for the changed position. The process is repeated for the next layer, and soon a second simulation resides in the computer, communicating with the first and with the remaining brain tissue. Layer after layer the brain is simulated, then excavated. Eventually your skull is empty, and the surgeon's hand rests deep in your brainstem. Though you have not lost consciousness, or even your train of thought, your mind has been removed from the brain and transferred to a machine. In a final, disorienting step the surgeon lifts its hand. Your suddenly abandoned body dies. For a moment you experience only quiet and dark. Then, once again, you can open your eyes. Your perspective has shifted. The computer simulation has been disconnected from the cable leading to the surgeon's hand and reconnected to a shiny new body of the style, color, and material of your choice. Your metamorphosis is complete.

Your new mind has a control labeled "speed." It had been set at 1, to keep the simulations synchronized with the old brain, but now you change it to 10,000, allowing you to communicate, react, and think ten thousand times faster. You now seem to have hours to respond to situations that previously seemed instantaneous. You have time, during the fall of a dropped object, to research the advantages and disadvantages of trying to catch it, perhaps to solve its differential equations of motion. When your old biological friends speak with you, their sentences take hours—you have plenty of time to think about the conversations, but they try your patience. Boredom is a mental alarm that keeps you from wasting your time in profitless activity, but if it acts too soon or too aggressively it limits your attention span, and thus your intelli-

gence. With help from the machines, you change your mind-program to retard the onset of boredom. Having done that, you will find yourself comfortably working on long problems with sidetracks upon sidetracks. In fact, your thoughts routinely become so involved that you need an increase in your memory. These are but the first of many changes. Soon your friends complain that you have become more like the machines than the biological human you once were. That's life.

NO

John R. Searle

IS THE BRAIN'S MIND
A COMPUTER PROGRAM?

Can a machine think? Can a machine have conscious thoughts in exactly the same sense that you and I have? If by "machine" one means a physical system capable of performing certain functions (and what else can one mean?), then humans are machines of a special biological kind, and humans can think, and so of course machines can think. And, for all we know, it might be possible to produce a thinking machine out of different materials altogether—say, out of silicon chips or vacuum tubes. Maybe it will turn out to be impossible, but we certainly do not know that yet.

In recent decades, however, the question of whether a machine can think has been given a different interpretation entirely. The question that has been posed in its place is, Could a machine think just by virtue of implementing a computer program? Is the program by itself constitutive of thinking? This is a completely different question because it is not about the physical, causal properties of actual or possible physical systems but rather about the abstract, computational properties of formal computer programs that can be implemented in any sort of substance at all, provided only that the substance is able to carry the program.

A fair number of researchers in artificial intelligence (AI) believe the answer to the second question is yes; that is, they believe that by designing the right programs with the right inputs and outputs, they are literally creating minds. They believe furthermore that they have a scientific test for determining success or failure: the Turing test devised by Alan M. Turing, the founding father of artificial intelligence. The Turing test, as currently understood, is simply this: if a computer can perform in such a way that an expert cannot distinguish its performance from that of a human who has a certain cognitive ability—say, the ability to do addition or to understand Chinese—then the computer also has that ability. So the goal is to design programs that will simulate human cognition in such a way as to pass the Turing test. What is more, such a program would not merely be a model of the mind; it would literally be a mind, in the same sense that a human mind is a mind.

From John R. Searle, "Is the Brain's Mind a Computer Program?" *Scientific American* (January 1990). Copyright © 1990 by Scientific American, Inc. Reprinted by permission. All rights reserved.

By no means does every worker in artificial intelligence accept so extreme a view. A more cautious approach is to think of computer models as being useful in studying the mind in the same way that they are useful in studying the weather, economics or molecular biology. To distinguish these two approaches, I call the first strong AI and the second weak AI. It is important to see just how bold an approach strong AI is. Strong AI claims that thinking is merely the manipulation of formal symbols, and that is exactly what the computer does: manipulate formal symbols. This view is often summarized by saying, "The mind is to the brain as the program is to the hardware."

* * *

Strong AI is unusual among theories of the mind in at least two respects: it can be stated clearly, and it admits of a simple and decisive refutation. The refutation is one that any person can try for himself or herself. Here is how it goes. Consider a language you don't understand. In my case, I do not understand Chinese. To me Chinese writing looks like so many meaningless squiggles. Now suppose I am placed in a room containing baskets full of Chinese symbols. Suppose also that I am given a rule book in English for matching Chinese symbols with other Chinese symbols. The rules identify the symbols entirely by their shapes and do not require that I understand any of them. The rules might say such things as, "Take a squiggle-squiggle sign from basket number one and put it next to a squoggle-squoggle sign from basket number two."

Imagine that people outside the room who understand Chinese hand in small bunches of symbols and that in response I manipulate the symbols according to the rule book and hand back more small bunches of symbols. Now, the rule book is the "computer program." The people who wrote it are "programmers," and I am the "computer." The baskets full of symbols are the "data base," the small bunches that are handed in to me are "questions" and the bunches I then hand out are "answers."

Now suppose that the rule book is written in such a way that my "answers" to the "questions" are indistinguishable from those of a native Chinese speaker. For example, the people outside might hand me some symbols that unknown to me mean, "What's your favorite color?" and I might after going through the rules give back symbols that, also unknown to me, mean, "My favorite is blue, but I also like green a lot." I satisfy the Turing test for understanding Chinese. All the same, I am totally ignorant of Chinese. And there is no way I could come to understand Chinese in the system as described, since there is no way that I can learn the meanings of any of the symbols. Like a computer, I manipulate symbols, but I attach no meaning to the symbols.

The point of the thought experiment is this: if I do not understand Chinese solely on the basis of running a computer program for understanding Chinese, then neither does any other digital computer solely on that basis. Digital computers merely manipulate formal symbols according to rules in the program.

What goes for Chinese goes for other forms of cognition as well. Just manipulating the symbols is not by itself enough to guarantee cognition, perception, understanding, thinking and so forth. And since computers, qua computers, are symbol-manipulating devices, merely running the computer program is not enough to guarantee cognition.

This simple argument is decisive against the claims of strong AI. The first premise of the argument simply states the formal character of a computer program. Programs are defined in terms of symbol manipulations, and the symbols are purely formal, or "syntactic." The formal character of the program, by the way, is what makes computers so powerful. The same program can be run on an indefinite variety of hardwares, and one hardware system can run an indefinite range of computer programs. Let me abbreviate this "axiom" as

Axiom 1. Computer programs are formal (syntactic).

This point is so crucial that it is worth explaining in more detail. A digital computer processes information by first encoding it in the symbolism that the computer uses and then manipulating the symbols through a set of precisely stated rules. These rules constitute the program. For example, in Turing's early theory of computers, the symbols were simply 0's and 1's, and the rules of the program said such things as, "Print a 0 on the tape, move one square to the left and erase a 1." The astonishing thing about computers is that any information that can be stated in a language can be encoded in such a system, and any information-processing task that can be solved by explicit rules can be programmed.

* * *

Two further points are important. First, symbols and programs are purely abstract notions: they have no essential physical properties to define them and can be implemented in any physical medium whatsoever. The 0's and 1's, qua symbols, have no essential physical properties and a fortiori have no physical, causal properties. I emphasize this point because it is tempting to identify computers with some specific technology—say, silicon chips—and to think that the issues are about the physics of silicon chips or to think that syntax identifies some physical phenomenon that might have as yet unknown causal powers, in the way that actual physical phenomena such as electromagnetic radiation or hydrogen atoms have physical, causal properties. The second point is that symbols are manipulated without reference to any meanings. The symbols of the program can stand for anything the programmer or user wants. In this sense the program has syntax but no semantics.

The next axiom is just a reminder of the obvious fact that thoughts, perceptions, understandings and so forth have a mental content. By virtue of their content they can be about objects and states of affairs in the world. If the content involves language, there will be syntax in addition to semantics, but linguistic understanding requires at least a semantic framework. If, for example, I am thinking about the last presidential election, certain words will go through my mind, but the words are about the election only because I attach specific meanings to these words, in accordance with my knowledge of English. In this respect they are unlike Chinese symbols for me. Let me abbreviate this axiom as

Axiom 2. Human minds have mental contents (semantics).

Now let me add the point that the Chinese room demonstrated. Having the symbols by themselves—just having the syntax— is not sufficient for having the semantics.

Merely manipulating symbols is not enough to guarantee knowledge of what they mean. I shall abbreviate this as

Axiom 3. Syntax by itself is neither constitutive of nor sufficient for semantics.

At one level this principle is true by definition. One might, of course, define the terms syntax and semantics differently. The point is that there is a distinction between formal elements, which have no intrinsic meaning or content, and those phenomena that have intrinsic content. From these premises it follows that

Conclusion 1. Programs are neither constitutive of nor sufficient for minds.

And that is just another way of saying that strong AI is false.

It is important to see what is proved and not proved by this argument.

First, I have not tried to prove that "a computer cannot think." Since anything that can be simulated computationally can be described as a computer, and since our brains can at some levels be simulated, it follows trivially that our brains are computers and they can certainly think. But from the fact that a system can be simulated by symbol manipulation and the fact that it is thinking, it does not follow that thinking is equivalent to formal symbol manipulation.

Second, I have not tried to show that only biologically based systems like our brains can think. Right now those are the only systems we know for a fact can think, but we might find other systems in the universe that can produce conscious thoughts, and we might even come to be able to create thinking systems artificially. I regard this issue as up for grabs.

Third, strong AI's thesis is not that, for all we know, computers with the right programs might be thinking, that they might have some as yet undetected psychological properties; rather it is that they must be thinking because that is all there is to thinking.

Fourth, I have tried to refute strong AI so defined. I have tried to demonstrate that the program by itself is not constitutive of thinking because the program is purely a matter of formal symbol manipulation—and we know independently that symbol manipulations by themselves are not sufficient to guarantee the presence of meanings. That is the principle on which the Chinese room argument works.

I emphasize these points here partly because it seems to me the Churchlands [see "Could a Machine Think?" by Paul M. Churchland and Patricia Smith Churchland, *Scientific American* (January 1990), page 321] have not quite understood the issues. They think that strong AI is claiming that computers might turn out to think and that I am denying this possibility on commonsense grounds. But that is not the claim of strong AI, and my argument against it has nothing to do with common sense.

I will have more to say about their objections later. Meanwhile I should point out that, contrary to what the Churchlands suggest, the Chinese room argument also refutes any strong-AI claims made for the new parallel technologies that are inspired by and modeled on neural networks. Unlike the traditional von Neumann computer, which proceeds in a step-by-step fashion, these systems have many computational elements that operate in parallel and interact with one another according to rules inspired by neurobiology. Although the results are still modest, these "parallel distributed processing, or connectionist," models raise useful questions about how complex, parallel network systems like those in brains might actually function in the production of intelligent behavior.

The parallel, "brainlike" character of the processing, however, is irrelevant to the purely computational aspects of the process. Any function that can be computed on a parallel machine can also be computed on a serial machine. Indeed, because parallel machines are still rare, connectionist programs are usually run on traditional serial machines. Parallel processing, then, does not afford a way around the Chinese room argument.

What is more, the connectionist system is subject even on its own terms to a variant of the objection presented by the original Chinese room argument. Imagine that instead of a Chinese room, I have a Chinese gym: a hall containing many monolingual, English-speaking men. These men would carry out the same operations as the nodes and synapses in a connectionist architecture as described by the Churchlands, and the outcome would be the same as having one man manipulate symbols according to a rule book. No one in the gym speaks a word of Chinese, and there is no way for the system as a whole to learn the meanings of any Chinese words. Yet with appropriate adjustments, the system could give the correct answers to Chinese questions.

There are, as I suggested earlier, interesting properties of connectionist nets that enable them to simulate brain processes more accurately than traditional serial architecture does. But the advantages of parallel architecture for weak AI are quite irrelevant to the issues between the Chinese room argument and strong AI.

The Churchlands miss this point when they say that a big enough Chinese gym might have higher-level mental features that emerge from the size and complexity of the system, just as whole brains have mental features that are not had by individual neurons. That is, of course, a possibility, but it has nothing to do with computation. Computationally, serial and parallel systems are equivalent: any computation that can be done in parallel can be done in serial. If the man in the Chinese room is computationally equivalent to both, then if he does not understand Chinese solely by virtue of doing the computations, neither do they. The Churchlands are correct in saying that the original Chinese room argument was designed with traditional AI in mind but wrong in thinking that connectionism is immune to the argument. It applies to any computational system. You can't get semantically loaded thought contents from formal computations alone, whether they are done in serial or in parallel; that is why the Chinese room argument refutes strong AI in any form.

* * *

Many people who are impressed by this argument are nonetheless puzzled about the differences between people and computers. If humans are, at least in a trivial sense, computers, and if humans have a semantics, then why couldn't we give semantics to other computers? Why couldn't we program a Vax or a Cray so that it too would have thoughts and feelings? Or why couldn't some new computer technology overcome the gulf between form and content, between syntax and semantics? What, in fact, are the differences between animal brains and computer systems that enable the Chinese room argument to work against computers but not against brains?

The most obvious difference is that the processes that define something as a computer—computational processes —are completely independent of any reference to a specific type of hardware implementation. One could in principle make a computer out of old beer cans strung together with wires and powered by windmills.

But when it comes to brains, although science is largely ignorant of how brains function to produce mental states, one is struck by the extreme specificity of the anatomy and the physiology. Where some understanding exists of how brain processes produce mental phenomena— for example, pain, thirst, vision, smell —it is clear that specific neurobiological processes are involved. Thirst, at least of certain kinds, is caused by certain types of neuron firings in the hypothalamus, which in turn are caused by the action of a specific peptide, angiotensin II. The causation is from the "bottom up" in the sense that lower-level neuronal processes cause higher-level mental phenomena. Indeed, as far as we know, every "mental" event, ranging from feelings of thirst to thoughts of mathematical theorems and memories of childhood, is caused by specific neurons firing in specific neural architectures.

But why should this specificity matter? After all, neuron firings could be simulated on computers that had a completely different physics and chemistry from that of the brain. The answer is that the brain does not merely instantiate a formal pattern or program (it does that, too), but it also *causes* mental events by virtue of specific neurobiological processes. Brains are specific biological organs, and their spe-

cific biochemical properties enable them to cause consciousness and other sorts of mental phenomena. Computer simulations of brain processes provide models of the formal aspects of these processes. But the simulation should not be confused with duplication. The computational model of mental processes is no more real than the computational model of any other natural phenomenon.

One can imagine a computer simulation of the action of peptides in the hypothalamus that is accurate down to the last synapse. But equally one can imagine a computer simulation of the oxidation of hydrocarbons in a car engine or the action of digestive processes in a stomach when it is digesting pizza. And the simulation is no more the real thing in the case of the brain than it is in the case of the car or the stomach. Barring miracles, you could not run your car by doing a computer simulation of the oxidation of gasoline, and you could not digest pizza by running the program that simulates such digestion. It seems obvious that a simulation of cognition will similarly not produce the effects of the neurobiology of cognition.

All mental phenomena, then, are caused by neurophysiological processes in the brain. Hence,

Axiom 4. Brains cause minds.

In conjunction with my earlier derivation, I immediately derive, trivially,

Conclusion 2. Any other system capable of causing minds would have to have causal powers (at least) equivalent to those of brains.

This is like saying that if an electrical engine is to be able to run a car as fast as a gas engine, it must have (at least) an equivalent power output. This conclusion says nothing about the mechanisms. As a matter of fact, cognition is a biological phenomenon: mental states and processes are caused by brain processes. This does not imply that only a biological system could think, but it does imply that any alternative system, whether made of silicon, beer cans or whatever, would have to have the relevant causal capacities equivalent to those of brains. So now I can derive

> Conclusion 3. Any artifact that produced mental phenomena, any artificial brain, would have to be able to duplicate the specific causal powers of brains, and it could not do that just by running a formal program.

Furthermore, I can derive an important conclusion about human brains:

> Conclusion 4. The way that human brains actually produce mental phenomena cannot be solely by virtue of running a computer program.

* * *

I first presented the Chinese room parable in the pages of *Behavioral and Brain Sciences* in 1980, where it appeared, as is the practice of the journal, along with peer commentary, in this case, 26 commentaries. Frankly, I think the point it makes is rather obvious, but to my surprise the publication was followed by a further flood of objections that—more surprisingly—continues to the present day. The Chinese room argument clearly touched some sensitive nerve.

The thesis of strong AI is that any system whatsoever—whether it is made of beer cans, silicon chips or toilet paper—not only might have thoughts and feelings but *must* have thoughts and feelings, provided only that it implements the right program, with the right inputs and outputs. Now, that is a profoundly antibiological view, and one would think that people in AI would be glad to abandon it. Many of them, especially the younger generation, agree with me, but I am amazed at the number and vehemence of the defenders. Here are some of the common objections.

a. In the Chinese room you really do understand Chinese, even though you don't know it. It is, after all, possible to understand something without knowing that one understands it.

b. You don't understand Chinese, but there is an (unconscious) subsystem in you that does. It is, after all, possible to have unconscious mental states, and there is no reason why your understanding of Chinese should not be wholly unconscious.

c. You don't understand Chinese, but the whole room does. You are like a single neuron in the brain, and just as such a single neuron by itself cannot understand but only contributes to the understanding of the whole system, you don't understand, but the whole system does.

d. Semantics doesn't exist anyway; there is only syntax. It is a kind of prescientific illusion to suppose that there exist in the brain some mysterious "mental contents," "thought processes" or "semantics." All that exists in the brain is the same sort of syntactic symbol manipulation that goes on in computers. Nothing more.

e. You are not really running the computer program—you only think you are. Once you have a conscious agent going through the steps of the program. It ceases to be a case of implementing a program at all.

f. Computers would have semantics and not just syntax if their inputs and outputs were put in appropriate causal relation to the rest of the world. Imagine that we put the computer into a robot, attached television cameras to the robot's head, installed transducers connecting the television messages to the computer and had the computer output operate the robot's arms and legs. Then the whole system would have a semantics.

g. If the program simulated the operation of the brain of a Chinese speaker, then it would understand Chinese. Suppose that we simulated the brain of a Chinese person at the level of neurons. Then surely such a system would understand Chinese as well as any Chinese person's brain.

And so on.

All of these arguments share a common feature: they are all inadequate because they fail to come to grips with the actual Chinese room argument. That argument rests on the distinction between the formal symbol manipulation that is done by the computer and the mental contents biologically produced by the brain, a distinction I have abbreviated—I hope not misleadingly—as the distinction between syntax and semantics. I will not repeat my answers to all of these objections, but it will help to clarify the issues if I explain the weaknesses of the most widely held objection, argument c—what I call the systems reply. (The brain simulator reply, argument g, is another popular one, but I have already addressed that one in the previous section.)

* * *

The systems reply asserts that of course *you* don't understand Chinese but the whole system—you, the room, the rule book, the bushel baskets full of symbols —does. When I first heard this explanation, I asked one of its proponents, "Do you mean the room understands Chinese?" His answer was yes. It is a daring move, but aside from its implausibility, it will not work on purely logical grounds. The point of the original argument was that symbol shuffling by itself does not give any access to the meanings of the symbols. But this is as much true of the whole room as it is of the person inside. One can see this point by extending the thought experiment. Imagine that I memorize the contents of the baskets and the rule book, and I do all the calculations in my head. You can even imagine that I work out in the open. There is nothing in the "system" that is not in me, and since I don't understand Chinese, neither does the system.

The Churchlands in their companion piece produce a variant of the systems reply by imagining an amusing analogy. Suppose that someone said that light could not be electromagnetic because if you shake a bar magnet in a dark room, the system still will not give off visible light. Now, the Churchlands ask, is not the Chinese room argument just like that? Does it not merely say that if you shake Chinese symbols in a semantically dark room, they will not give off the light of Chinese understanding? But just as later investigation showed that light was entirely constituted by electromagnetic radiation, could not later investigation also show that semantics are entirely constituted of syntax? Is this not a question for further scientific investigation?

Arguments from analogy are notoriously weak, because before one can make the argument work, one has to establish that the two cases are truly analogous. And here I think they are not. The account of light in terms of electromagnetic radiation is a causal story right down to the ground. It is a causal account of the physics of electromagnetic radiation. But the analogy with formal symbols fails because formal symbols have no physical, causal powers. The only power that symbols have, qua symbols, is the power to cause the next step in the program when the machine is running. And there is no question of waiting on further research to reveal the physical, causal properties of 0's and 1's. The only relevant properties of 0's and 1's are abstract computational properties, and they are already well known.

The Churchlands complain that I am "begging the question" when I say that uninterpreted formal symbols are not identical to mental contents. Well, I certainly did not spend much time arguing for it, because I take it as a logical truth. As with any logical truth, one can quickly see that it is true, because one gets inconsistencies if one tries to imagine the converse. So let us try it. Suppose that in the Chinese room some undetectable Chinese thinking really is going on. What exactly is supposed to make the manipulation of the syntactic elements into specifically Chinese thought contents? Well, after all, I am assuming that the programmers were Chinese speakers, programming the system to process Chinese information.

Fine. But now imagine that as I am sitting in the Chinese room shuffling the Chinese symbols, I get bored with just shuffling the—to me—meaningless symbols. So, suppose that I decide to interpret the symbols as standing for moves in a chess game. Which semantics is the system giving off now? Is it giving off a Chinese semantics or a chess semantics, or both simultaneously? Suppose there is a third person looking in through the window, and she decides that the symbol manipulations can all be interpreted as stock-market predictions. And so on. There is no limit to the number of semantic interpretations that can be assigned to the symbols because, to repeat, the symbols are purely formal. They have no intrinsic semantics.

Is there any way to rescue the Churchlands' analogy from incoherence? I said above that formal symbols do not have causal properties. But of course the program will always be implemented in some hardware or another, and the hardware will have specific physical, causal powers. And any real computer will give off various phenomena. My computers, for example, give off heat, and they make a humming noise and sometimes crunching sounds. So is there some logically compelling reason why they could not also give off consciousness? No. Scientifically, the idea is out of the question, but it is not something the Chinese room argument is supposed to refute, and it is not something that an adherent of strong AI would wish to defend, because any such giving off would have to derive from the physical features of the implementing medium. But the basic premise of strong AI is that the physical features of the implementing medium are totally irrelevant. What matters are programs, and programs are purely formal.

The Churchlands' analogy between syntax and electromagnetism, then, is confronted with a dilemma; either the syntax is construed purely formally in terms of its abstract mathematical properties, or it is not. If it is, then the analogy breaks down, because syntax so construed has no physical powers and hence no physical, causal powers. If, on the other hand, one is supposed to think in terms of the physics of the implementing medium, then there is indeed an analogy, but it is not one that is relevant to strong AI.

* * *

Because the points I have been making are rather obvious—syntax is not the same as semantics, brain processes cause mental phenomena—the question arises, How did we get into this mess? How could anyone have supposed that a computer simulation of a mental process must be the real thing? After all, the whole point of models is that they contain only certain features of the modeled domain and leave out the rest. No one expects to get wet in a pool filled with Ping-Pong-ball models of water molecules. So why would anyone think a computer model of thought processes would actually think?

Part of the answer is that people have inherited a residue of behaviorist psychological theories of the past generation. The Turing test enshrines the temptation to think that if something behaves as if it had certain mental processes, then it must actually have those mental processes. And this is part of the behaviorists' mistaken assumption that in order to be scientific, psychology must confine its study to externally observable behavior. Paradoxically, this residual behaviorism is tied to a residual dualism. Nobody thinks that a computer simulation of digestion would actually digest anything, but where cognition is concerned, people are willing to believe in such a miracle because they fail to recognize that the mind is just as much a biological phenomenon as digestion. The mind, they suppose, is something formal and abstract, not a part of the wet and slimy stuff in our heads. The polemical literature in AI usually contains attacks on something the authors call dualism, but what they fail to see is that they themselves display dualism in a strong form, for unless one accepts the idea that the mind is completely independent of the brain or of any other physically specific system, one could not possibly hope to create minds just by designing programs.

Historically, scientific developments in the West that have treated humans as just a part of the ordinary physical, biological order have often been opposed by various rearguard actions. Copernicus and Galileo were opposed because they denied that the earth was the center of the universe; Darwin was opposed because he claimed that humans had descended from the lower animals. It is best to see strong AI as one of the last gasps of this antiscientific tradition, for it denies that there is anything essentially physical and biological about the human mind. The mind according to strong AI is independent of the brain. It is a computer program and as such has no essential connection to any specific hardware.

Many people who have doubts about the psychological significance of AI think that computers might be able to understand Chinese and think about numbers but cannot do the crucially human things, namely—and then follows their favorite human specialty—falling in love, having a sense of humor, feeling the angst of postindustrial society under late capitalism, or whatever. But workers in AI complain—correctly—that this is a case of moving the goalposts. As soon as an AI simulation succeeds, it ceases to be of psychological importance. In this debate both sides fail to see the distinction between simulation and duplication. As far as simulation is concerned, there is no difficulty in programming my computer so that it prints out, "I love you, Suzy"; "Ha ha"; or "I am suffering the angst of postindustrial society under late capitalism." The important point is that simulation is not the same as duplication, and that fact holds as much import for thinking about arithmetic as it does for feeling angst. The point is not that the computer gets only to the 40-yard line and not all the way to the goal line. The computer doesn't even get started. It is not playing that game.

POSTSCRIPT

Will It Be Possible to Build a Computer That Can Think?

Science fiction has played with the idea of "thinking machines" for decades, but is this idea nothing but science fiction? Some scientists do not think so, although they are quick to grant that the technology is not yet nearly ready to produce a convincing example. Still, they are trying, at least in restricted subsets of human intelligence such as chess playing. In fact, in February 1996 IBM's "Deep Blue," a chess-playing supercomputer, won and drew games against the human world champion, Garry Kasparov. Although it lost the six-game match, Deep Blue still demonstrated advanced skill at something that most people are willing to call "thinking." Is chess playing a kind of thinking? When the idea of artificial intelligence was new, workers in the field agreed that it was and set out to achieve it. However, even partial success was enough to rouse critics who said that if a machine could do it, it could not be "real" thinking.

Moravec develops his ideas at much greater length in his book *Mind Children* (Harvard University Press, 1988) and in a number of papers. In the book, he focuses on the development of motor and sensory apparatus for robots, forecasts the transfer of human minds into immensely capable machines, and speculates on the replacement of biological intelligence by machine intelligence. He also discusses some of the ideas behind the growing field of "artificial life." Steven Levy, in *Artificial Life* (Pantheon, 1992), expands on this last topic.

Moravec's speculations reach far into the future, culminating in a time when humans will exist as streamlined minds residing in "cyberspace," a world simulated within computers, and when the very definition of "reality" must be changed to encompass the new conditions of human life. For an interesting discussion along the same lines, see Frederick Pohl and Hans Moravec, "Souls in Silicon," *Omni* (November 1993).

Not everyone is willing to go as far as Moravec. Searle's essay presented here was paired in the January 1990 issue of *Scientific American* with Paul M. Churchland and Patricia Smith Churchland's "Could a Machine Think?" According to this article, the authors "reject the Turing test as a sufficient condition for conscious intelligence [because it is] very important... that the right sorts of things be going on inside the artificial machine." Unlike Searle, however, the Churchlands believe that true "artificial intelligence, in a nonbiological but massively parallel machine, remains a compelling and discernible prospect."

Searle is by no means alone in objecting to the idea of the mind as a computer program (also known as "strong AI"). Roger Penrose, a renowned physicist and mathematician at the University of Oxford in England, attacks the idea of strong AI vigorously and at length in *The Emperor's New Mind: Concerning Computers, Minds, and the Laws of Physics* (Penguin Books, 1991) and concludes, "Is it not 'obvious' that mere computation cannot evoke pleasure or pain; that it cannot perceive poetry or the beauty of an evening sky or the magic of sounds; that it cannot hope or love or despair; that it cannot have a genuine autonomous purpose? ... Perhaps when computations become extraordinarily complicated they can begin to take on the more poetic or subjective qualities that we associate with the term 'mind.' Yet it is hard to avoid an uncomfortable feeling that there must always be something missing from such a picture."

PART 4

Risky Business

Many people worry that technology is often accompanied by unexpected—and unfortunate—side effects. Whether a technology is old or new and whether its side effects are old or new, the worry rarely fades away. This concern raises the question of whether society should accept a particular technology at a price—in lives or health or environmental degradation—or reject it.

Such questions arise in many areas. This section begins with an evaluation of risk itself. Then two issues that have aroused many people are considered: genetic engineering and electric power.

- Are Worst-Case Estimates of Risk the Best Method for Making Environmental Decisions?

- Should Genetic Engineering Be Banned?

- Are Electromagnetic Fields Dangerous to Your Health?

ISSUE 12

Are Worst-Case Estimates of Risk the Best Method for Making Environmental Decisions?

YES: Robert Costanza and Laura Cornwell, from "The 4P Approach to Dealing With Scientific Uncertainty," *Environment* (November 1992)

NO: Wendy Cleland-Hamnett, from "The Role of Comparative Risk Analysis," *EPA Journal* (January–March 1993)

ISSUE SUMMARY

YES: Robert Costanza, a professor of environmental studies, and policy analyst Laura Cornwell argue that when uncertainty about potential future damage to health or the environment is high, those who are potentially responsible should be required to post a bond adequate to cover the costs associated with the worst possible results.

NO: Wendy Cleland-Hamnett, the acting deputy assistant administrator for policy, planning, and evaluation at the U.S. Environmental Protection Agency, insists that worst-case scenarios are far too unlikely to be used as the basis for policy.

Science and technology have helped provide the people of the modern world with access to a level of health, wealth, and consumer goods unparalleled in all of human history. Unfortunately, improved health has led to overpopulation, and the industrialization that has provided the wealth and consumer goods has resulted in extensive damage to the environment. In order to progress and to attain prosperity, society continually runs the risk of reducing the quality of life for future generations—possibly even destroying them. Some less sweeping risks to human health and the environment include medications that can have serious side effects; power plants that may pollute the air and aggravate respiratory diseases; and the possibility that the continued use of chlorofluorocarbon aerosol propellants and refrigerants will destroy Earth's protective ozone layer and eventually lead to an epidemic of skin cancer.

Some risks are accepted because they have been around for a long time and people are used to them. New risks are generally found to be more alarming, and in this age of science and technology, society is surrounded by new risks. It is perhaps not too surprising that some people strive to reject such risks, even when they are small or unlikely or when they represent a trade-off against large benefits, simply because they are new. That is, many people do not approach risks realistically. Few people ever worry about the risks associated with population and prosperity. Most commuters rate the risks of driving a car fairly low, despite statistics indicating that far more people die in automobile accidents than (for instance) in airplane crashes. Rare risks, however, such as the chance of having a child with a serious birth defect or of getting cancer from cellular telephones or nuclear power plants, often rouse much greater concerns.

Most people do not seem to evaluate risks according to their odds. Rather, an activity is rated safer if the individual is perceived to be in control (as when driving a car) or if it is chosen voluntarily (as with people who choose to smoke). Activities are considered riskier when the possible damage is severe (such as death). Often, things that are not well understood are considered riskiest of all, no matter what the real dangers may be.

Life carries with it certain unavoidable risks. Some people insist that voluntarily adding any risk at all is intolerable. This is the idea behind the Delaney Clause, which forbids adding to food products any substance shown to cause cancer in any animal at any dose, even if the resulting increase in a consumer's chance of developing cancer is only one in many millions. For a point/counterpoint discussion on the Delaney Clause, see Al Meyerhoff, "Let's Reform a Failed Food Safety Regime," and Clausen Ely, "An Obscure EPA Policy Is to Blame," *EPA Journal* (January/February/March 1993).

One area in which people try to avoid all possible risk—or to hold someone accountable for unfortunate events—is vaccines. At one time, whooping cough, measles, diphtheria, and other childhood diseases killed many thousands of children every year in the United States alone. Vaccines have vastly reduced that toll. The first measles vaccine, for instance, hit the U.S. market in 1963 and within five years reduced the number of cases by 95 percent. Unfortunately, vaccines occasionally have had rare—sometimes fatal—side effects. The resulting lawsuits have led to multimillion-dollar damage awards, and concerns about liability have led many pharmaceutical companies to stop making vaccines, despite the existence of the National Vaccine Injury Compensation Program, a government effort to compensate victims without penalizing manufacturers.

Should society ban vaccines because of their risks? Surely not, for the risks they bear with them are many times less than the risks they avoid. But then, what should society's attitude be toward those risks or toward risk in general? In the following selections, Robert Costanza and Laura Cornwell argue in favor of the "precautionary polluter pays principle," which states that risk producers must pay in advance for the worst possible results of their activities. Wendy Cleland-Hamnett argues that policymakers must be realistic and make decisions based on more likely problems, not on unlikely worst cases.

YES

Robert Costanza and
Laura Cornwell

THE 4P APPROACH TO DEALING WITH SCIENTIFIC UNCERTAINTY

One often sees contradictory stories in the media from "reputable scientific sources" who claim, one day, that "Global warming will occur, and the results will be catastrophic unless something is done immediately," and, on another day, that "There is no direct evidence for global warming, and people should not waste money on something that may or may not happen." On yet another day, one hears that "Toxic chemical X causes cancer," followed on the next day by the statement that "Toxic chemical X occurs in too low a concentration in the environment to cause cancer." These seemingly contradictory statements from the scientific community send the social decisionmaking process into a tailspin. On the one hand, because scientists cannot agree on what is happening, should policymakers wait until better information is available before acting? On the other hand, if society fails to act, the situation may deteriorate rapidly and irreversibly. What are people to do in these all-too-common situations, and why has science failed to provide the certain and unbiased answers on which good policymaking depends? What is wrong with the link between science and policy, and how can it be improved? Is a different, nonregulatory approach needed for managing the environment?

There are several lines of thought in environmental science and economics about how to develop an effective approach to dealing with uncertainty. Two of the most renowned are the "precautionary principle," which has gained wide acceptance in international environmental circles, and the "polluter pays principle," which has long been advocated by environmental economists. Although both of these principles have gained wide acceptance in theory, practical applications have been severely hampered. One criticism is that, "though the precautionary principle provides a useful overall orientation, it is an insufficient basis for policy and largely lacks legal content." Large uncertainties about ecological damages also have caused applications of the polluter pays principle to founder on questions of "how much" and "when." However, an environmental deposit-refund or assurance bonding system could shift the burden of proof, incorporate uncertainty into what the

From Robert Costanza and Laura Cornwell, "The 4P Approach to Dealing With Scientific Uncertainty," *Environment*, vol. 34, no. 9 (November 1992), pp. 12–20. Copyright © 1992 by The Helen Dwight Reid Educational Foundation. Reprinted by permission of Heldref Publications, 1319 18th St., NW, Washington, DC 20036-1802. Notes omitted.

polluters pay for and when they pay it, and thus provide strong and effective economic incentives for both environmental precaution and technological innovation.

SCIENTIFIC UNCERTAINTY

One of the main reasons for the problems with current methods of environmental management is scientific uncertainty—not just its existence, but the radically different expectations and modes of operation that scientists and policymakers have developed to deal with it. To solve this problem, these differences must be exposed and understood, and better methods to incorporate uncertainty into policymaking and environmental management must be designed.

To understand the scope of the problem, it is necessary to differentiate between risk, which is an event with a known probability (sometimes referred to as statistical uncertainty), and true uncertainty, which is an event with an unknown probability (sometimes referred to as indeterminacy). For instance, every time you drive your car, you run the risk of having an accident because the probability of car accidents is known with very high certainty. The risk involved in driving is well known because there have been many car accidents with which to calculate the probabilities. These probabilities are known with enough certainty that they are used by insurance companies, for instance, to set rates that will assure those companies of a certain profit. There is little uncertainty about the possibility of car accidents. If you live near the disposal site of some newly synthesized toxic chemical, however, your health may be in jeopardy, but no one knows to what extent. Because no one knows the proba-

bility of your getting cancer, for instance, or some other disease from this exposure, there is true uncertainty. Most important environmental problems suffer from true uncertainty, not merely risk.

Uncertainty may be thought of as a continuum ranging from zero for certain information to intermediate levels for information with statistical uncertainty and known probabilities (risk) to high levels for information with true uncertainty or indeterminacy. Risk assessment has become a central guiding principle at the U.S. Environmental Protection Agency (EPA) and other environmental management agencies, but true uncertainty has yet to be adequately incorporated into environmental protection strategies.

Scientists treat uncertainty as a given, a characteristic of all information that must be honestly acknowledged and communicated. Over the years, scientists have developed increasingly sophisticated methods to measure and communicate uncertainty arising from various causes. In general, however, scientists have uncovered more uncertainty rather than the absolute precision that the lay public often mistakenly associates with scientific results. Scientific inquiry can only set boundaries on the limits of knowledge. It can define the edges of the envelope of known possibilities, but often the envelope is very large, and the probabilities of what's inside (the known possibilities) actually occurring can be a complete mystery. For instance, scientists can describe the range of uncertainty about global warming and toxic chemicals and maybe say something about the relative probabilities of different outcomes, but, in most important cases, they cannot say which of the possible outcomes will occur with any degree of accuracy.

Current approaches to environmental management and policymaking, however, avoid uncertainty and gravitate to the edges of the scientific envelope. The reasons for this bias are clear. Policymakers want to make unambiguous, defensible decisions, which are often codified into laws and regulations. Although legislative language is often open to interpretation, regulations are much easier to write and enforce if they are stated in absolutely certain terms. For most of criminal law, the system works reasonably well. Either Cain killed his brother or he did not; the only question is whether there is enough evidence to demonstrate guilt beyond a reasonable doubt (with essentially zero uncertainty). Because the burden of proof is on the prosecution, it does little good to conclude that there was an 80-percent chance that Cain killed his brother. But many scientific studies come to just these kinds of conclusions. Science defines the envelope while the policy process gravitates to an edge—usually the edge that best advances the policymaker's political agenda. But to use science rationally to make policy, the whole envelope and all of its contents must be dealt with.

The problem is most severe for environmental regulation. Building on the legal traditions of criminal law, policymakers and environmental regulators desire certain information when designing environmental regulations. But much of environmental policy is based on scientific studies of the likely health, safety, and ecological consequences of human actions. Information gained from these studies is therefore only certain within the studies' epistemological and methodological limits. Regulators are increasingly confronted with decisionmaking outside the limits of scientific certainty, particularly with the recent shift in environmental concerns from visible, known pollution to more subtle threats, such as radon.

Problems arise when regulators ask scientists for answers to unanswerable questions. For example, the law may mandate that the regulatory agency devise safety standards for all known toxins when little or no information is available on the impacts of these chemicals. When trying to enforce the regulations after they are drafted, governments confront the problem of true uncertainty about the impacts. It is usually impossible to determine with any certainty if the local chemical company contributed to the death of some of the people in the vicinity of its toxic waste dump. Similarly, one cannot prove the connection between smoking and lung cancer in any direct, causal way, at least in the legal sense, but only as a statistical relationship. And of course, global warming may or may not happen after all.

Most environmental regulations, particularly those in the United States, demand certainty. When scientists are pressured to supply this nonexistent commodity, there is not only frustration and poor communication but also mixed messages in the media. Because of uncertainty, environmental issues are often manipulated by political and economic interest groups. Uncertainty about global warming is perhaps the most visible current example of this phenomenon.

The precautionary principle describes one theory of how the environmental regulatory community should deal with the problem of true uncertainty. The principle states that, rather than await certainty, regulators should act in anticipation of any potential environmental harm to prevent it. The precautionary principle is so frequently invoked in international environmental resolutions that it has come to be seen by some as a basic normative principle of international environmental law. But the principle offers no guidance as to what precautionary measures should be taken. It "implies the commitment of resources now to safeguard against the potentially adverse future outcomes of some decision" but does not say how many resources should be committed or which adverse future outcomes are most important.

Yet the size of the stakes is a primary determinant of how uncertainty is dealt with in the political arena. Normal applied science applies only under circumstances of low uncertainty and low stakes. Higher uncertainty or higher stakes result in a much more politicized decisionmaking environment. Moderate uncertainty or stakes correspond to "applied engineering" and "professional consultancy," which allow a good measure of judgment and opinion to deal with risk. Currently, however, there is no way to deal with either high stakes or high uncertainty, which require a new approach that could be called "post-normal" or "second-order" science. This "new" science is really just the application of the essence of the scientific method to new territory. The scientific method does not, in its basic form, imply anything about the precision of the results achieved. It does, however, imply a forum of free inquiry, without preconceived answers or agendas, aimed at determining the envelope of knowledge and the magnitude of ignorance.

Implementing second-order science requires a new approach to environmental protection, one that acknowledges the existence of true uncertainty rather than denying it and includes mechanisms to safeguard against potentially harmful effects but, at the same time, encourages the development of low-impact technologies and the reduction of uncertainty about impacts. The precautionary principle sets the stage for this approach, but the real challenge is to develop scientific methods to determine the potential costs of uncertainty and to adjust incentives so that the appropriate parties pay this cost of uncertainty and have appropriate incentives to reduce its detrimental effects. Without this adjustment, the full costs of environmental damage will continue to be left out of the accounting, and the hidden subsidies from society to those who profit from environmental degradation will continue to provide strong incentives to degrade the environment beyond sustainable levels.

DEALING WITH UNCERTAINTY

How should scientists and policymakers deal with the enormous uncertainty inherent in environmental issues? First, uncertainty should be accepted as a basic component of environmental decision-making at all levels and be better communicated. But environmental management should also change, and understanding of the link between ecological and economic systems must grow. Thus, economic and other incentives could be used more efficiently and effectively to achieve environmental goals.

The effort to integrate ecology and economics to improve environmental and economic management and to ensure long-term sustainability has become focused in the transdisciplinary field of ecological economics. This new field promises to permit a deeper understanding of the ecological functions and values that the precautionary principle is intended to protect and the development of more efficient and effective mechanisms to implement the principle. One goal of ecological economics is to estimate the long-term social and ecological costs and benefits of various human activities for comparison with the private short-term costs and benefits that are too often the only consideration in decisionmaking. To do this, the field must develop methods for the valuation of ecological damage based on a second-order scientific understanding of the functioning of linked ecological economic systems at several temporal and spatial scales. This understanding involves developing a description of the envelope of knowledge and the boundaries of ignorance about these interactions. For the purposes of pricing ecological functions and values for use with the precautionary principle, the edge of this envelope that describes the worst-case scenario, as far as ecological impacts are concerned, is the one of primary interest. Research focused on the "worst edge" should lead to much more effective use of science in anticipating and heading off problems.

For example, were worst-edge research the norm, scientists could easily have anticipated the greenhouse effect and taken steps to minimize its potential impacts. Indeed, the effect and humanity's potential impact on it were first described almost 100 years ago, but it remained a scientific curiosity until the 1980s, when enough data and models had been assembled to demonstrate that the effect was, in fact, likely to cause global warming. There is still much uncertainty about the magnitude of the warming and especially about its ultimate impacts, but science can do a very good job of anticipating potential problems if it focuses on that function rather than on demonstrat-

ing impacts that have already occurred. Current research should therefore focus on the worst edge of climatic and economic impacts that might result from releases of greenhouse gases, as well as on the range of uncertainty about these impacts and on ways to reduce the uncertainty.

Over the past two decades, there has been extensive discussion about the efficiency that theoretically can be achieved in environmental management through the use of market mechanisms. These mechanisms are designed to alter the pricing structure of the present market system to incorporate the long-term social and ecological costs of an economic agent's activities. Suggested incentive-based mechanisms include pollution taxes, tradable pollution-discharge permits, financial responsibility requirements, and deposit-refund systems.... Some new versions of these incentive-based alternatives should help policymakers deal in a precautionary way with the pervasive uncertainty inherent in environmental problems.

An innovative incentive-based instrument currently being researched to manage the environment for precaution under uncertainty is called a flexible environmental assurance bonding system. This variation of the deposit-refund system is designed to incorporate both known and uncertain environmental costs into the incentive system and to induce positive environmental technological innovation. It works by charging an economic agent directly for known environmental damages and levying an assurance bond equal to the current best estimate of the largest potential future environmental damages. The bond would be kept in an interest-bearing escrow account for a predetermined length of time.

In keeping with the precautionary principle, this system requires a commitment of resources up front to offset the potentially catastrophic future effects of current activity. Portions of the bond (plus interest) would be returned if and when the agent could demonstrate that the suspected worst-case damages had not occurred or would be less than was originally assessed. If damages did occur, portions of the bond would be used to rehabilitate or repair the environment and possibly to compensate injured parties. Funds tied up in bonds could still be used for other economic activities. The only cost would be the difference (plus or minus) between the interest on the bond and the return that could be earned by the business had it invested in other activities. On average, this difference would be minimal. In addition, the "forced savings" that the bond would require could actually improve overall economic performance in economies like that of the United States that chronically undersave.

By requiring the users of environmental resources to post a bond adequate to cover uncertain future environmental damages (with the possibility for refunds), the burden of proof and the cost of the uncertainty are shifted from the public to the resource user. At the same time, agents are not charged in any final way for uncertain future damages and can recover portions of their bond (with interest) in proportion to how much better their environmental performance is than the predicted worst-case scenario.

Deposit-refund systems are not a new concept; they have been successfully applied to a range of consumer, conservation, and environmental policy objectives. The most well-known examples are the systems for beverage containers and used lubricating oils that have proven to be quite effective and efficient.

Another precedent for environmental assurance bonds are the producer-paid performance bonds often required for federal, state, or local government construction work. For example, the Miller Act (40 U.S.C. 270), a 1935 federal statute, requires contractors performing construction work for the federal government to secure performance bonds. Performance bonds provide a contractual guarantee that the principal (the entity that is doing the work or providing the service) will perform in a designated way. Bonds are frequently required for construction work done in the private sector as well.

Performance bonds are frequently posted in the form of corporate surety bonds. Surety companies, which cosign these bonds, are licensed under various insurance laws and, under their charter, have legal authority to act as a financial guarantee for those posting the bond. The unrecoverable cost of this service is usually from one to five percent of the bond amount. However, under the Miller Act, any contract above a designated amount ($25,000 in the case of construction) can be backed by other types of securities, such as U.S. bonds or notes, in lieu of a bond guaranteed by a surety company. In this case, the contractor provides a duly executed power of attorney and an agreement authorizing collection on the bond or notes if the contractor defaults on the contract. If the contractor performs all of the obligations specified in the contract, the securities are returned to the contractor, and the usual cost of the surety is avoided.

Environmental assurance bonds would work in a similar manner, by providing a contractual guarantee that the principal would perform in an environmentally benign manner, but would be levied according to the best estimate of the largest potential future environmental damages....

The bond would be held until some or all of the uncertainty was removed. This would provide a strong incentive for principals to reduce the uncertainty about their environmental impacts as quickly as possible, either by funding independent research or by changing their processes to ones that are less damaging. The establishment of a quasi-judicial body would be necessary to resolve disputes about when and how much of the bonds should be refunded. This body would use the latest independent scientific information on the worst-case ecological damages that could result from a business's activities, but the burden of proof would fall on the economic agent that stands to gain from the activity, not on the public. EPA already has a protocol for worst-case analysis. In 1977, the U.S. Council on Environmental Quality required worst-case analysis for implementing the National Environmental Policy Act of 1969. This requirement forced EPA to consider the worst environmental consequences of an action when scientific uncertainty was involved.

One potential argument against the bond is that it would favor relatively large businesses that could afford to handle the financial responsibility of activities that are potentially hazardous to the environment. This is true, but it is exactly the desired effect, because businesses that cannot handle the financial responsibility should not be passing the cost of potential environmental damage on to the public. In the construction industry, the use of performance bonds would prevent small fly-by-night businesses from cutting corners and endangering the public to underbid responsible businesses.

This is not to say that small businesses would be eliminated; far from it. They could either band together to form associations to handle the financial responsibility for environmentally risky activities, or, preferably, they could change to more environmentally benign activities that did not require large assurance bonds. This encouragement of the development of new, environmentally benign technologies is one of the main attractions of the bonding system, and small, start-up businesses would certainly lead the way.

APPLYING THE "4P" APPROACH

Strong economic incentives would be provided by the proposed environmental assurance bond to reduce pollution, to research the true costs of environmentally damaging activities, and to develop innovative, cost-effective pollution control technologies. The bonding system extends the polluter pays principle to make the polluter pay for uncertainty as well. Thus is born the "precautionary polluter pays principle" (4P), which would allow a much more proactive approach to environmental problems because the bond would be paid up front, before the damage is done. By unleashing the creative resources of businesses, 4P would foster pollution prevention and the development of new, cleaner technologies (rather than merely cleanup). Because these technologies would be economically attractive in the short run, competition in the marketplace would lead to environmental improvement rather than degradation. The 4P approach would deal more appropriately with scientific uncertainty than do the current command-and-control systems.

The 4P approach has several potential applications. Three of them—growth management, toxic chemicals, and global warming—are high-stakes, high-uncertainty problems for which effective management mechanisms do not currently exist.

Traditional approaches to growth management have centered on zoning and other forms of land-use restrictions. Although the results of planning and zoning are better than totally uncontrolled growth, the approach leaves much to be desired, and one can certainly argue that most planning and zoning have not improved environmental conditions. 4P suggests a flexible impact bond system in addition to regional planning. A developer would post an initial impact bond that is large enough to cover the worst-case environmental and economic impacts of the proposed development. The developer would be refunded portions of the bond to the extent that the possible impacts did not occur. Innovative developers who designed projects with lower environmental impacts would be directly rewarded by refunds of their impact bonds. Developers who defaulted on their bonds would do poorly in economic competition with their more innovative competitors, and their bonds would be used to pay for whatever impacts they caused. Impact fees have been tried before, but, in most cases, they have been flat, inflexible, one-time fees that offered no incentive to developers to produce anything but the standard fare. They also generally covered only a small fraction of the real impacts of the development. A flexible impact bonding system would solve these problems and help manage growth in a rational yet flexible way, without taking the right to develop away but merely imposing the true costs of that growth on the parties that stand to gain from it while providing strong economic incentives for them to reduce their impacts to a minimum.

Another particularly difficult environmental management problem is the control of toxic chemicals from both point sources, such as factories, and nonpoint sources, such as agricultural and urban areas. Toxic chemicals can be damaging to ecosystems and human health in extremely low concentrations, and there is enormous uncertainty about their cumulative and individual impacts. The standard management approach is to develop lists of toxic chemicals and standards for their allowable concentrations in the environment. But because the list is so long (there are thousands of such chemicals in common use) and there is so much uncertainty about setting safe standards—as well as about who is producing and releasing what quantities of which chemicals and how the chemicals interact once they come in contact in the environment—this approach has not been very effective.

4P suggests a flexible toxic chemical bonding system. The bond would be sized according to the best current estimates of the worst-case damages from the release of the chemicals. Refunds would be based on the extent to which each potential polluter performed better than the worst case. This system would give polluters strong incentives to reduce their releases through recycling and more efficient use. Farmers could no longer afford to overuse agricultural chemicals just to be sure they were killing all pests. Industries could no longer afford to release new chemicals with poorly known impacts into the environment. Individual home owners would pay a high price for using potentially dangerous chemicals on their lawns and would be forced to find more environmentally benign alternatives, which, under the bonding system, would be relatively cheaper. This system would be designed to complement other regulatory schemes; would be self-policing and self-funding; and would provide strong incentives to correct environmental problems for which there are few good management alternatives.

Finally, the problem of global warming is probably the most severe current example of a high-stakes, high-uncertainty problem. A tax on carbon dioxide emissions has been proposed as an economic incentive to lessen this problem, but current ideas about the tax do not account for uncertainty. The 4P approach suggests that a bond for carbon dioxide emissions, with the size of the bond based on worst-case estimates of the magnitude of future damages, would work better than a tax, whose size would be based on much more uncertain estimates of what levels of emissions will not produce long-term problems. In this way, the efficiency advantages of economic incentives can be reaped without unduly penalizing current economic agents for the costs of unknown future damages.

There are several other potential applications of 4P. Any situation with large true uncertainty is a likely candidate, and these situations abound in today's world. To deal with these situations, scientific understanding must grow, and approaches to environmental management must change accordingly. Scientists can only define the envelope of ignorance. Given that envelope, policymakers should plan for the worst while providing incentives for firms to produce the best.

NO

Wendy Cleland-Hamnett

THE ROLE OF COMPARATIVE RISK ANALYSIS

EPA's support for using comparative risk analysis to help set the Agency's priorities has been no secret. Building on the lessons and insights gained in the 1988 *Unfinished Business* report, the Science Advisory Board's [SAB's] 1990 *Reducing Risk* report, and our experience in implementing strategic initiatives, we have seen how valuable it can be to have a grasp of the relative risk of various problems in narrowing our focus to the most important ones—especially as fiscal reality has dictated that we must.

Of course, other forces play critically important roles in directing policy, including statutory mandates, traditional considerations of costs and benefits, the state of technology, environmental equity, and, above all, public values and concerns. But comparative risk analysis, and its promise of objective, relevant, and even-handed guidance, has definitely "made it to the table" at EPA. The challenge for the Agency and its stakeholders will be in deciding the precise role it will play in delineating our priorities.

The particular ways we have tried to use relative risk and the conditions under which we operate are not universally understood. Some think risk ranking affects our entire budget, and some think it derives from a backroom dialogue with cloistered scientific gurus. Perhaps most often it is viewed as the only factor we intend to include in our decision making. It is important to note that we have never understood priority setting to be one dimensional, where comparative risk analysis is the last word. In *Reducing Risk*, the SAB made it clear that establishing the relative risks of different environmental problems was only "one tool" that could help make integrated and targeted national environmental policy a reality. It also stressed that the "dichotomy" that exists between the perceptions of the public and the "experts" on which risks are important "presents an enormous challenge to a pluralistic, democratic country."

As good as our intentions have been over the last few years, there is ample room for EPA to do a better job in meeting the challenge of piloting the

From Wendy Cleland-Hamnett, "The Role of Comparative Risk Analysis," *EPA Journal* (January–March 1993).

doctrine of risk through a democratic society. A quotation from Thomas Jefferson provides valuable insight:

> I know of no safe depository of the ultimate powers of the society but the people themselves; and if we think them not enlightened enough to exercise their control with a wholesome discretion, the remedy is not to take it from them, but to inform their discretion.

This piece of wisdom implies, among other things, that a democratic government operates at its peril if it becomes so arrogant that it makes important decisions without informing, involving, and taking guidance from average citizens, and it should never underestimate the citizens' ability to understand. Jefferson is warning us not to lose touch. He is not recommending that all technical decisions of a government agency be made only through town meetings. But his statement is a persuasive argument for broader inclusion of the public in the basic decisions that determine the direction of all the policy minutiae that follows.

It is becoming clearer to those involved in this debate that risk-based decision making should be based on a synthesis of inputs broader and deeper than was envisioned in the past. Risk-based priority setting will be a major element of the kind of informed and effective dialogue that raises the quality of environmental action across the board, especially in the state and federal legislatures. To achieve this, though, we need a more participatory model of prioritization—a risk system much broader than the stereotypical one in which "experts" make their pronouncements about risks with clinical dispassion; one which is an organic part of a broad-based, decision-making process in which equity, social concerns, fiscal feasibility, technological innovation, and legislative mandates are fully considered alongside the science.

To ensure a proper place for comparative risk in developing environmental priorities, we must build the strongest possible foundation of individual risk assessments. I see three basic guiding principles in the building of that foundation. The first involves an early step in the risk assessment process, the characterization of risk. A memorandum on the subject issued in February 1992 provided that EPA needs to offer more useful information when characterizing a given risk—we need to give more accurate predictions than a single point estimate would allow, and we need to evaluate more realistic exposure situations than the unlikely worst-case scenarios sometimes used as the basis for policy. We must characterize individual risks using straightforward, consistent terminology identifying uncertainties and data gaps so that both experts and citizens can more easily compare one risk to another.

This challenge remains enormously important as more attention is focused on the need to take into account both hard science factors and societal elements in the comparison of risks. The question "What is really at stake here?" will need to be answered realistically and usefully, again and again, in terms that all can understand.

The second guiding principle is the need to bring varied expertise into the risk assessment process from the earliest stage. Our work in relative risk stands much less chance of acceptance if the common perception persists that assessments of specific risks emerge from a black box. Therefore, just as the whole enterprise of priority setting needs to be broadly inclusive, the work

TWO FACES OF RISK

The terms *risk assessment* and *comparative risk analysis* are sometimes confused. Actually, they have very different meanings.

Risk assessment, which in rudimentary form, at least, is older than EPA itself, is a complex process by which scientists determine the harm that an individual substance can inflict on human health or the environment. For human health risk assessment, the process takes place in a series of steps that begins by identifying the particular hazard(s) of the substance. Subsequent steps examine "dose-response" patterns and human exposure considerations, and the conclusion is a "risk characterization" that is both quantitative and qualitative. The risk characterization then becomes one of the factors considered in deciding whether and how the substance will be regulated.

Risk assessments are not infallible. For one thing, information on the effects of small amounts of a substance in the environment is often not available, and data from animal experiments must be extrapolated to humans. Such extrapolations cannot be made with absolute certainty.... [C]onsiderable research is being focused on improving the risk assessment process.

Unlike risk assessment, which for years has provided regulators the basis for deciding whether or not an individual substance needs to be controlled, **comparative risk analysis** and its derivative relative risk have arrived on the scene only recently. Very simply described, comparative risk analysis is a procedure for ranking environmental problems by their seriousness (relative risk) for the purpose of assigning them program priorities. Typically, teams of experts put together a list of problems then sort the problems by types of risk—cancer, noncancer health, materials damage, ecological effects, and so on. The experts rank the problems within each type by measuring them against such standards as the severity of effects, the likelihood of the problem occurring among those exposed, the number of people exposed, and the like. The relative risk of a problem is then used as a factor in determining what priority the problem should receive. Other factors include statutory mandates, public concern over the problem, and the economic and technological feasibility of controlling it.

Not unexpectedly, comparative risk analysis has its critics. As one skeptic asked in the pages of *EPA Journal* two years ago: "How does one compare a case of lung cancer in a retired petrochemical worker to the loss of cognitive function experienced by an urban child with lead poisoning? How do we make choices between habitat and health?" Nonetheless, in its September

Box continued on next page.

1990 report *Reducing Risk*, EPA's Science Advisory Board urged the Agency to order its priorities on the basis of reducing the most serious risks. The board argued, in part: "... There are heavy costs involved if society fails to set environmental priorities based on risk. If finite resources are expended on lower priority problems at the expense of higher priority risks, then society will face needlessly high risks. If priorities are established based on the greatest opportunities to reduce risk, total risk will be reduced in a more efficient way, lessening threats to both public health and local and global ecosystems...."

—Eds [of *EPA Journal*]

of our Agency professionals in working through the important issues of specific risks needs to be exposed to the critical eye of independent experts, peers, and colleagues in their fields. This both enhances the quality of the work and maximizes the number of people who understand what the work attempts to accomplish.

The Agency's existing peer review process should be expanded as far as possible into the earliest segments of the life cycle of our risk-related work, and active peer involvement in the characterization and assessment of individual risks should become standard procedure. We are implementing the recommendations made by the SAB and an independent panel in the March 1992 report *Credible Science, Credible Decisions* by establishing science advisors for the Administrator and Assistant Administrators, and I hope future administrations build on this collegial network.

We have also participated extensively in interagency organizations such as the Risk Assessment Working Group of the Federal Coordinating Council on Science Engineering and Technology (FCCSET), mindful that cross-pollinating expertise and real coordination on cross-cutting issues with other parts of the government can improve the quality of our work. This cooperation must continue and must extend not only to specific risk assessments but also to the important guidelines that are establishing the state of the art in process and methods for cancer, noncancer, and ecological risk end points.

The third guiding principle we must observe in building a foundation of credible risk assessment is the need for basic research and state-of-the-environment data. One of the most fundamental reasons for the controversy surrounding the uses of relative risk is the persistent belief that our risk assessments are based on default assumptions rather than on hard facts. Simply put, facts and hard conclusions from data are better than estimates based on extrapolations and interpolations. Facts are what our research operations must give our risk assessors if their work is to have dependable credibility at the priority-setting table. These facts can then be brought to life through advanced computer visualizations in geographic information systems, which will allow us to target risks and develop more meaningful geographic strategies.

Even if these principles are followed and our risk assessments become more widely accepted, there will remain major legislative barriers to the widespread use of relative risk, which makes it imperative that Congress be an integral part of the dialogue. As it stands now, EPA policy makers implementing risk-based priority setting can have an impact only at the margins of funding. The two funds set up for construction of wastewater treatment plants and the cleanup of abandoned hazardous waste sites under Superfund dwarf all other EPA spending areas, accounting in fiscal year (FY) 1990 for over 70 percent of the Agency's $6 billion budget. Only 16 percent of the full budget is allocated toward the higher risk areas identified by the SAB in *Reducing Risk*. In FY 1992, for example, indoor radon, indoor air, stratospheric ozone, and climate change accounted for a little more than 2 percent of our total budget, although they were listed by the SAB as high risk.

Adding to the pressure is spending for congressional projects: In FY 1993, Congress added about 100 specific items while approving an essentially flat budget from FY 1992. These new responsibilities have to be met at the expense of both existing Agency priorities and new initiatives. To be sure, there is not always a direct correlation between funding levels and results—[some] EPA programs... prove that rich results can be achieved through small budgetary investments. These budgetary facts do indicate, however, that comparative risk has a long way to go before it becomes a dominant element of priority setting at EPA.

Nevertheless, there are a number of things going on within EPA to prepare the way for a more inclusive and more credible role for comparative risk in pri-ority setting. The current dioxin reassessment..., sparked by net findings on the mechanisms of dioxin toxicity, has been widely praised as evidence that the Agency will practice what it preaches concerning dedication to good science and meaningful risk assessment, and has involved both extensive peer review and public participation. Agency professionals used the techniques of inclusion in the development of the forthcoming neurotoxicity and immunotoxicity guidelines, and EPA demonstrated its willingness to reach out to peers outside the Agency by involving a professional association; the Society for Risk Analysis, in issues associated with the cancer risk-assessment guidelines.

Successful development of an inclusive system of risk assessment at EPA in the future will require sustained attention to some very ambitious and large-scale initiatives. The principles in the February 1992 memorandum on risk characterization must be fully implemented. Development of information for EPA's computerized health risk-assessment database—the Integrated Risk Information System, or IRIS—is currently subject to very little peer review or public involvement, and this vulnerability must be addressed if we are to bring the credibility of the information up to par with the influence that this very important database has developed since it became public in 1988.

The Environmental Monitoring and Assessment Program, or EMAP, is a centerpiece of the Agency's enhanced focus on risks to the ecological health of regions and ecosystems. Yet the massive amounts of information gained from the environmental indicators it monitors form so broad a cut of cloth that there is a real challenge to link this information to new, concrete understandings about risk, and then to develop indicators that measure the progress of our prevention programs. And, in the wake of the June 1992 United Nations Conference on Environment and Development in Rio de Janeiro, risk assessment will necessarily be an international issue as well, and the Agency will have a direct stake in the attempt to build upon the work of the U.N.'s Organization for Economic Cooperation and Development in coordinating risk assessment activities by scientists and governments around the globe.

Government cannot do everything, and the question of which things matter the most is inevitable. Environmental decision making in a democracy is not a math problem. As a result, comparative risk will never be the only criterion for setting priorities. But if EPA's findings are built upon a foundation of good science and the public is fully informed and involved in the dialogue, then comparative risk will be an increasingly important factor. By building integrated strategies based upon solid facts, and by harnessing the power of communities and markets, I am absolutely confident EPA can stimulate entire new generations of clean production and give new expression to the concept of "sustainable development."

POSTSCRIPT

Are Worst-Case Estimates of Risk the Best Method for Making Environmental Decisions?

Many people involved in negotiating public acceptance of new technological ventures say that reducing ignorance or uncertainty is more useful than Costanza and Cornwell's "precautionary polluter pays principle." William J. Madia, in "Making the Right Choices," *Vital Speeches of the Day* (May 15, 1993), argues that education—informing the public about the nature of a venture and its genuine associated risks—tends to reduce fears.

Many others agree that education is crucial. The Institute of Electrical and Electronic Engineers (IEEE) even includes in its code of ethics the pledge that IEEE members will "improve the understanding of technology, its appropriate application, and potential consequences." See Joseph R. Herkert, "Ethical Risk Assessment: Valuing Public Perceptions," *IEEE Technology and Society Magazine* (Spring 1994).

Public perceptions of risk remain an important aspect of risk-as-issue, and most analysts agree that the public has a right to consent to the risks it confronts. Public information efforts are therefore an essential part of all modern risk management programs. To support such efforts, the Environmental Protection Agency publishes reports such as Dorothy E. Patton's "The ABCs of Risk Assessment," *EPA Journal* (January/February/March 1993) and encourages states to identify their most pressing risks. In California, the result of this encouragement was a 600-page report, *Toward the Twenty-First Century: Planning for the Protection of California's Environment*, released in 1994. Five other states have prepared similar reports; 15 have such reports in the works; and 11 are planning them. See Richard Stone, "California Report Sets Standard for Comparing Risks," *Science* (October 14, 1994).

Even given adequate efforts to provide information to the public, technological efforts are plagued by the negative public reactions captured in the acronyms NIMBY (Not In My Back Yard), NIMTOF (Not In My Term Of Office), and BANANA (Build Absolutely Nothing Anywhere Near Anything). Yet M. Granger Morgan, in "Risk Analysis and Management," *Scientific American* (July 1993), argues, "If anyone should be faulted for the poor quality of responses to risk, it is probably not the public but rather risk managers in government and industry."

Two Internet sites of interest to those who wish to know more about risk are: http://www.hampshire.org/risk01.htm and http://mijuno.larc.nasa.gov/dfc/rsk.html.

ISSUE 13

Should Genetic Engineering Be Banned?

YES: Andrew Kimbrell, from *The Human Body Shop: The Engineering and Marketing of Life* (HarperSanFrancisco, 1993)

NO: James Hughes, from "Embracing Change With All Four Arms: A Post-Humanist Defense of Genetic Engineering," *Paper Presented at the University of Chicago Health and Society Workshop* (May 6, 1994)

ISSUE SUMMARY

YES: Andrew Kimbrell, policy director of the Foundation on Economic Trends in Washington, D.C., argues that the development of genetic engineering is so marked by scandal, ambition, and moral blindness that society should be deeply suspicious of its purported benefits.

NO: James Hughes, assistant director of research at the MacLean Center for Clinical Medical Ethics in the Department of Medicine at the University of Chicago, argues that the potential benefits of genetic engineering greatly outweigh the potential risks.

In the early 1970s scientists first discovered that it was technically possible to move genes—biological material that determines a living organism's physical makeup—from one organism to another and thus (in principle) to give bacteria, plants, and animals new features and to correct genetic defects of the sort that cause many diseases, such as cystic fibrosis. Most researchers in molecular genetics were excited by the potentialities that suddenly seemed within their grasp. However, a few researchers—as well as many people outside the field—were disturbed by the idea; they thought that genetic mix-and-match games might spawn new diseases, weeds, and pests. Some people even argued that genetic engineering should be banned at the outset, before unforeseeable horrors were unleashed.

Researchers in support of genetic experimentation responded by declaring a moratorium on their own work until suitable safeguards could be devised. Once those safeguards were in place in the form of government regulations, work resumed. Before long, it became clear that the hazards were less than had been feared, although the benefits were going to take years of hard work to achieve. James D. Watson and John Tooze document the early years of this research in *The DNA Story: A Documentary History of Gene Cloning* (W. H. Freeman, 1981). For a shorter, more recent review of the story, see Bernard D.

Davis, "Genetic Engineering: The Making of Monsters?" *The Public Interest* (Winter 1993).

By 1989 the technology had developed tremendously: researchers could obtain patents for mice with artificially added genes ("transgenic" mice); firefly genes had been added to tobacco plants to make them glow (faintly) in the dark; and growth hormone produced by genetically engineered bacteria was being used to grow low-fat pork and increase milk production by cows. While these developments were being made, a storm of protest was gathering strength. Critics argued that genetic engineering was unnatural and violated the rights of both plants and animals to their "species integrity"; that expensive, high-tech, tinkered animals gave the competitive advantage to big agricultural corporations and drove small farmers out of business; and that putting human genes into animals, plants, or bacteria was downright offensive. See Betsy Hanson and Dorothy Nelkin, "Public Responses to Genetic Engineering," *Society* (November/December 1989).

By 1990 the first proposals to add genes to *human* cells in order to restore normal function were being made (Inder M. Verma, "Gene Therapy," *Scientific American,* November 1990). Not long after that, the first gene therapy attempts were approved by the National Institutes of Health (NIH), despite objections that altering a human being's genes meant violating that person's nature and identity at the deepest possible level. To avoid producing genetic changes that would be passed on to future generations, which cannot consent to the changes, researchers have been restricted to modifying only somatic (body) cells, not germ cells (sperm and eggs). Still, in 1994 Mark A. Findeis, a group leader at OsteoArthritis Sciences in Cambridge, Massachusetts, described numerous genetic therapies under development in "Genes to the Rescue," *Technology Review* (April 1994).

Anti-genetic-engineering activist Jeremy Rifkin, president of the Foundation on Economic Trends in Washington, D.C., has stressed that because we do not know the future undesirable side effects of genetic engineering, and because those side effects may be horrible, we should reject the technology. In the following selections, Andrew Kimbrell echoes this alarmist view of genetic engineering and argues that its history is so marked by scandal, ambition, and moral blindness that it poses an exceedingly disturbing precedent for the future.

James Hughes, representing the voice of optimism, argues that genetic engineering offers "such good that the risks are dwarfed" and finds "faith in the potential unlimited improvability of human nature and expansion of human powers far more satisfying than a resignation to our current limits."

YES

ENGINEERING OURSELVES

In an age of protests, this was the first of its kind. It was early March 1977, and hundreds of demonstrators had flocked to the futuristic, domed auditorium of the National Academy of Sciences (NAS). The protesters chanted slogans such as "We will not be cloned," and they carried signs bearing warnings, including "Don't Tread on My Genes."

The object of the protest was a three-day symposium being held under the auspices of the NAS. The forum was intended to bring together scientists, government officials, and business leaders to discuss the future prospects of genetically altering life-forms, including humans. The chairman of the meeting, Dr. David Hamburg, president of the NAS Institute for Medicine, undoubtedly had anticipated that this would be the usual scientific conference, a collegial discussion of current scientific and legislative issues that had been cropping up as a result of advances in genetic manipulation. It was not to be.

The demonstrators, led by activist Jeremy Rifkin, crowded the auditorium with their signs and dominated the session with their chants and shouted questions to the symposium's panels. They relentlessly prodded the scientists and bureaucrats, urging them to confront the moral and ethical implications of engineering the genetic code of life. They also repeatedly demanded that speakers disclose who was financing their research. (The forum was supported in part by funds from a variety of drug manufacturers.) Finally, under a barrage of questions about the eugenic [breed- or race-improving] and discriminatory potential of biotechnology, the chairman had no choice but to offer the podium to Rifkin and others to air their concerns.

Speaking up with the protesters were many prominent scientists. At a press conference prior to the demonstration, Nobel Prize winner George Wald called the use of genetic engineering "the biggest break in nature that has occurred in human history." Renowned biochemist Dr. Erwin Chargoff warned against the use of genetic research to attempt to control the evolution of humans and other life-forms.

The activists and scientists who voiced their concerns that day were part of a growing chorus of those who feared the engineering of life. As early as

From Andrew Kimbrell, *The Human Body Shop: The Engineering and Marketing of Life* (HarperSanFrancisco, 1993). Copyright © 1993 by Andrew Kimbrell. Reprinted by permission of HarperCollins Publishers, Inc. Notes omitted.

1967, Marshall Nirenberg, the Nobelist who first described the "language" of the genetic code, had delivered a stern lecture about engineering human beings, along with a remarkably prescient prophecy:

> My guess is that cells will be programmed with synthetic messages within 25 years.... The point that deserves special emphasis is that man may be able to program his own cells long before he will be able to assess adequately the long-term consequences of such alterations, long before he will be able to formulate goals, and long before he can resolve the ethical and moral problems which will be raised.

The fears of the early gene engineering critics focused on proposals to engineer the human germline—to permanently alter the genetic makeup of an individual that is passed on to succeeding generations. Many scientists were predicting that, by manipulating the genes in sperm, eggs, or embryos, future physicians would be able to excise "bad" genes from the human gene pool. Critics envisioned a future human body shop industry in eliminating the genes responsible for sickle-cell anemia or cystic fibrosis by mass engineering of these "problem" genes from the sex cells (the sperm and ova) of individuals. Future genetic engineers could also add foreign genes to a patient's genome, genes from other humans or even different species. These genes might protect an individual from various diseases, or confer desired qualities like better looks or brains. Ultimately, they believed that as scientists learned more about the relationship of genes to disease and other human traits, there would be an inevitable push to treat life-forms as so many machines whose working parts, genes, could be engineered or replaced if they were "defective."

Moreover, it was clear that if the genetic engineering of human beings should come, and most believed it would, there would be a quantum leap in both negative and positive eugenics. No longer would it be necessary to attempt to carefully control generations of breeding to create "good" characteristics, or to resort to sterilization, abortion, or genocide in order to remove abnormal or undesirable traits. Individuals could be altered through genetic surgery that would repair or replace bad genes and add good ones. Nobel Prize winner Jean Rostand's early visions of the eugenic potential of gene engineering went even further: "It would be no more than a game for the 'man farming biologist' to change the subject's sex, the colour of his eyes, the general proportions of body and limbs and perhaps the facial features." Many agreed with scientists such as Wald and Chargoff that the genetic alteration of people could eventually change the course of evolution. In 1972, ethicist Dr. Leon Kass wrote, "The new technologies for human engineering may well be 'the transition to a wholly new path of evolution.' They may therefore mark the end of *human* life as we and all other humans know it."

For over two decades, scientists, activists, ethicists, and the media have engaged in the debate over the medical and moral questions surrounding the germline genetic engineering of human beings. Editorials have appeared with headlines questioning "Whether to Make Perfect Humans" and how to arrive at "The Rules for Reshaping Life." Many critics have continued to argue against the entire enterprise of "the remaking of man." They question the wisdom of having scientists decide which part of the human genome should be eliminated and which enhanced. And if not scientists, who, they ask, will determine which human genes are bad and which good? They warn that even supposedly "bad" genes may bring extraordinary benefits to humanity. Recently, it was discovered that cystic fibrosis genes appear to provide individuals with protection from melanoma, an increasingly common form of skin cancer. Research conducted in the 1980s determined that sickle-cell anemia genes appear to help provide individuals with immunity to malaria. Excising such genes from the human gene pool in the effort to eliminate human disease could backfire with potentially catastrophic results.

There is also the question of how and when society will ensure that the powerful technology of germline gene engineering will be limited to the treatment of serious human diseases.... [G]enetic screening of embryos is already being used for eugenic purposes, including sex selection; and genetically engineered drugs are being used for cosmetic purposes in a way that helps foster certain forms of discrimination. Who will ensure that germline therapy is not abused in the same discriminatory and eugenic way? Will those with under normal height or I.Q. become key targets of the future entrepreneurs of germline therapy? Other novel legal questions arise from the prospect of germline therapy, issues similar to those being asked in reference to advances in prenatal genetic screening. Do children have the right to an unmanipulated germline? Or, conversely, do they have a right to the best germline that genetic surgery can offer and money can buy?

As the debate around germline gene therapy continues, another form of human genetic engineering has already begun. This form of genetic manipulation does not involve sex cells, but rather those cells that do not partake in reproduction. These cells are called *somatic cells*. Engineering these cells is both easier and far less controversial than attempting to manipulate germ cells. Altering somatic cells triggers far less concern about eugenics, in that the cells being repaired or added affect only the single individual being engineered. They do not affect the inheritance of genetic traits. Early uses of somatic cell engineering include providing individuals with healthy or repaired genes that might replace those that are faulty and causing disease.

Though somatic cell gene therapy does not affect the genetic inheritance of future generations, there are still fears. Will individuals with "poor" genetic readouts —those predisposed to a variety of disorders or abnormal traits—be under pressure by parents, education providers, insurance companies, and employers to undergo gene therapy to remove their "bad" genes? Will the therapy be used "cosmetically" to add or eliminate nondisease traits, such as growth, skin color, or intelligence? Will victims of discrimination be pressured by societal prejudice to alter in themselves those traits society views as negative?

The early concerns about germline and somatic cell genetic engineering relied primarily on future projections of the potential abuse of the technology. However, two early cases involving misuse of gene therapy contributed significantly to the controversy that marked the early years of experimentation on the genetic manipulation of humans. The first scandal involving the nascent technology happened over two decades ago.

[In the next section of the original source, which is not reprinted here, Kimbrell discusses two instances of early gene therapy experimentation, one in 1970 and one in 1980, that were considered unethical because of the scientists' seeming lack of regard for the treated patients. The first case, which involved Dr. Stanfield Rogers, led to the first proposed legislation on genetic engineering and eventually provoked the National Institutes of Health (NIH) to produce guidelines regulating the use of human gene engineering. The later case, which involved Dr. Martin Cline of the University of California, also contributed to a promulgation of legislative and regulatory action on human gene engineering, including the establishment of a White House commission led by ethicist Alexander Morgan Capron and of the Biomedical Ethics Review Board to explore the ethical implications of human gene technology.—Ed.]

Throughout the 1980s, the criticisms of gene therapy continued. In 1983, Jeremy Rifkin organized a religious and scientific coalition against the use of genetic engineering on humans. The coalition and its signed statement opposing germline engineering were front-page stories around the United States. Unlike Capron's commission, the coalition's resolution on germline therapy was unambiguous: "Resolved, the efforts to engineer specific genetic traits into the germline of the human species should not be attempted." Its logic on prohibiting heritable gene alterations was also straightforward: "No individual, group of individuals, or institutions can legitimately claim the right or authority to make such decision on behalf of the rest of the species alive today or for future generations." The resolution, which was presented to Congress, was signed by a remarkable variety of religious leaders, including mainstream Jewish, Catholic, and Protestant religious organizations, as well as by many prominent scientists.

Six years later, an important and detailed religious statement on biotechnology was issued by the World Council of Churches (WCC). It contained a strong policy statement calling on all churches to support a "ban on experiments involving the genetic engineering of the human germline." The WCC was also deeply concerned about somatic cell gene experiments. The report called upon member churches to urge "strict control on experiments involving genetically engineered somatic cells, drawing attention to the potential misuse of... [this technique] against those held to be 'defective.'" The timing of the WCC statement could not have been more pertinent, for 1989 was to be the year that the age of human genetic engineering officially began.

PLAYING GOD?

On January 30, 1989, almost twelve years after the first demonstration on human genetic engineering, another such protest took place. The protesters came to a meeting of the National Institutes of Health Recombinant DNA Advisory Committee (RAC). Since publishing its guidelines in 1976, RAC had met dozens of times to discuss and approve experiments in genetic engineering. The advisory committee, composed mainly of scientists, held meetings that were usually staid affairs replete with lengthy discussion of arcane data and procedures.

This RAC meeting was like no other. There, demanding to be heard by the NIH scientists and genetic engineers, were fifteen of the nation's most prominent leaders in disability rights, many themselves suffering from disabilities. Additionally, several biotechnology activists were present to demand accountability of the scientists on the RAC. Many of the scientists appeared visibly uncomfortable at the prospect of discussing human gene engineering with people concerned about a new age of eugenics—and all under the unaccustomed glare of TV cameras. Those present knew that they were at a historic moment in the genetic engineering revolution, for this RAC meeting had as an agenda item discussion of approval for the world's first legally sanctioned genetic engineering experiment on humans.

The experiment involved genetic engineering but was not intended to be a cure. Researchers wished to insert novel genetic "markers" into certain immune cells taken from the bodies of terminally ill cancer patients, and then transfuse those cells back into the patients. With the help of the markers, they hoped to track which cells were working effectively and which were not. The procedure was to be carried out by the NIH's prime genetic engineering team of Drs. French Anderson, Steven A. Rosenberg, and Michael Blaese.

Minutes after RAC chairman Dr. Gerard J. McGarrity called the meeting to order, critics began to express deep concern that the NIH had begun the historic process of approving human gene engineering protocols while still doing nothing to put in place a review process on the ethical and legal implications of human genetic alteration. Jeremy Rifkin announced that his Foundation on Economic Trends had filed suit that morning, calling on a federal court to halt the experiment until the NIH committed itself to allowing the public a greater voice in decisions on gene therapy. Rifkin also noted that the lawsuit was based on the fact that the historic experiment was approved by a secret mail ballot, the first in RAC's history. He repeated the concerns he and other demonstrators had expressed over a decade before: "Genetic engineering raises unparalleled ethical and social questions for the human race. They cannot be ignored by the NIH. If we are not careful we will find ourselves in a world where the disabled, minorities, and workers will be genetically engineered." Another protesting voice at the meeting was Evan Kemp, then Commissioner of the Equal Opportunity Commission (EEOC), and himself disabled:

> The terror and risk that genetic engineering holds for those of us with disabilities are well grounded in recent events.... Our society seem to have an aversion to those who are physically and mentally different. Genetic engineering could lead to the elimination of the rich diversity in our peoples. It is a real and frightening threat.

Those present asked the RAC to set up an outside review board for human genetic engineering experiments that would include experts in the rights of minorities, workers, and the disabled. They insisted that the RAC scientists, though astute on advances in genetics, were no experts in the public policy implications of their work. "This group cannot play God when it comes to deciding what genes should be engineered in and out of individual patients," Rifkin said during heated arguments with members of the committee. "What will be the criteria for good or bad genes? Who will decide what genes, and which people, will be engineered?" he continued. "The people in this room are just not qualified to raise these monumental social issues. You're just not going to be able to maintain that control of power within a small group. We need to broaden this group." A few members of the RAC board became belligerent, denying, sometimes angrily, the suggestion that they lacked the expertise to oversee the larger social and political implications of their work. Others simply ignored the proposal. When the vote came, the RAC board unanimously (twenty in favor, three abstentions) turned down the proposal to set up a public policy review committee.

The RAC critics lost the NIH vote, but they won the battle in court. On May 6, the NIH settled the law case filed against the NIH, agreeing to immediately make changes in the RAC guidelines that would forbid mail or secret ballots and would also provide more review for gene therapy experiments. The legal settlement cleared the way for the first legally sanctioned gene engineering experiment on humans. The gene "marker" experiment took place a few days later, on May 22, 1989.

CLAIMING IMMUNITY

The second gene experiment on humans was performed just over a year after the first. It was the first official attempt to use somatic cell human gene engineering as a therapy for disease. On September 14, 1990, a four-year-old girl from Cleveland with the immune disorder popularly known as the "bubble boy syndrome" was injected with a billion cells into which a new gene had been inserted. The girl was born without the gene that controls successful functioning of certain immune cells called T lymphocytes. The rare condition (it affects only about twenty children worldwide), known as adenosine deaminase (ADA) deficiency, leaves victims helpless in the face of disease and infection. Many children suffering from ADA deficiency have been kept alive by isolating them in a germ-free capsule, as was "David," the famous "Boy in the Bubble" at Baylor College of Medicine in Houston, Texas.

Dr. French Anderson and a team at NIH intravenously infused the child with blood cells containing the missing ADA gene in hope that it would help her recover normal functioning of her immune system. On the surface the medical procedure looked little different from a normal blood transfusion. The procedure, which took place in the Pediatric Intensive Care Unit of the Clinical Center of NIH, in Bethesda, Maryland, lasted twenty-eight minutes. One hour later the young patient was wandering around the hospital playroom, eating M&Ms.

The young girl who had become the first human gene therapy patient to be legally engineered with human genes became something of a celebrity, as did Dr. Anderson. The media reported the historic occasion in glowing terms. Soon reporters were writing about "Dr. Anderson's Gene Machine." After some initial reports of success, it was not uncommon to hear that genetic engineering had cured the "bubble boy syndrome." A second patient began gene treatment in January 1991. It was hard to imagine a more altruistic beginning for a technological development that so many had feared as the beginning of a new eugenic movement.

The experiment had its dark side, however, including some unfortunate parallels with Rogers's scandalous experiments on children in the early 1970s. A careful examination revealed that Anderson's procedure may have been more hype than cure. The "bubble boy syndrome" cases were now a misnomer:

None of the handful of existent cases required the bubble to protect the immunologically impaired children from disease. Since the mid-1980s, these children were being adequately treated with a new drug therapy. Anderson, however, had started his research into ADA before the drug therapy was available. Many felt that he continued on with his protocol more out of stubbornness and ambition than medical necessity. Months before the experiment took place, members of the Human Genome Subcommittee had openly questioned Anderson on the rationale for subjecting children to the risks of gene therapy when they were already being treated successfully. So concerned were the RAC members about the effectiveness of Anderson's therapy that they restricted Anderson and his team to working only with patients who were already receiving the drug therapy. This in turn led to the question of how Anderson could accurately assess the results of his experiment. One scientist noted that it would be a little like attempting to assess the results of aspirin on a patient who was being treated with antibiotics.

Whether or not Anderson is using his patients as gene therapy guinea pigs, his experiments appear to violate the general bioethical rule that the expected benefits to an individual from an experimental therapy should equal or exceed the potential harm. The experiment's protocol was clear. The procedure did not offer children suffering from the genetic disorder a cure, but merely a supplemental therapy. The beneficial results of the experiment are at best marginal. A cure awaits improvements in bone marrow transplantation.

By contrast, the dangers to children from Anderson's experiment could be quite real. Anderson and others involved in inserting genes into patients use animal retroviruses to carry those genes. The retrovirus used in all early gene therapy experiments, including the ADA experiment, is one called murine leukemia virus (MuLV). It is a retrovirus obtained from mice. Anderson engineers the ADA gene into the retrovirus and then injects the gene package into a patient. Once inside the patient, the retrovirus invades cells and drops off the genes. Genetic engineers like Anderson attempt to render these carrier retroviruses harmless, but there are still concerns that these viruses could cause cancer or other serious disease in patients. Except in the case of Anderson's ADA experiments, MuLV had only been approved for use in terminally ill patients in whom the retrovirus could do little additional harm. Yet Anderson used this suspect retrovirus on children who were living relatively normal lives with potentially long life spans ahead of them.

In December 1991, less than a year after Anderson began genetically engineering his second patient, an unsettling report was made public. A researcher, Arthur Nienhaus, described his discovery that the MuLV virus had caused cancer in primate. The researcher suspects that the cancer may have been caused by a contaminant that leaked into the virus during production. Anderson and others were quick to note that they used a different system to produce their MuLV, one less prone to contamination. However, the discovery bolsters the view that much more needs to be learned before MuLV is widely used as a gene therapy tool.

In a rare demonstration of scientific breaking of ranks, several fellow genetic engineers openly expressed their displeasure with the Anderson experiment. One gene therapy expert called the Anderson procedures "absolutely crazy." Dr. Arthur Bank, professor of medicine and human genetics at Columbia University, charged that gene therapy researchers at NIH were driven by ambition and not by good science. "The main impetus [for the ADA experiment] is the need for French Anderson to be the first to do gene therapy in man.... This may turn out to be bad news for all of us," Bank told a genetics conference within a week after the experiment had started. Dr. Stuart Orkin, professor of pediatric medicine at Harvard Medical School, noted, "A large number of scientists believe the experiment is not well founded scientifically.... I'm quite surprised that there hasn't been more of an outcry against the experiment by scientists who are completely objective." Dr. Richard Mulligan, a pioneer in gene therapy work and a member of the RAC board—the only one who voted against the experiment—was more direct. "If I had a daughter, no way I'd let her get near these guys if she had that defect."

Anderson has more than his experiments to defend. Critics of the approvals of the first gene therapy experiments also point out that over a five-year period, Anderson has almost singlehandedly pioneered delivering federally funded human gene engineering research to a private company with which he is a collaborator. In 1987, Anderson did what many viewed as "scientifically unthinkable" when he joined forces with venture capitalist Wallace Steinberg to help build a human gene engineering company, Genetics Therapy, Inc. (GTI), a company one observer has called the "ultimate body shop."

Steinberg had long headed the venture capital arm of Johnson & Johnson and was looking for a new market challenge in what promised to be the cutting-edge industry of the future—human genetic engineering. Traditionally, government scientists have regarded joining forces with private investors as unseemly if not unethical. Anderson's relationship to human gene engineering entrepreneurs has cast a shadow over both the science and the procedures that led to the approval of the first of several human gene therapy experiments. Concerns about conflict of interest were heightened in late 1990 when GTI hired former NIH/RAC chairman Gerard McGarrity. McGarrity had been a leading supporter of GTI's and Anderson's gene therapy experiments, and as chairman of RAC had helped shepherd the therapy proposals through the NIH approval process. In 1991, GTI's numerous maneuvers paid off: Sandoz Pharma, Ltd., one of the world's major multinational companies, bought $10 million of GTI stock and agreed to provide $13.5 million over the subsequent three years in project funding. GTI ended 1991 with cash and marketable securities of $20.8 million.

Human gene engineering is progressing quickly. Currently, over a dozen somatic cell gene engineering experiments are ongoing on three continents. Numerous other gene engineering protocols are being developed for approval in the near future. Large-scale use of gene engineering to cure disease or cosmetically change individuals is still several years away; nevertheless, the scandal, ambition, and moral blindness that have characterized the early history of human genetic engineering set a profoundly disturbing precedent for the future.

Moreover, many of the protections against abuses in the use of gene technology put in place in the 1980s are fast disappearing. The Congressional Biomedical Ethics Board, established in 1985, was disbanded in 1990. Additionally, in 1991 Dr. Anderson and others successfully urged the disbanding of the RAC Human Gene Therapy Subcommittee. Finally, in the face of a massive influx of profit-seeking and potential conflicts of interest, the viability of RAC as a responsible regulatory agency of human gene engineering is in considerable doubt.

In the future we will be genetically engineering ourselves in numerous ways—applications of biotechnology with which our society is ill prepared to deal. As researchers successfully locate genes responsible for height, weight, and I.Q., there are still no restrictions that would prevent an industry from altering these traits through somatic gene therapy. Further, researchers are now more determined than ever to begin the first germline gene engineering experiments on humans. There is general consensus that such research will become a reality over the next decade. We have no national or international mechanisms that will prevent germline engineering from permanently altering our human genome, no restrictions on the unlimited genetic alteration of sperm and eggs, or the engineering of embryos. Despite continuing controversy, publicity, and massive public funding of gene technology research, the questions demonstrators shouted at scientists over fifteen years ago have still not been answered.

NO

James Hughes

EMBRACING CHANGE WITH ALL FOUR ARMS: A POST-HUMANIST DEFENSE OF GENETIC ENGINEERING

INTRODUCTION

Nine years ago, while I rode a bus through the small, crooked, immaculate and beautiful streets of Kyoto, Jeremy Rifkin convinced me that genetic technology would determine the shape of the future. I was reading his *Algeny*, an alarmist attack on the coming of the gene age, alongside *What Sort of People Should There Be?*, a moderate defense of genetic engineering by Jonathan Glover. In a sense, in the nine years since, I have recoiled from the radical Rifkin to embrace the reformist Glover.

While extreme, Rifkin is a bellwether of Luddite tendencies in bioethics and the political Left, two of the movements within which I construct my worldview. Among bioethicists the anti-technological agenda has focused on abuses and social dangers in medical research and practice, and our alleged need to accept death and technological limits. The post-60s, environmentalist Left focuses on the ways that technology serves patriarchy, racism, imperialism, corporate profits, structural unemployment, the authoritarian state, and domination by scientific discourse. The response of bioethicists and the Left to genetic engineering has been particularly fevered, driven by accusations of eugenics and the defilement of sacred boundaries.

Since that bus ride in Kyoto my initial horrified agreement with Rifkin has shifted to determined agreement with Glover, that we can control genetic technology and make it a boon rather than a bane. Instead of a *Brave New World*, I see genetic engineering offering a grand, albeit somewhat unpredictable, future. While many of the concerns of ethicists and the Left about this technology are well-founded, I now believe they are answerable. While I still acknowledge the need for democratic control and social limits, I am now convinced that banning genetic engineering would be a profound mistake.

From James Hughes, "Embracing Change With All Four Arms: A Post-Humanist Defense of Genetic Engineering," *Eubios Journal of Asian and International Bioethics*, vol. 6, no. 4 (July 1996). Copyright © 1996 by James Hughes. Reprinted by permission.

Those who set aside angst about changing human nature, and embrace the possibility of rapid diversification of types of life, are establishing a new moral and political philosophy for the 21st century, a system some refer to as "post-humanism." Like all philosophical systems, post-humanism incorporates prior philosophic and political systems but recasts them around new definitions of personhood, citizenship, and the limits of social solidarity and human knowledge. Like Glover, post-humanists view the coming of genetic technology the way most Americans now view organ transplants or chemotherapy; there are many practical questions about how the technologies get developed and tested, who needs them, and how we pay for them, but there is no question that they should be available. In this essay I will be trying to imagine what liberal democracies could be like if we allow a post-humanist flowering of genetic technology.

DISTINCTIONS WITHOUT A DIFFERENCE

Many writers on these technologies draw distinctions between "negative" and "positive" genetic modification, and the modification of the somatic versus germ-line cells. Negative genetic modification has been defined as the correction of a genetic disease, while positive modification has been defined as the attempt to enhance human ability beyond its normal limits. The somatic/germ-line distinction has been made to address the alleged ethical difference in modifying only one's own body, versus modifying one's progeny as well.

Both distinctions have been made by those who wanted to draw a line to demarcate the ethical boundaries of genetic research. The distinctions are quite fuzzy, however. Take for instance Culver and Gert's effort to define "malady" to distinguish when a genetic therapy is or isn't "enhancement":

> A person has a malady if and only if he has a condition, other than his rational beliefs and desires, such that he is suffering, or at increased risk of suffering, an evil (death, pain, disability, loss of freedom or opportunity or loss of pleasure) in the absence of distinct sustaining cause.

Doesn't any cause of illness, suffering and death, or inadequacy in the face of one's goals, fit this criterion? Take for instance a potential future genetic therapy that turned off a hypothetical aging switch, doubling the human life span; is this therapy for the diseases which result from the activation of the aging switch, such as Alzheimers or cancer, or an unconscionable intervention into the natural span of life?

As to the modification of one's own genes versus future progeny, the argument is made that current generations would be violating the self-determination of future generations by doing so. The first response is that our choice of breeding partners already "determines" the biology of future generations. Take the case of a couple who both carry a gene for latent inheritable mental illness. The only difference between their choosing not to breed with one another, and choosing to have germ-line therapy on themselves or their child to correct the illness, is that the latter choice is a far happier one.

The second response to the somatic/germ-line distinction is that advancing genetic technology will make it possible for future generations to change their genes back if they don't like them. Only modifications which remove decision-making autonomy from future generations altogether would truly raise issues of "self-determination," and I will discuss such fascist scenarios below.

These distinctions are extremely fuzzy, and do not represent important ethical boundaries. In this essay I want to defend genetic therapy and enhancement, as well as self-modification by competent adults and modification of one's progeny. Even the most liberal, and most recent, of international bioethics consensus documents, the 1995 draft UNESCO Declaration on the Protection of the Human Genome, draws the line at germ-line enhancement.

Therefore ground-zero of the terrain that I want to defend is germ-line enhancement, the modification of the genetic code such that the parent passes on the enhancements to their progeny. The defense of this practice necessarily addresses the concerns about many other technologies, such as:

- In-Vitro Fertilization
- Surrogate Mothering
- Extra-uterine Gestation
- Genetic Screening and Diagnosis
- Genetic Selection, including Sex Selection
- Cloning of Embryos

In a more fundamental sense I am writing in defense of our control of our bodies, individually and collectively. I want to build a broad enough defense to cover any technology offering modification of human abilities, whether a specific genetic application has been imagined for that purpose or not.

ETHICAL STARTING POINTS FOR A DEFENSE

Rule Utilitarianism

In general I assume the ethical stance of Millsian rule utilitarianism: acts are ethical which lead to the greatest good or happiness for the greatest number. Rule utilitarianism means that, when confronted with a distasteful case, such as throwing a Christian to a lion for the amusement of thousands of Romans, I fall back on general rules of thumb: "In general, societies that respect individual rights and liberties will lead to greater happiness for all."

In the case of genetic engineering my broad assertion is that gene-technologies can, and probably will, give people longer, healthier lives, with more choices and greater happiness. In fact, these technologies offer the possibility that we will be able to experience utilities greater and more intense than those on our current mental pallet. Genetic technology will bring advances in pharmaceuticals and the therapeutic treatment of disease, ameliorating many illnesses and forms of suffering. Somewhat further in the future, our sense organs themselves may be re-engineered to allow us to perceive greater ranges of light and sound, our bodies re-engineered to permit us to engage in more strenuous activities, and our minds re-engineered to permit us to think more profound and intense thoughts. If utility is an ethical goal, direct control of our body and mind suggests the possibility of unlimited utility, and thus an immeasurable good.

PRIVACY, SELF-DETERMINATION AND BODILY AUTONOMY

But there are other rules to consider, rules which are the basis of other ethical systems. Most utilitarians, and many others, accept the general rule that liberal societies, which allow maximum self-determination, will maximize social utility. The rule of, or right to, self-determination also argues that society should have very good reasons before interfering with competent adults applying genetic technology to themselves and their property. Self-determining people should be allowed the privacy to do what they want to with their bodies, except when they are not competent, or their actions will cause great harm to others.

Acknowledging self-determination as an ethical starting point addresses half of the revulsion to genetic engineering: the concern that people will be forced to conform to eugenic policies. I will discuss this fear of racist and authoritarian regimes at greater length, but suffice it to say here that individuals should not be forced to have or abort children, or to modify their own or their children's genetic code. I am addressing the desirable genetics policies of liberal societies, not of authoritarian regimes.

Within liberal societies, competent adults should generally be allowed to do as they like with their bodies, including genetically modify them. The potential risks to others from such modifications, which I will try to discuss below, are all soluble, and not sufficient to warrant contravening the right of bodily autonomy.

I also view the embryo and fetus as the biological property of the parents, and exclusively of the mother when in utero. Again, the rights of the future child and of society may restrict what we allow parents to do to their prenatal property. But I would again argue that the risks to society and to the children themselves of prenatal genetic manipulation are negligible for the near future, and regulable as they become apparent.

FREEDOM FROM BIOLOGICAL NECESSITY

Genetic technology promises freedom and self-determination at an even more basic level: freedom from biological necessity. Social domination pales before our domination by the inevitability of birth, illness, aging and death, burdens that genetic technology offers to ameliorate. As for Marx, the goal of this revolution is to move from the realm of necessity to the realm of freedom.

Social domination also builds on a biological foundation. Patriarchy is, in part, based on women's physical vulnerability, and their special role in reproduction. While industrialization, contraception and the liberal democratic state may have removed the bulk of patriarchy's weight, genetic technology offers to remove the rest. Similarly, while racism, ageism, heterosexism, and so on may be only 10% biological and 90% social construction, at least the biological factors can be made a matter of choice by genetic and biological technology.

JUSTICE AND A BETTER SOCIETY

While the biological factors in most forms of inequality are probably slight, genetic technology does promise to create a more equal society in a very basic way: by eliminating congenital sources of illness and disability that create the most intractable forms of inequality in society. We can go to great lengths to give the ill and disabled full access to society, but their disabilities place basic limits on how equal their social participation and power can be. Our ability to ameliorate these sources of congenital inequality may even impose obligations on us to do so, at least for those who are cognitively impaired and incompetent. Admittedly, we will probably have surmounted most disabilities through non-genetic technological fixes long before we do so through genetic therapy. But the general principle is that genetic technology promises to make it possible to give all citizens the physical and cognitive abilities for equal participation, and perhaps even to bring about a general enhancement of the abilities essential to empowered citizenship.

A CRITICAL DEFENSE

Unlike those libertarians who hold self-determination as a cardinal principle, I adopt more of a social democratic stance, and foresee legitimate limits that we can and should place on these technologies. For instance, some characteristics of society, such as social solidarity and general equality, are so important that they warrant the regulation of these technologies in the furtherance of these goals. Collective interests should also be pursued through active means, such as government subsidies for the research, development and application of genetic technologies.

Nor am I an unquestioning advocate of technological progress. Some technologies are so inscribed with harmful ends that no amount of regulation and social direction can make them worth the risk. If I were convinced that genetic technology, like nuclear weapons technology, had no

redeeming qualities and only great risks then I would embrace a complete ban.

But the potential benefits of genetic technology far outweigh the potential risks. In short, I advocate a position of critical support, a position which reflects the suspicious optimism that most Americans have toward genetic technology.

ARGUMENTS AGAINST GENETIC TECHNOLOGY

There are at least two kinds of criticisms of genetic technology, fundamentalist and non-fundamentalist. The fundamentalist or "bio-Luddite" concerns, such as those of Jeremy Rifkin, I reject fundamentally. On the other hand, I accept the validity of many of the non-fundamental concerns, but see the problems they suggest as soluble. Few of these concerns about genetic technology raise new questions for medical ethics. The same questions have been raised by previous medical research and therapy, and those challenges have been met without bans on those technologies.

Some non-fundamentalist critics believe that, cumulatively, the risks posed by new genetic technologies are great enough to warrant postponing genetic research for some indefinite period of study and preparation. With these concerns I will argue that, with adequate technology assessment and anticipatory regulation, there will be adequate time to regulate genetic technology as we proceed; none of the risks are sufficiently weighty, individually or cumulatively, to outweigh the potential benefits.

The fundamentalist or bio-Luddite concerns I will address are:

- Bio-Luddism 1: Medicine Makes People Sick

- Bio-Luddism 2: Sacred Limits of the Natural Order
- Bio-Luddism 3: Technologies Serve Ruling Interests
- Bio-Luddism 4: The Genome Is Too Complicated to Engineer

The non-fundamentalist or pragmatic concerns I will discuss are:

- Gene Angst 1: Fascist Applications
- Gene Angst 2: The Value of Genetic Diversity
- Gene Angst 3: Genetic Discrimination and Confidentiality
- Gene Angst 4: Discrimination Against the Disabled
- Gene Angst 5: Unequal Access, Priority Setting and the Market
- Gene Angst 6: The Decline of Social Solidarity

Bio-Luddism 1: Medicine Makes People Sick

One extreme bio-Luddite position was elaborated by Ivan Illich: medicine itself makes us sick and should be done away with. A variant on this argument is that genetic screening will eventually determine that all of us are "at risk," making everyone see themselves as sick. More troubling, genetic diagnosis might create a two-tier social system, divided between those with relatively clean genes and those with genetic disease. In other words, genetic diagnosis will make us all genetically diseased. This would be even more problematic if the genetic diagnosis was for a disease which was not yet curable.

Some medicine makes some people sicker, but I hold fast to the modernist promise that scientific progress generally improves our lives and that knowledge is better than ignorance. It is unlikely that we will ever force people to know their likelihood of developing disease, though perhaps we should educate parents and physicians to be cautious about informing children of their risks. In any case, we all know that we are at risk of dying, and with or without genetic diagnosis people view the medical history of their parents and relatives as harbingers of things to come. Both knowing and refusing to know one's genetic makeup are empowering choices for competent adults; denying people the option of making this choice does not improve their lives.

This argument also presumes just the first, screening phase of the new eugenics, and not the latter correction phase. Far from making everyone sick, the advance of genetic therapy promises to make everyone well.

Bio-Luddism 2: Sacred Limits of the Natural Order

Rifkin has joined forces with religious leaders to assert another fundamentalist tenet, that genetic engineering transgresses sacred limits beyond which we should not "play God." I don't believe that divine limits are discernible, and I don't believe in any "natural order" except the one we've got. As Love and Rockets point out: "you can't go against nature, 'cause when you go against nature, it's part of nature too." There are no "natural limits" in our taking control of our biology or ecology. There is no "natural" way to have a baby or die. Even if there was a natural way to birth or die I don't believe we are morally compelled to adopt it.

Bio-Luddism 3: Technologies Serve Ruling Interests

Some hesitate to argue that medical technology is bad in and of itself, but argue instead that the powerful always shape and apply technologies to further their domination of the less powerful. While this is probably true, the conclusion is that all technology should be abandoned. The wealthy and powerful have more access to telephones than the poor and powerless, and telephones are used by the wealthy and powerful to collect more wealth and power. But I see the answer to be subsidized phone service and social reform, not banning the telephone.

Bio-Luddism 4: The Genome is Too Complicated to Engineer

A fourth fundamentalist conviction is that the genome is too complicated to engineer, and therefore there are certain to be unpleasant, unintended consequences. This argument is directly parallel to the deep ecologists' conclusion that human management of the complex global eco-system is impossible, and that our only hope is to leave the planet alone to its own self-organization.

The genome and eco-system are both very complicated, and the ability to do more than correct local defects in either may be many decades away. But eventually we will have the capacity to write genetic code and re-engineer eco-systems, and to computer-model the structural consequences of our interventions on future bodies and planets. Of course, it will be difficult to decide when the consequences of a genetic blueprint are sufficiently well-understood that it is safe for use, and our current regulatory scheme is probably not yet adequate to the task.

Our understanding of the genome and ability to predict consequences must be very robust before we allow human applications or the release of animal applications. While Elias and Annas object to "positive" germ-line therapy, which I would defend, they propose three sensible preconditions on the application of gene-engineering:

1. that there should be considerable prior experience with human somatic cell gene therapy, which has clearly established its safety and efficacy; and

2. that there should be reasonable scientific evidence using appropriate animal models that germ-line gene therapy will cure or prevent the disease in question and not cause any harm, and

3. all applications should be approved by the NIH's [National Institutes of Health] Working Group on Gene Therapy and local Institutional Review Boards, with prior public discussion.

Those of us who believe in the possibility of effective public regulation may differ widely as to the appropriate standards the public and these regulatory bodies may use. But liberals and conservatives differ fundamentally from those bio-Luddites who believe that the natural world is so complicated, and governments so unwise, that all intervention must be forbidden.

Gene Angst 1: Fascist Applications

Another concern expressed by many critics of genetic technology is the dire consequences of the re-emergence of fascist, racist and authoritarian regimes, and their use of engineering to produce compliant, genetically uniform subjects. The first point to make about fascist uses of eugenic ideology or technology is that nothing a democratic society does to forbid itself genetic technology will have any impact on future or contemporary fascist regimes. Indeed, if there is any "national security" to be gained from genetic technology then it would behoove liberal democracies to gain them as well. For instance, public health campaigns to detect and correct the genetic predisposition to alcoholism, or to enhance the intelligence of children, could make nations much more powerful and productive than their more conservative neighbors; would it not be in the interest of democracy itself for democracies to pursue these measures?

Yet, what if the fascist regimes found strength in breeding different castes a la *Brave New World*, and democracies could only meet the challenge by becoming equally repugnant? This is a possibility, and it raises the important point: the way to stop fascist uses of genetics is to prevent the rise of fascism, not to restrict the emergence of genetic technology. As we see today with Iraq and North Korea, firm agreements by right-thinking nations that only the United States is sufficiently moral to be allowed the ownership of nuclear and chemical weapons has little impact on recalcitrant regimes. If we cannot effectively prevent the proliferation of nuclear technology, with its large radioactive facilities visible to satellites, we will have even less success with genetic laboratories. I support the strengthening of the legal, judicial and military might of U.N. so that it might begin to enforce global law, but I think the proper task for such a New World Order is the suppression of fascist regimes likely to use genetics for nefarious ends, not the policing and suppression of outlawed genetic technologies.

Genetic science does not itself encourage racism or authoritarianism. In fact, the advance of scientific knowledge may even erode the pseudo-scientific basis on which most eugenics has rested. Presumably the advance of genetic science will tell us whether there is a genetic basis for gender and racial differences in abilities, or not, and how important these are. If there are genetic factors in gender or racial difference, they will most likely be revealed as minor beside the social factors, and the genetic factors will become ameliorable through a technical fix. Some insist that knowledge itself, or knowledge about forbidden topics, will lead to fascism; I prefer the modernist optimism that knowledge is at least neutral towards, and sometimes a scourge of, obscurantism.

Gene Angst 2: The Value of Genetic Diversity

Another concern that is often expressed vis-a-vis genetic engineering is the alleged aesthetic or biological virtues of genetic diversity. Many refer to the evidence from ecology that ecosystems are more stable when they contain a greater diversity of gene-lines. Some suggest, for instance, that our very survival as a species might hinge on genetic diversity if we faced some blight that only a few were resistant to.

The first objection to this argument is that diversity is not a sufficiently compelling ethical or aesthetic virtue that it can trump the prevention of disease, or the improvement of the quality of our lives. We "reduced diversity" when we eradicated smallpox and polio, with no regrets. We "reduce diversity" when we insist on compulsory education because we don't value the diversity of extreme class inequality.

The second objection to the diversity argument is that any loss of adaptiveness through biological diversity will be compensated for by an increase in biological knowledge and control. It is unlikely that a future society would have the ability to create "superior genes" and yet be unable to meet the challenge of infectious disease.

Third, the regime of genetics I have outlined is a liberal one, which should produce as much diversity as it reduces. While I support public provision of genetic screening for disease, I oppose any eugenic coercion. People desire different attributes and abilities, for themselves and their children; for every Aryan parent that chooses a blond, blue-eyed Barbie phenotype, I expect there would be a Chinese parent choosing a classic Chinese ideal of beauty. True, this might lead to the convergence toward a few physical and mental ideals, though I suspect that phenotypic fashions will change quickly. But I see no ethical difference between permitting people to change their genes in conformity with social fashions, and permitting them to change their clothes, makeup and beliefs to do so.

Yet, perhaps there is some aesthetic and or even civic virtue in diversity. If it is valued by the public, let us establish incentives for diversity. If the number of parents choosing to raise blond boys is offensive to public opinion, we can give tax incentives for parents who bear dark-haired girls. In any case, we will quickly know if there are broad trends that we find offensive, and I trust our ability to craft non-coercive policy responses to re-establish any valued diversity we feel may be eroding.

Gene Angst 3: Genetic Discrimination and Confidentiality

Many opponents of genetic investigation are concerned that growing genetic knowledge will lead to discrimination against the "genetically diseased and disabled." Some assert that genetic therapy itself will increase this discrimination by bringing intense pressure to bear on those with genetic diseases to have the disease corrected, and not burden society and future generations with their diseases.

It is certainly true that employers are already attempting to discover the genetic risks of their employees, and deny employment or health insurance on the basis of this risk profile. A bill guaranteeing the confidentiality of genetic information has been introduced in Congress, and while it has not yet passed, some form of confidentiality is certain to be guaranteed by the turn of the millennium. In addition, the Americans with Disabilities Act and similar legislation will clearly be mustered to defend workers from genetic discrimination.

Keeping genetic information confidential from health insurers is trickier, since they would be reimbursing for any special screening or treatment that genetic risks called for. Unregulated, the use of genetic risk information could greatly strengthen the ability of insurers to exclude the illness-prone from their risk pools, or charge them premiums equivalent to the costs of their potential treatments. Again, however, popular insurance reform legislation before Congress will ban "risk-rating" and excluding clients with "pre-existing conditions." These two reforms will likely reduce the number of insurance companies in the country by half or more, and make genetic discrimination in health insurance a more or less moot point. Some have suggested further that the pervasiveness of genetic information will make private health insurance impossible; to which I say, good riddance.

There are undoubtedly many other nefarious uses to which knowledge of someone's genetic make-up can be put. But genetic information is only one small category of the information about our lives which is potentially in the public domain, and potentially injurious. The regulation of genetic technology really has very little to do with whether we establish data privacy in the 21st century.

Gene Angst 4: Discrimination Against the Disabled

Opponents of sex selection and of eugenic efforts against genetic disease argue that these decisions are acts of prejudice against women and the disabled, and perpetuate the second-class status of women and the disabled by focusing on genetic rather than social amelioration. In the first place, embryos and fetuses are not persons, and therefore their rights cannot be violated as persons or as members of oppressed social groups. While parents may make reproductive decisions for many reasons we disapprove of, such as aborting a fetus because the father was accidentally of the "wrong" race, this is not a reason to intervene.

The alleged link between choosing to abort a disabled child, or correcting their disability through genetic therapy, and the perpetuation of oppression of the disabled seems tenuous at best. Perhaps by reducing the population of disabled we reduce their power at the ballot box. But a parent's moral obligation to give their children the greatest quality of life, and the fullest range of abilities, includes not only the obligation to treat a disabled child with respect and love, but also the obligation to keep them from having disabilities in the first place. It also seems likely that a society with fewer disabled would increase rather than decrease their per capita expenditures on the disabled.

Gene Angst 5: Unequal Access, Priority Setting and the Market

As a social democrat, one of my gravest concerns is how social inequality will constrain access to genetic technology, and how genetic technology may reinforce social inequality. Establishing the appropriate balance of state and market in genetics starts with the creation of a national health budget, most likely through the creation of a national health system, such as the [President Bill] Clinton plan or some other form of national health insurance. Such a system allows the ethical determination of utility trade-offs, from what the level of health care expenditures should be, to what should be included in the basic package of guaranteed medical services and what should be consigned to the private medical market.

If we had such a system, I don't think most fertility treatments would make the cut, nor would future positive genetic "enhancements." On the other hand, genetic screening and corrective genetic therapy would clearly be socially acceptable, cost-effective, and therefore a plausible positive right. This leaves me in a quandary; I want fertility treatments and positive genetic enhancement to be legal and available, but I'm not prepared to argue that they are a positive right worthy of public subsidy. Yet, if gene products are left in the market, only the wealthy will have access to them, with the upper-classes having more life opportunities and potentially becoming genetically healthier and more intelligent than the poor, which is unethical in an equal opportunity society.

These problems are really a sub-category of the larger task of determining which medical tests and procedures should be:

- required by law, e.g. vaccinations
- publicly funded, but not obligatory, e.g. abortion in progressive states
- encouraged, but unsubsidized, e.g. exercise
- discouraged, but not banned, e.g. smoking
- banned., e.g. heroin

Any assignment of genetic technologies to the categories between obligatory and forbidden allows for potential inequality. Most opponents of genetic technology, when pressed, would stop short of banning these technologies out-right, and thus leave them to be inequitably distributed by the market. At the other extreme, there are no audible voices calling for a program of mandatory, universal genetic redesign. This leaves me with Glover in the usual social democratic, mixed-market middle: try a little public, and a little private, and we will tinker with it as we proceed.

Gene Angst 6: The Decline of Social Solidarity

Finally some critics suggest that parents would become alienated from their genetically engineered children. Dator and other post-humanists suggest that genetic engineering and other technologies may create conflict between humans and post-humans, and threaten social solidarity. I think this is a serious concern, and one goal of the social regulation of genetic technology would be to moderate

the rapidity with which society genetically advances and diversifies. The gaps between the bodies and abilities of parents and children should not be so great as to make parenting impossible. Also the unenhanced public's concerns will inevitably be a factor in regulating the enhancement of the modified minorities. While some of these conservative concerns may be warranted, if the enhanced feel they have no responsibility to the unenhanced and seek to dominate or exploit them, we must also avoid allowing simple chauvinism and fear of the unknown to stop genetic enhancement.

While tremendous social conflicts can be imagined, they are not that different from the conflicts between ethnic minorities and majorities, or between the First World and the Third, or between social classes. Like other sources of social division, the relations between new genetic communities will hopefully be mediated by the same institutions, courts and legislatures, minority rights and majority rule. The real challenge faced by a post-human ethic is to define new parameters for which forms of life should be considered property, social wards (neither property nor competent persons, such as children), and persons with full citizenship.

CONCLUSION

While humanists and economists urge us to embrace financial and existential limits, and give up the quixotic quest for immortality, the post-humanists say "Some alive today may never die." The potential problems created by new medical technology are numerous, and we must work hard to ensure that our societies are free and equal enough that these tools create more good than harm. But I believe this to be an achievable goal, and that genetic technology offers, if not immortality, such good that the risks are dwarfed. Like all speculation (and all utilitarian judgments are based on social speculation) this optimism is founded on numerous points of faith. But I find faith in the potential unlimited improvability of human nature and expansion of human powers far more satisfying than a resignation to our current limits.

POSTSCRIPT

Should Genetic Engineering Be Banned?

Genetic engineering has had and will have applications in agriculture (improved crop plants and animals) and in the pharmaceutical industry (drug production). In the last few years, much of the excitement and the alarm have centered on its use to treat diseases by modifying human genes. Gene therapy has not yet become a multimillion-dollar industry, but there have been some successes. In October 1993 researchers reported that giving hemophiliac dogs—dogs with a hereditary defect that delays blood clotting—a copy of the gene for the blood-clotting agent they lacked improved the ability of their blood to clot. In March 1994 a similar approach repaired mice that had an autoimmune condition similar to the human disease lupus erythematosus. In April 1994 researchers announced that giving a woman with familial hypercholesterolemia—a rare genetic disorder that is marked by very high levels of blood cholesterol and early death from heart attack—the proper version of her defective gene reduced her cholesterol levels by 20 percent. For more detailed discussions of how researchers are transferring genes into human cells, see Mark A. Findeis, "Genes to the Rescue," *Technology Review* (April 1994) and Mario R. Capecchi, "Targeted Gene Replacement," *Scientific American* (March 1994).

By 1995 over 100 genetic therapies were being tested in humans. However, technical difficulties remain, and the successes have not been decisive (see Eliot Marshall, "Gene Therapy's Growing Pains," *Science*, August 25, 1995).

The technology is still young, its growth is still largely ahead, and its promise is yet to be fulfilled. *Will* that promise be fulfilled? Many people remain worried about the negative possibilities: In Germany tough regulations have made genetic engineering research of any kind almost impossible to carry out. In England a cancer research project was shut down in February 1994 because of fears that common cold viruses engineered to carry cancer genes might escape and cause a cancer plague (the actual risk was almost zero because the virus had been made unable to reproduce in cells, but government regulators judged the lab's containment measures to be inadequate). The availability of genetic information has raised fears of discrimination by insurers and employers (see Kathy L. Hudson et al., "Genetic Discrimination and Health Insurance: An Urgent Need for Reform," *Science*, October 20, 1995). And religious groups have objected to the patenting of genes (see Ronald Cole-Turner, "Religion and Gene Patenting," *Science*, October 6, 1995).

For more information on genetic engineering and the Human Genome Project, visit the following Internet site: http://www.er.doe.gov/production/oher/bioinfo_center.html.

ISSUE 14

Are Electromagnetic Fields Dangerous to Your Health?

YES: Paul Brodeur, from *The Great Powerline Coverup: How the Utilities and the Government Are Trying to Hide the Cancer Hazard Posed by Electromagnetic Fields* (Little, Brown, 1993)

NO: Jon Palfreman, from "Apocalypse Not," *Technology Review* (April 1996)

ISSUE SUMMARY

YES: Writer Paul Brodeur argues that there is an increased risk of developing cancer from being exposed to electromagnetic fields given off by electric power lines and that the risk is significant enough to warrant immediate measures to reduce exposures to the fields.

NO: Jon Palfreman, senior producer at WGBH, the public television station in Boston, Massachusetts, argues that there is no convincing evidence that electromagnetic fields pose any risk to human health.

Electromagnetic fields (EMFs) are emitted by any device that uses electricity. They weaken rapidly as one gets further from the source, but they can be remarkably strong close to the source. Users of electric blankets, before the blankets were redesigned to minimize EMFs, were among those who were most exposed to EMFs. People who use computers regularly are another highly exposed population. And, since EMF strength depends also on how much electricity is flowing through the source, so are people who live near power lines, especially high-tension, long-distance transmission lines.

Early research shows the difficulties of nailing down any possible side effects of EMF exposure. In 1979 researchers at the University of Colorado Health Center in Denver, Colorado, reported that, in a study of 344 childhood cancer deaths, children whose homes were exposed to higher EMF levels were two to three times more likely to die of leukemia or lymphoma. At the time, however, no one could suggest any mechanism by which EMFs could cause cancer, especially since the body generates its own EMFs of strength similar to those produced in the body by high-tension lines. Some other studies found similar links between EMF exposure and cancer; some did not.

Inconsistency has been the curse of research in this area. Speaking on research into the effects of extremely low frequency (ELF) EMFs on cells in the laboratory (which was performed in an effort to find mechanisms by which EMFs might cause cancer), Larry Cress of the U.S. Food and Drug Administration's Center for Devices and Radiological Health said, "Many researchers have been able to reproduce their effects most, but not all, of the time. And we don't see a dose response, as with some radiation, such as x-ray. Or, one laboratory may see an *increase* in something in a cell when the field is turned on, while another laboratory sees a corresponding *decrease* when the field is turned on." See Dixie Farley, "The ELF in Your Electric Blanket [and Other Appliances]," *FDA Consumer* (December 1992).

In 1992 the Committee on Interagency Radiation Research and Policy Coordination, an arm of the White House's Office of Science and Technology Policy, released *Health Effects of Low Frequency Electric and Magnetic Fields,* a report that concluded, "There is no convincing [published] evidence . . . to support the contention that exposures to extremely low frequency electric and magnetic fields generated by sources such as household appliances, video terminals, and local powerlines are demonstrable health hazards."

However, at about the same time, Swedish researchers announced that a study of leukemic children showed an association between their disease and the distances of their homes from power lines. The researchers also reported finding that the risk of leukemia increases in adults with exposure to EMFs in the workplace. Critics have objected that the correlations in such studies are weak—that they could easily be due to nothing more than coincidence or that they might reflect exposure to something other than EMFs whose levels nevertheless fluctuate in step with EMF levels (perhaps herbicides used to control the growth of vegetation under power lines or vapors given off by electrical insulation).

Yet the associations are there for scientists, as well as for journalists such as Paul Brodeur, to consider. In July 1990 Brodeur published a long article in *The New Yorker* in which he describes clusters of cancer cases that seemed to be linked to EMFs from power lines and reviews both the evidence and the responses of public utility representatives. In a later article, reprinted here, Brodeur summarizes his earlier report, adds further cases, and urges immediate measures to reduce what he feels are dangerous EMF exposures.

Jon Palfreman, senior producer at Boston's WGBH public television station, researched this issue for a program called "Currents of Fear." In his selection, he argues that the weight of evidence indicates that electromagnetic fields are not hazardous.

YES   Paul Brodeur

THE GREAT POWERLINE COVERUP

In my Annals of Radiation about the health hazard posed by the sixty-hertz magnetic fields that are given off by high-current and high-voltage power lines (July 9, 1990) I cited evidence suggesting that a cancer cluster had occurred among residents of Meadow Street in Guilford, Connecticut. During the past twenty years, seven tumors—two malignant brain tumors, two cases of meningioma (a rare and generally nonmalignant tumor of the brain), a malignant eye tumor, an ovarian tumor, and a tumor of the tibia—have been recorded among children and adults living on that street, which is only two hundred and fifty yards long and has only nine houses on it. Because all seven tumors developed in people who were living or had lived for significant periods of time in five of six adjacent houses situated near an electric-power substation and next to some main distribution power lines carrying high current from the substation, I suggested that the cancer among the residents of Meadow Street was associated with chronic exposure to the magnetic fields that are given off by such wires. To support that contention, I cited the fact that during the past decade some two dozen epidemiological studies had been conducted and published in the medical literature of the United States and other parts of the world showing that children and workers exposed to power-line magnetic fields were developing cancer—chiefly leukemia, lymphoma, melanoma, brain tumors, and other central-nervous-system cancers—at rates significantly higher than those observed in unexposed people, and the fact that between 1985 and 1989 no fewer than twelve studies had shown more brain tumors than were to be expected among people exposed to electric and magnetic fields at home or at work.

At a public meeting held in the Guilford Public Library on August 20th, David R. Brown, chief of the Connecticut Department of Health Services' Division of Environmental Epidemiology and Occupational Health, and Sandy Geschwind, an epidemiologist with the division, declared that there was no cancer cluster on Meadow Street. To support their contention, they distributed a document entitled "Guilford Cancer Cluster Preliminary Investigation," claiming that "there was not a cluster of the same kind of tumors on Meadow Street," and that from 1968 through 1988 "Guilford as a whole did

From Paul Brodeur, *The Great Powerline Coverup: How the Utilities and the Government Are Trying to Hide the Cancer Hazard Posed by Electromagnetic Fields* (Little, Brown, 1993). Copyright © 1993 by Paul Brodeur. Reprinted by permission of Little, Brown and Company. This article first appeared in *The New Yorker* (November 19, 1990).

not experience a higher than expected number of brain cancer or meningioma cases." The document stated, further, that "mapping of these brain tumor and meningioma cases showed that they did not cluster in a particular area but were scattered throughout the town."

At the meeting, Geschwind gave a presentation in which she said that one of the brain cancers on Meadow Street was not a primary tumor but an esophageal cancer that had metastasized. She also said that the malignant eye tumor in question was a melanoma—a type of cancer that she claimed had never been associated with exposure to electromagnetic fields—and she assured her listeners that meningioma had never been associated with exposure to such fields. Toward the end of her presentation, Geschwind displayed a map showing the location of ten meningiomas and nineteen other brain and central-nervous-system tumors listed by the Connecticut Tumor Registry as having occurred in Guilford between 1968 and 1988, and told the hundred or so members of her audience—they included a dozen newspaper and television reporters—that the map proved that there was "absolutely no clustering" in Guilford and that the state investigation showed "no cancer cluster on Meadow Street."

However, the fact that Guilford as a whole—the town now has a population of twenty thousand five hundred, living in seventy-three hundred dwellings—did not experience a higher than expected number of meningiomas and other brain and nervous-system tumors during those twenty-one years does not address the situation on Meadow Street, Second, while there is no reason to doubt Geschwind's assertion that one of the two brain cancers among Meadow Street residents was

not a primary tumor, eye melanoma—the one in question was a malignant tumor involving the optic nerve, an extension of the brain—has been found to be "notably high for electrical and electronics workers," who are known to be exposed to strong magnetic fields. The finding appeared in a highly regarded study entitled "Epidemiology of Eye Cancer in Adults in England and Wales, 1962–1977," which was conducted by Dr. A. J. Swerdlow, a physician at the Department of Community Medicine of the University of Glasgow, in Scotland. Swerdlow reported his findings in 1983, in Volume 118, No. 2, of the *American Journal of Epidemiology*, which is published by the Johns Hopkins University School of Hygiene and Public Health, in Baltimore. Moreover, melanoma of the skin is one of three types of cancer listed by scientists of the Environmental Protection Agency in a recent draft report, "An Evaluation of the Potential Carcinogenicity of Electromagnetic Fields," as being prevalent among workers in electrical and electronic occupations, and thus associated with exposure to magnetic fields.

The conclusion of Brown and Geschwind that there is no cancer cluster among people who have lived on Meadow Street seems disingenuous, to say the least. As Geschwind noted, the Connecticut Tumor Registry recorded ten cases of meningioma and nineteen other primary tumors of the brain and central nervous system among Guilford residents between 1968 and 1988—a span in which the average population of the town was seventeen thousand five hundred. Thus the meningioma rate in Guilford is consistent with the Connecticut statewide incidence, of 2.6 cases per hundred thousand people per year—I was in error when I gave it in my article as one case per hundred thousand—and the incidence of other brain and central-nervous-system tumors in Guilford is also close to the number that would normally be expected. The fact that three of the twenty-nine primary brain and central-nervous-system tumors that occurred in Guilford during those twenty-one years developed among a handful of people who lived in four of five adjacent houses on Meadow Street that are situated near a substation and very close to a pair of high-current distribution lines, called feeders, together with the fact that a malignant eye tumor, involving a tract of brain tissue, occurred in a woman who had lived in a sixth adjacent dwelling, next to a third feeder line, surely suggests that there is a cancer cluster of some significance on Meadow Street.

Finally, and somewhat ironically, further evidence of cancer clustering associated with exposure to power-line magnetic fields can be found in the very map that Geschwind displayed in an effort to persuade the people of Guilford that no cancer cluster existed there. Among those listening to her presentation was Robert Hemstock, a Guilford resident, who, in January of this year, first sounded the alarm about a cluster on Meadow Street. When Geschwind held up the map, Hemstock noticed that three of the twenty-nine cancers on it appeared to have occurred along the route of a feeder line that carried high current from the Meadow Street substation to other towns during the nineteen-sixties, seventies, and early eighties, when the substation was being operated by its owner, the Connecticut Light & Power Company, as a bulk-supply station for large-load areas in Madison and Clinton —neighboring towns with a total population of about twenty thousand dur-

ing that period. He also noticed that an unusually large proportion of the other brain tumors on the map appeared to have occurred among people living along the routes of other primary distribution lines emanating from the substation.

After the meeting, Hemstock shared his observation with Don Michak, a reporter for the Manchester Enfield *Journal Inquirer,* who on August 23rd asked the Department of Health Services for a copy of the map. As it happened, Brown had displayed the map the day before at a Rotary Club meeting in Guilford, and told the Rotarians that he saw no need for the department to make any further inquiry into the incidence of cancer on Meadow Street. However, Health Services officials refused to release the map to Michak, on the ground that to do so might violate the confidentiality of cancer victims by revealing their addresses. The *Journal Inquirer* reported this development in an article by Michak on September 6th, and on September 10th it published an editorial pointing out that if the withheld map showed that the distribution of cancer cases in Guilford corresponded to the Meadow Street substation and to a power line running north from it "the public's concern might be overwhelming not only in Guilford but throughout Connecticut and even nationally." The editorial went on to question Health Services' rationale for secrecy, declaring that the map "is just a matter of dots superimposed on a map of Guilford; it apparently doesn't include names and addresses," and that "anyone seeking to use the map to find people who have or had cancer would have to knock on doors in the area of the dots on the map and ask such people to identify themselves." After observing that "the health department undermined its own rationale by displaying the map at the public hearing in Guilford in the first place," the editorial concluded by stating that if the department failed to make the map available "the public will have to assume that the department wants to protect something else more than it wants to protect public health."

In September, a reporter for the New Haven *Register* obtained a copy of the map from an assistant to the Guilford health officer. (The assistant later said that she had given it out by mistake.) The *Register* reporter also went to the Connecticut Light & Power Company's office in Madison and obtained a company map of the routes of existing high-current and high-voltage distribution lines in Guilford. On October 3rd, the *Register* published its own map—one combining the locations of the brain tumors and other central-nervous-system tumors with the routes of Connecticut Light & Power's distribution lines. It clearly showed that Hemstock's observation was correct—that an inordinately high number of the meningiomas and other brain and central-nervous-system tumors that had occurred in Guilford over the twenty-one-year period between 1968 and 1988 had developed in people living close to primary distribution wires.

This correlation notwithstanding, Brown and Geschwind denied that the map furnished any evidence of a link between the occurrence of such tumors and proximity to power lines in Guilford. "You can't use the map to show that kind of association," Geschwind told the *Register*. She added that such tumors could be found on streets near main distribution power lines because those streets were densely populated, and heavily populated areas would have proportionally higher cancer rates.

To the contrary, anyone who knows the addresses of the twenty-nine brain-and-other-central-nervous-system-tumor victims in Guilford, and follows the routes of the feeder lines and primary distribution wires leading from the Meadow Street substation, will find not only that there is a strong correlation between the occurrence of these tumors and living close to high-current or high-voltage wires but also that most of the tumors have not occurred in areas of notably dense population. The feeder that carried high current from the substation to Madison and Clinton was abandoned a few years ago; it ran across Meadow Street from the substation and proceeded east for about a mile and a half, to a point near the junction of Stone House Lane, South Union Street, and Sawpit Road. (Up to that point, the poles and the wires of the line remain in place, but they have been removed from the rest of the route—across an uninhabited salt marsh and the East River, which is the eastern boundary of Guilford, to a substation on Garnet Park Road, in Madison.) This feeder line ran for a mile and a half through Guilford, and it passed close —within a hundred and fifty feet or so —to only twelve houses. One of the ten meningiomas and two of the nineteen other brain and central-nervous-system tumors listed by the Tumor Registry as having occurred in Guilford between 1968 and 1988 afflicted people living in three of those twelve dwellings. All three are situated within about forty feet of the high-current wires. Moreover, a former Meadow Street resident who developed eye cancer at the age of forty-four, and has since died of it, lived for fourteen years in one of the twelve houses close to the abandoned feeder line. It is at 56 Meadow, and is situated only about thirty feet from the wires....

All told, seven of the ten meningiomas and ten of the nineteen other brain and central-nervous-system tumors—that is, seventeen of the total of twenty-nine—have afflicted people living near high-current or high-voltage power lines in Guilford. The total combined length of the lines is about forty-five miles, and along this distance some seven hundred and twenty-two out of a total of eight hundred and six houses are situated within a hundred and fifty feet of the wires. It seems obvious that in a town of seventy-three hundred dwellings the occurrence of this proportion of meningiomas and other brain and central-nervous-system tumors in residents of just over eight hundred dwellings strung out along some forty-five miles of roadway cannot be ascribed to heavy population—as the Connecticut Department of Health Services has done. It also seems obvious that people living in houses close to high-current wires and high-voltage transmission lines in Guilford are especially susceptible to developing meningiomas and other brain tumors. Particularly disturbing in this regard is the fact that in March of 1989—too late to be counted among the twenty-nine tumors listed by the Registry on the map that the Connecticut Department of Health Services displayed to reassure the townspeople of Guilford—a seventeen-year-old girl living in a house close to one of the high-current feeder lines was found to be suffering from an astrocytoma, the same type of malignant brain tumor that has afflicted a seventeen-year-old girl living near the same line on Meadow Street.

Instead of continuing to extend the presumption of benignity to power-line magnetic fields, the Connecticut Department of Health Services could require its Division of Environmental Epidemiology and Occupational Health to conduct a thorough study of the apparent strong association between the occurrence of meningiomas and other brain and central-nervous-system tumors, on the one hand, and, on the other, chronic exposure to the magnetic fields given off by high-current and high-voltage power lines in Guilford. Moreover, since Connecticut is one of the few states that have collected data on the occurrence of such tumors over a significant period, the department has a unique opportunity to perform an important service for public health nationwide by conducting a detailed investigation of the seventeen hundred and three meningiomas and the four thousand one hundred and two other brain and central-nervous-system tumors that have been diagnosed among Connecticut residents over the twenty-one years between 1968 and 1988, in order to determine whether, as is clearly the case in Guilford, a disproportionately high percentage of them have developed in people living close to wires giving off strong magnetic fields. If such an association should prevail throughout the state, meningioma and other brain tumors would have to be considered marker diseases for exposure to power-line magnetic fields.

* * *

Later in my article I described a cluster of seven brain cancers that had been reported to have occurred over the past fifteen or twenty years among the residents of Trading Ford and Dukeville—two small communities near Salisbury, in Rowan County, North Carolina—who had either worked at a nearby power-generating plant, owned by the Duke Power Company, or lived in a company village, Dukeville, that was situated close to the plant and adjacent to a large substation and some high-voltage transmission lines giving off strong magnetic fields. I suggested that officials of the North Carolina Department of Environment, Health, and Natural Resources' environmental-epidemiology section were remiss in not having investigated this brain-cancer cluster during the eight and a half months since it was reported in the Salisbury *Post* on July 12 and 18, 1989, especially since one of the officials, Dr. Peter D. Morris, had made a point of stating that such a cluster might be significant if all the cancer victims had worked in the same plant twenty years earlier. I also suggested that the health experience of the three hundred or so people who lived in the company village or worked at the plant, or did both, should be thoroughly investigated, because, in addition to the seven of those people who had died of brain cancer, four others, who simply lived near the plant or the high-voltage transmission lines radiating from it, had died of the disease, and because a preliminary inquiry revealed that there had also been at least eight deaths from leukemia, lymphoma, and other cancers among these people.

In a recent letter to the editor of *The New Yorker* three officials of the environmental-epidemiology section stated that they had evaluated the seven cases of brain cancer, in order to "determine whether or not they should be included in our study of brain cancer in Rowan County from 1980 through 1989," and had found that "two of the seven cases had metastatic brain cancer, a different type of tumor originating in another part of the body and later spreading to the brain." They went on to say that four of the remaining cases were excluded from their study because the di-

agnoses of two of them were made prior to 1979, an unconfirmed diagnosis of another was made prior to 1979, and one of the victims lived outside Rowan County at the time of diagnosis.

In the final report of their study, which is entitled "Rowan County Brain Cancer Investigation," the North Carolina health officials state that Rowan County did not have a significantly greater incidence of malignant brain cancer between 1980 and 1989 than each of the five surrounding counties. During a press conference at the Rowan County Health Department on October 25th, Dr. Morris told the Salisbury *Post* that brain cancer in the Trading Ford–Dukeville area during the ten-year period "was not studied as a separate cluster."

The rationale of the North Carolina health officials is as faulty as that of their counterparts in Connecticut, because they not only have failed to address the brain-cancer situation in Trading Ford and Dukeville in its entirety but also have submerged the small part they did address in the larger study of Rowan County. In order to understand how flawed their investigation has been, one must remember that the power plant, which was built in 1926, was partly shut down during the nineteen-fifties and sixties, and the eighty-six houses in Dukeville, which were built between 1926 and 1945, were moved elsewhere in 1955. Thus, in addition to the one case of primary brain cancer among Trading Ford and Dukeville residents that the North Carolina officials included in their study, and the four cases of brain cancer that they saw fit to exclude, other people who were exposed to the electric and magnetic fields from the plant, its substation, and its high-voltage transmission lines by virtue of working at the plant or living in the company village during the nineteen-thirties, forties, and fifties may well have developed the disease and died of it before 1979. By deciding not to include brain cancers diagnosed among residents of the Trading Ford–Dukeville area before 1979, the North Carolina health officials decided not to investigate the health experience of people who worked at or lived near the Duke Power Company plant—a decision that makes about as much epidemiological sense as a decision to study the incidence of gray hair in a given population after excluding all those persons in the study group who became gray more than ten years earlier.

* * *

Still later in my article I wrote that cancer among the student population of the Montecito Union School—an elementary school with four hundred pupils in Montecito, California—was "at least a hundred times what might have been expected." This was an error. The incidence of cancer at the school is considerably less than that, though far greater than it should be. Between 1981 and 1988, six cases of cancer are known to have occurred among children who attended the Montecito Union School: two children developed leukemia; three children developed lymphoma; and one child developed testicular cancer. As I wrote in my article, cancer is a rare event in children, occurring annually in about one of ten thousand children per year under the age of fifteen. However, as several readers have pointed out, the child-years at risk should be calculated at eight times four hundred students per year; that comes to thirty-two hundred child-years at risk. Six cases of cancer out of thirty-two hundred child-years

translates to 18.75 cases per ten thousand children per year. According to the National Cancer Institute's Surveillance, Epidemiology and End Results (SEER) data, the all-sites cancer rate for white children of both sexes, aged five to nine, between 1983 and 1987 in the San Francisco–Oakland area (the closest metropolitan area to Santa Barbara for which SEER data exist) was 11.9 cases per hundred thousand children per year. Thus the cancer rate over those eight years at the Montecito Union School—18.75 cases per ten thousand—is more than fifteen times the expected rate.

In their assessment of this cancer cluster officials of California's Department of Health Services' environmental-epidemiology-and-toxicology branch have maintained that magnetic-field levels at the school—which is situated within forty feet of a sixty-six-thousand-volt feeder line originating at an adjacent substation—were not unusually high, and that there was no evidence that they posed a health hazard. The fact is, however, that magnetic-field levels measured at the school's kindergarten patio by Enertech, an engineering consulting firm in the Bay Area, were between four and six milligauss; that is, approximately twice the levels that have been associated with a doubling of the expected rate of childhood cancer in three epidemiological studies cited by staff scientists of the Environmental Protection Agency as providing the strongest evidence that there may be a causal relationship between certain forms of childhood cancer —chiefly leukemia, nervous-system cancer, and lymphoma—and exposure to power-line magnetic fields. (Incidentally, on February 26th of this year I measured the magnetic fields at the kindergarten patio of the Montecito Union School, and found them to be about the same as those reported by Enertech.) It is also a fact that the magnetic-field levels at the kindergarten patio are at least equal to, and, for the most part, greater than, the exposure levels of forty-five hundred New York Telephone Company cable splicers, in whom cancer of all types—particularly leukemia—has been found to be higher than expected.

California health officials decided not to include the case of testicular cancer, which occurred in a second-grader, in their assessment of the cancer hazard at the Montecito Union School, and that decision seems arbitrary, in the light of the fact that cancer of all types was elevated in the childhood-cancer studies cited by the E.P.A. and also in the study of the telephone-cable splicers. It seems all the more arbitrary in the light of SEER data that estimate the chances of a seven- or eight-year-old child's developing testicular cancer to be nearly zero in one hundred thousand children per year. Also disturbing is the fact that since the publication of my article a teacher's aide with several years' experience in the kindergarten of the Montecito Union School has developed a brain tumor. This occurrence, together with the fact that four cases of leukemia have been reported among children

who attended the Montecito Union School in the late nineteen-fifties, should encourage the California officials to conduct a full-scale investigation of the health experience of all the children who have attended this school during the past thirty-five years, just as the cancer clusters that have been found among the residents of Guilford and Dukeville should occasion in-depth investigations of the health experience of all the people who have lived near high-voltage and high-current power lines in those communities over a similarly appropriate period.

While these studies are in progress, interim preventive measures should be undertaken to reduce the magnetic-field exposure of children in hundreds of schools and day-care centers across the nation which have been built perilously close to high-voltage and high-current power lines. That can be accomplished by rerouting such lines, or burying them in a manner that will prevent hazardous magnetic-field emissions. Needless to say, such measures should be supported by the parents of schoolchildren, by members of parent-teacher associations, and by officials of school districts, of city and state health departments, and of the federal Environmental Protection Agency.

NO

Jon Palfreman

APOCALYPSE NOT

With some 2 million miles of power lines carrying electricity from generating stations to homes and businesses across the United States, utilities go to great lengths—stringing wires on high towers, burying them underground, and fencing in substations—to avoid accidental electrocutions. But some concerned citizens, journalists, and scientists have warned for more than 15 years of a more pernicious danger emanating from power lines: electromagnetic fields.

A charged particle in motion (like an electron flowing in a wire) produces an electric and magnetic field, so a person standing underneath a power line is exposed to both. While the electric field can hardly penetrate skin, much less the walls of houses, a magnetic field will pass through just about anything and can permeate a human body as if it were free space. Thus, a broad consensus has developed that, if the electromagnetic radiation from power lines is dangerous, the magnetic fields must be doing the damage.

This was indeed the hypothesis of Nancy Wertheimer and Ed Leeper in 1979 when they published the first epidemiological study linking electromagnetic fields to childhood cancers. Wertheimer, a psychologist who now works with the Department of Preventive Medicine at the University of Colorado, and Leeper, a retired physicist, compiled a list of 344 children in the Denver area who had died of any form of cancer from 1950 through 1973 and compared them with children without cancer randomly selected from birth records. To estimate exposure to magnetic fields, they ranked the children's homes as a function of their distance from a substation or power line and the configuration and thickness of the wires near them. The results showed that, at the homes ranking highest—that is, likely to be immersed in the strongest magnetic fields—children died of cancer at about three times the rate of those residing in homes that ranked the lowest.

Since Wertheimer and Leeper's study, scientists have conducted some four dozen other epidemiological studies investigating these effects. About two-thirds have been occupational studies of workers such as cable splicers whose job potentially exposes them to strong magnetic fields. The rest are residential studies, investigating whether people living near power lines or substations

From Jon Palfreman, "Apocalypse Not," *Technology Review*, vol. 99, no. 3 (April 1996). Copyright © 1996 by *Technology Review*. Reprinted by permission of the author and *Technology Review*.

face increased risk. Many of the scientists participating in these studies have claimed to find positive correlations between estimates of magnetic-field exposure and disease.

The popular media have also carried reports of clusters of cancers and other diseases allegedly caused by power lines and substations. In widely read articles in the *New Yorker*, for instance, environmental journalist Paul Brodeur wrote about a high incidence of cancers among the residents of Meadow Street in Guilford, Conn., who lived near a substation, and about an elementary school in Fresno, Calif., also located near a substation, where 15 teachers and staff members had developed cancer.

These cancer clusters and their alleged association with substations and power lines hit home: many people reading such accounts identified with the citizens and wondered about the power lines on their streets. With so much smoke, they concluded, there must be a fire. Something must be going on. Yet these numerous studies have failed to satisfy any of the basic criteria, established in 1965 by the British epidemiologist Sir Austin Bradford Hill, for convincingly demonstrating cause and effect.

BIOLOGICAL IMPLAUSIBILITY

Among other things, the so-called Hill criteria declared that any proposed association between an environmental agent and disease should have a biologically plausible link. While acknowledging that this criterion is limited by the "biological knowledge of the day," Hill maintained that researchers must try to offer a reasonable hypothesis of how a proposed health effect could occur.

Given what we already know about the interaction of electromagnetic fields with living tissue, it seems unlikely that magnetic fields from power lines could cause cancer or other diseases. "There's probably nothing on earth, or in the universe, that we understand as well as electromagnetic fields and the interaction of electromagnetic fields with matter, including biological matter," says Robert Adair, a physicist at Yale. These interactions, he says, make up "all of chemistry and almost all of biology, excepting a few gravitational effects."

Adair is one of a growing group of physicists who have felt compelled to participate in the electromagnetic field debate. A few years ago, Adair and his Yale colleague physicist William Bennett found that the more they studied the area, the more skeptical they became. What makes the connection seem most improbable to Bennett is what he calls the "absolutely minuscule" strength of the magnetic fields in question.

Magnetic fields are measured in milligauss (thousandths of a gauss). The fields recorded in most homes, even ones near power lines, are of the order of a few milligauss at most. Even standing directly under most power lines, one is typically exposed to only 50 milligauss or less. Yet, as every school child knows, we live in the earth's magnetic field. This field in North America averages about 500 milligauss.

While this fact alone makes it sound as though electromagnetic fields from power lines would certainly be lost against this magnetic backdrop, the earth's magnetic field is relatively static. The magnetic field associated with power lines, on the other hand, is normally so-called alternating current (AC), vibrating to and fro some 60 times per second.

Some people argue this is the critical difference. As Brodeur puts it, "When you're standing underneath the power lines, every cell in your brain and body is entrained to the rhythm."

But according to Adair, despite the image of every cell in one's body moving back and forth 60 times a second, the effect is minuscule compared with temperature-induced oscillations that occur all the time—an effect with a magnitude thousands of times larger. "It's completely lost in the noise," Adair says. "The fact that we live at 98 degrees Fahrenheit means everything is always oscillating, bouncing back and forth because of thermal effects." Comparing the cell vibrations caused by power lines' electromagnetic fields to those caused by temperature fluctuations, Adair likens them to damage your cat might do to a tree by breathing on it in the middle of a windstorm.

Since the field is so weak, Bennett and Adair, like many other scientists, find it hard to see how it might cause cancer. Cancer is usually caused when very energetic radiation, or some chemical agent, directly breaks or rearranges DNA. But the forces holding DNA molecules together are millions of times larger than any force that electromagnetic fields from power lines could produce.

Participants on both sides of the debate generally agree that the electromagnetic fields emanating from power lines and electrical appliances do not have enough energy to initiate cancer. But some critics argue that electromagnetic fields from power lines might promote an existing cancer or perhaps affect the immune system in a novel way. Some proponents of this view, for example, argue there might be mechanisms in the human body capable of amplifying the signal so it can be heard above the background thermal noise. Such "hardware" has been discovered in sharks that can detect 60 Hz magnetic fields, but not yet in humans. Other scientists, like A. R. Liboff, a physicist at Michigan-based Oakland University, argue that there might be a resonant "window" effect whereby human cells are especially responsive to a frequency range that includes 60 Hz. To account for the power systems in Europe, where some epidemiological findings have come from, however, this window must necessarily include 50 Hz as well.

Bennett and Adair, together with the overwhelming majority of physicists, dismiss these theories outright. The 45,000-member American Physical Society, for instance, released a report on electromagnetic fields last May arguing that cancer fears were unfounded and lending little credence to the resonance hypotheses. But, as Hill stressed, biological plausibility is merely one of several factors that can establish a link between an environmental agent and disease. By itself, the lack of a plausible electromagnetic field-disease hypothesis is not enough to sink the possibility of a connection.

BULLET-PROOF STUDIES

According to the Hill criteria, researchers can also reveal a link between environmental factors and disease by using controlled procedures in the laboratory. For instance, it is widely agreed that exposure to AC electromagnetic fields in excess of 2,000 gauss—millions of times larger than those implicated in the epidemiological studies—can excite nerves. But early research suggesting that AC magnetic fields could adversely affect the development of chick embryos has not been borne out in subsequent studies and, in general, experiments reporting effects at fields lower than about 5 gauss have not been replicated.

Three years ago, a $65 million federal program operating under the auspices of the National Institute of Environmental Health Sciences began sponsoring a series of carefully designed laboratory studies, funding multiple versions of all the research to increase the likelihood that any findings would be independently replicated. As a key piece of this program, the Illinois Institute of Technology constructed, deep under the streets of Chicago, the world's largest facility designed to expose rodents to electromagnetic fields. Built almost entirely of nonmetallic materials (so not to interfere with the magnetic fields) and containing state-of-the-art monitoring equipment, the $9 million facility is capable of exposing 3,000 rodents at a time to measured doses of magnetic fields ranging from 20 milligauss to 10,000 milligauss —thousands of times the average exposure in most homes. Project leader David McCormick says he wanted a facility capable of producing "bullet-proof studies." And indeed, it appears everything imaginable has been controlled for: the earth's magnetic field in all the rooms has been mapped extensively; temperature, humidity, noise, and light levels are all controlled and monitored continuously lest they confound the results; and every year the National Institute of Standards and Technology checks the lab equipment's calibration.

By last spring, McCormick's group had completed five studies. In one, involving a total of 3,000 rodents, the team investigated whether magnetic fields such as those from power lines caused fetal abnormalities. Pathologists examined the animals' skeletons, heads, and visceral organs. According to McCormick, the results came up completely negative. "We found no adverse effects from the magnetic fields at all," he says.

The group also conducted a reproductive study in which they bred animals continuously exposed to magnetic fields. McCormick's team examined 12 sets of litters over three generations and looked at a variety of outcomes: the number of successful pregnancies, the number of litters delivered, the number of pups per litter, and several other parameters such as birth weight to assess the health of the pups once they were delivered. Again, as McCormick explains, "That study demonstrated no effects of the magnetic fields on reproductive performance in either sex."

To test the hypothesis that magnetic fields could promote an existing cancer, McCormick used two strains of transgenic mice genetically engineered to predispose them to lymphomas. McCormick exposed the transgenic mice to measured intensities of magnetic fields and compared them with an unexposed control group. The result was unambiguous— no evidence appeared that the magnetic fields had stimulated the development of lymphoma in either strain of mice. Similarly, McCormick's team was unable to demonstrate that electromagnetic fields caused any consistent effect on the animals' immune systems.

McCormick's laboratory is still conducting a study in which rats will spend two years—essentially their whole lives —exposed to a magnetic field to test for chronic long-term effects. The results won't be known until later this year.

Proponents of the electromagnetic field-disease hypothesis rightly argue that one should not rely on McCormick's results until they are replicated. Such studies are under way in the United States, Canada, and Scandinavia. But the thrust of the most recent—and most thorough—experimental evidence is unmistakable. McCormick's work is just the latest of a series of whole-animal studies that have failed to find any health effects from electromagnetic fields.

But whole-animal experiments, such as those undertaken by McCormick's group, are just one approach to unlocking the mysteries of magnetic fields. One provocative possibility, also the target of federal research funding, is that exposure to magnetic fields might somehow affect the cancer-causing genes called oncogenes. Research by Reba Goodman and Ann Henderson, molecular biologists at New York's Columbia University and Hunter College, respectively, had claimed just this: that the fields might be capable of stimulating a particular cancer gene known as the MYC oncogene, increasing its activity and perhaps its likelihood of causing cancer.

Two groups—one at Cambridge University in England and one at the Battelle Pacific Northwest Laboratories (PNL) in Washington—were intrigued enough to try to replicate these results. In his attempts, Jeffrey Saffer, a molecular biologist at PNL, controlled for factors such as temperature, humidity, noise, and vibrations by placing batches of human cells into two identical test chambers. Then, in each trial, he randomly assigned one chamber to receive exposure from 60 Hz magnetic fields. Next he analyzed the samples to see if there were any differences. The whole procedure was conducted blind to eliminate potential investigator bias.

When Saffer's first results failed to detect any effect, he repeated the experiment dozens of times, changing parameters such as field intensities, serum types and concentrations, and the type of cell culture. But despite these efforts, nothing worked. Finally, Saffer took an unusual step; he went to the laboratory of Reba Goodman and repeated the experiment using her cells, culture vessels, and exposure system. His result was the same. As Saffer puts it, "We were unable to find evidence for a change in MYC expression due to the magnetic field."

Saffer concluded that the effects reported by Henderson and Goodman probably resulted from inadequate experimental controls. (A full account of Saffer's work appeared in the October 1995 edition of the journal *Radiation Research* along with a report from the team in Cambridge, England, that also tried—and failed—to replicate the effect.)

Although other studies here and abroad have reported negative results as well, some critics argue that electromagnetic fields might affect human beings in ways that these experiments are failing to pick up. Public policy, they further argue, should not be determined in the laboratory but rather with reference to the many epidemiological studies investigating the link between 60-Hz magnetic fields and disease in humans.

STRENGTH, CONSISTENCY, AND SPECIFICITY

According to the Hill criteria, epidemiology alone can establish a causal connection even in the absence of biological plausibility or laboratory evidence, provided any association possesses the qualities of strength, consistency, and specificity.

A notable case of strength occurred, for instance, when workers exposed to vinyl chloride were found to contract a rare form of liver cancer at a rate some 200 times normal. Another clear modern example is the link between smoking and lung cancer. In his work with the epidemiologist Sir Richard Doll, Hill found that a person who smokes a pack of cigarettes per day is 14 times more likely to develop lung cancer than a nonsmoker. Moreover, Doll and Hill found that this number—the so-called risk ratio—increased as the dose grew. Smokers who consumed two packs a day, for instance, faced a significantly greater risk. This effect—a so-called dose-response in which more is worse—Hill argued, was also strong evidence of causality.

In the extensive search for a connection between electromagnetic fields and adverse health effects, though, even those studies that have found a link have risk ratios that hover between 1 and 2. Such low ratios might signal a real effect yet to be isolated, but they might also simply reveal statistical noise. Despite some 15 years of research on this topic, both possibilities "still remain viable," according to David Savitz, an epidemiologist at the University of North Carolina.

Traditionally, evidence of an effect increases as scientific studies improve, but that doesn't seem to have happened in this area. Some of the most recent and sophisticated studies, such as two large-scale investigations of pregnant women who use electric blankets, another source of exposure to electromagnetic fields that has caused concern, have yielded negative results.

But because no single study can be relied on as definitive, Hill wisely noted that consistency can help establish an epidemiological link. In the case of smoking, for example, hundreds of studies have reproduced what Doll and Hill found for lung cancer, revealing risk ratios in the range of 10 to 30.

Proponents of the hypothesis that electromagnetic fields cause cancer acknowledge the lack of strength in the association but argue that an unmistakable trend exists. As David Carpenter, dean of the School of Public Health at the State University of New York (SUNY) at Albany, puts it, "while I admit that the proof is not 100 percent, there is consistency in correlation between leukemia and brain tumors and exposure to magnetic fields both in residential and occupational settings."

But is there really a consistent trend? In the past few years, several very large occupational studies have been published attempting to link electromagnetic-field exposure to disease. One 1994 study of Canadian workers, led by Gilles Theriault at McGill University, found a small association with leukemia but no link with brain cancer. Another study by David Savitz and colleagues at the University of North Carolina found no link with leukemia but a small association with brain cancer. Research by Jack Sahl at the UCLA School of Public Health in 1993 found nothing at all. The picture is also inconsistent for specific diseases like childhood leukemia. Savitz found a weak association, but other researchers, such as M. P. Coleman at the International Agency for Research on Cancer, did not. An earlier study in 1986 by L. Tomenius, former medical officer for the county of Stockholm, Sweden, even found an inverse correlation (implying electromagnetic fields offer protection against leukemia).

In fact, these study findings aren't just inconsistent, they also lack specificity. In his criteria, Hill emphasizes that actual epidemiological links must be specific: a particular kind of disease associated with a particular exposure offers a strong argument in favor of causation. Less compelling, on the other hand, are findings claiming that a whole range of diseases are linked to a diverse set of exposures. Judged in this light, the studies of electromagnetic fields and health effects have revealed few such specific links. Childhood leukemia and adult brain cancer have been implicated in several studies while others cite weak evidence for a range of ailments including adult leukemia, eye cancer, central nervous system tumors, neuroblastomas, meningiomas, lung cancer, male breast cancer, female breast cancer, Alzheimer's, and Parkinson's disease.

So what about the reported "clusters" of disease that are purported to be related to exposure to electromagnetic fields? One thing virtually all epidemiologists agree on is that, while clusters of disease may point to fruitful topics of study, their existence alone is not scientifically valid as a method to prove a connection between an environmental agent and disease. Epidemiologists like to tell their students the cautionary tale of the Texas sharpshooter, who fires bullets at the side of a barn and then draws in the target afterward to maximize his number of bulls' eyes. The point of the analogy is that diseases like cancers occur randomly in the population. Arbitrarily drawing boundaries in space and time by counting up the numbers of cancers in a given zip code, street, or school over a period of time is rather like the Texas sharpshooter; such arbitrary selection makes chance variations look like meaningful clusters. Just by chance some zip codes will have more than the average number of cancers. Just by chance, others will have fewer.

The problem is especially acute when the number of cases involved is small, as with rare cancers. In the case of Meadow Street, which is 250 yards long and contains only nine houses, journalist Paul Brodeur revealed that over several decades the residents suffered two malignant brain tumors and a nonmalignant brain tumor. The implication was that these were related in some way to the substation across the street. In fact, epidemiologists in Connecticut have argued persuasively that this number of brain cancers was not out of the ordinary. Even SUNY epidemiologist David Carpenter, who is convinced of a connection between electromagnetic fields and cancer, does not base his conviction on cluster studies, noting that "by statistics alone, it's very possible that there will be a number of cancers in one block and none in the next ten blocks."

To get around the problem of chance variation, epidemiologists typically study large numbers of individuals exposed to a candidate carcinogen or toxin and compare them with an equally large control group not exposed (or exposed to a much lower dose). By using large numbers of cases they can minimize the possibility that any differences between the groups could have appeared merely by chance.

Achieving statistical power is just the first problem, though. Epidemiologists must also eliminate confounders—other factors that might skew the results, such as the age, sex, and socioeconomic status of the study populations. Some diseases affect old people more frequently than young people, or women more than men, or poor people more than rich people. It is possible, for example, that people who live in houses near power lines are not as affluent or as well-educated as people who live away from them. If this is true, it might well account for any differences in health observed.

Investigators also have to rule out other potential environmental confounders ranging from traffic density to toxins. PCBs were widely used in electrical transformers, for example, and herbicides are sometimes used to clear tracts of land for power lines. Should a correlation be found between power lines and health effects, it would be essential to rule out these potential sources of disease.

Finally, when assessing exposure, investigators ideally ought not to know whether the person or household is a member of the exposed group or a control. Wertheimer and Leeper, for instance, did know which individuals had died of cancer at the time they were classifying houses according to wire codes, and that knowledge could have introduced bias. For this reason alone, many scientists discount their first study.

THE MULTIPLE COMPARISONS FALLACY

A 1992 study by epidemiologists Maria Feychting and Anders Ahlbom at the Karolinska Institute in Stockholm initially seemed to overcome most of these general obstacles and one major specific one: namely, that researchers investigating exposure to electromagnetic fields have had great difficulty agreeing how best to measure such exposure. In some cases, for instance, they have settled for crude, surrogate measures like job titles that include the word "electrical." Other times they have employed on-site measurements of field strengths. Ideally, of course, researchers would like to know an individual's true exposure to electromagnetic fields at the time disease allegedly started but, because this may

have happened far in the past, it is normally deemed impossible.

In Scandinavia, however, electric utilities maintain complete historical records of the amount of electricity actually pulsing through particular power lines at any given time. Using a computer program, the Swedish power company Vattenfalls actually used such data about current flowing in its high-voltage transmission lines in past years to calculate the magnetic field at given distances from the wire.

Seizing this opportunity, Feychting and Ahlbom undertook to study everyone with cancer who had lived within 300 meters of Sweden's high-voltage transmission line system over a 25-year period, calculating the actual magnetic fields that children and adults were exposed to at the time of their cancer diagnosis and before. The calculation did not include exposure from local distribution lines, domestic appliances, the wires in the houses, or from sources outside the home (such as trains, underground cables, or office appliances), but it did go far enough to capture a significant part of the subjects' historic exposure to electromagnetic fields. The study also took great pains to avoid confounding variables and sources of bias.

The results, published to worldwide attention in 1992, reported an apparently clear association between magnetic field exposure and childhood leukemia, with a risk ratio of nearly four for the highest exposed group. Surely, here was proof that even physicists and biological naysayers would have to accept. In the aftermath, the Swedish government announced it was investigating whether to move children away from schools near power lines.

But some four years after the Swedish research was published, it serves as a case study of what scientists call the multiple comparisons fallacy. A basic axiom of experimental sciences is that you must specify, in advance, the hypothesis that you are testing. But observational epidemiology sometimes mixes up two distinct kinds of experiments: those designed to generate hypotheses and those designed to test them.

Why does it matter? The answer can be found in the original contractor's report of the Feychting and Ahlbom study. Unlike the final published paper, which gives only a summary of their methods, this remarkable document reveals the comprehensiveness with which they attacked the problem. The study looked at twelve separate cancer rates (four in children and eight in adults), and used three different exposure scales (measured fields using gauss meters, calculated historic fields using the Vattenfalls' records, and measured distances from lines). Within each exposure scale there were further subdefinitions (such as cutoff points for "unexposed," "exposed," "more exposed," and "most exposed").

This initial report generated some 800 separate risk ratios, comparing the incidence of the twelve cancer rates with an astounding number of separate environmental categories—including many hairsplitting distinctions. For example, special categories were made for children who lived in single-family homes versus those who lived in apartments.

Such a method sounds thorough but, because there is no clearly stated hypothesis, we don't know which among these hundreds of comparisons the authors are testing. Unfortunately, by considering all of them, the researchers introduce a great deal of statistical noise. "By the standard way we do statistics, even if nothing is going on, we would expect 5 percent of those 800 to be statistically elevated, and 5 percent to be statistically decreased," explains John Moulder, a radiation biologist at the Medical College of Wisconsin. In other words, random statistical variation would predict some 30 or 40 elevated risk ratios above 1 (implying that electromagnetic fields cause a particular disease) and 30 or 40 decreased ones below 1, (implying that electromagnetic fields protect against that disease). Given such statistical variation, then, it becomes hard to know whether, by one measure of exposure, a finding that leukemia is up in a group of children is real or is merely the result of random noise.

Similarly, if there were no relationship between power lines and cancer, some "significantly" decreased rates of cancer would still be expected. In fact, such examples can be found in the report. Presented in isolation as evidence that electromagnetic fields "protected" against leukemia, these could be just as misleading as presenting the ones with positive risk ratios. In this regard, though, it appears that Feychting and Ahlbom were rather selective in their reporting.

For example, in the contractor's report, the researchers compare leukemia rates with calculated magnetic fields at the time of diagnosis, one year before diagnosis, five years before diagnosis, and ten years before diagnosis. They find a statistically significant correlation with calculated fields at the time of diagnosis, but not at one, five or ten years before diagnosis. The authors select only the first for publication, but on what justification? Since cancers generally take several years before they show clinical signs, a correlation between electromagnetic field exposure at the time of a cancer diagnosis should be no more significant than at one year, five years, or even 10 years before diagnosis.

Seen in this context, the published associations look far less compelling. Equally mystifying, while Feychting and Ahlbom reported a "significant correlation" between leukemia and some calculated electromagnetic fields, the authors found no association with magnetic fields they actually measured. In fact, they reported an inverse relationship with measured fields (that is, it appeared that there was less childhood leukemia in homes where they measured large fields). Moreover, they failed to find any positive association with calculated fields for children who lived in apartments, only for those in single-family homes.

Two other Scandinavian studies published in 1993 that made use of calculated historic electromagnetic fields reported inconclusive results. A Danish study by Jorgen Olsen at the Danish Cancer Control Agency found no significant increase for leukemia or brain cancer or for overall childhood cancers when 2.5 milligauss was used as the cut-off point to define exposure (as specified in the study design). However, after reanalyzing the data, the researchers determined that the overall incidence of childhood cancer was significantly elevated if 4 milligauss was used as the cut-off point. Meanwhile, though, a Finnish study led by Pia Verkasalo at the University of Helsinki found no significant increase in the incidence of a range of childhood cancers.

It is unclear how many epidemiological studies investigating electromagnetic fields commit the multiple comparisons fallacy or how many of the seemingly positive correlations found can be explained this way. Original contractors' reports are not always available. Yet the issue is fundamental. Outside of epidemiology, most scientists are unanimous: you cannot confuse a study that tests a hypothesis with one that merely generates them.

FAILING THE TEST

It is important to note that not all the Hill criteria need to be satisfied to establish causality. As Wisconsin's Moulder explains, in some cases "the epidemiology has been so strong that we've concluded something was a carcinogen without any laboratory evidence or any mechanisms. There are other cases when we've decided that something was a carcinogen just based on laboratory data without any actual epidemiological data." But, as he underscores, "you need some real strengths somewhere."

After scores of studies that span more than a decade, though, the contention that electromagnetic fields cause adverse health effects so far fails to meet any of the Hill criteria. The theory lacks biological plausibility. The experimental evidence so far is strongly negative. The epidemiological evidence is weak, inconsistent, and nonspecific. And the epidemiology is plagued by problems such as possible bias, lack of clearly defined measures of exposure, and multiple comparison artifacts.

Even if we suppose that magnetic fields from power lines do cause cancer, the fact that the connection has been so hard to prove means that, by definition, the risk cannot be large. As a worst case, for instance, assuming that Feychting and Ahlbom's conclusions are correct, a Swedish child would face an increased risk of contracting leukemia on the order of one in a million.

The public would certainly be within its rights to want to know about such a risk but would be hard-pressed to know what to do about it. Would moving the Swedish children to another location make them safer? "Absolutely not," says Peter Valberg, a biophysicist and risk analyst with Harvard School of Public Health. "The idea that you would bus the children as far as one mile would not make any sense in terms of the comparable risks. We know from real actuarial statistics that being on a bus does carry some real health hazards in terms of injury and death," Valberg says. And in fact Swedish authorities now agree—they decided not to make any policy changes based on the 1992 study.

In the United States, as President Clinton anticipates a long-awaited Environmental Protection Agency (EPA) report on electromagnetic fields, he faces a delicate policy dilemma. If he dismisses public concerns as unfounded, he might appear unsympathetic to people convinced that electromagnetic fields caused their health problems. On the other hand, he cannot support a position that is scientifically untenable. Unfortunately, even after the EPA report is released, Clinton's easiest option is to continue to say that more study is needed and allocate the research funds, either to the EPA or to another program administered by an agency like the National Institutes of Health.

The trouble with that course is that it makes little sense to continue researching this issue when so many urgent medical problems need attention. A policy of "keep on studying" not only focuses citizens' fears on phantom risks rather than on real ones like smoking, driving, or toxic chemical exposure, but it also drains considerable sums of money from mainstream medical research into a scientific backwater.

POSTSCRIPT

Are Electromagnetic Fields Dangerous to Your Health?

Is the EMF scare nothing more than media hype, as suggested by Sid Deutsch in "Electromagnetic Field Cancer Scares," *Skeptical Inquirer* (Winter 1994)? Or do EMFs pose a genuine hazard? If they do, the threat is not yet clear beyond a doubt. However, society cannot always wait for certainty. Gordon L. Hester, in "Electric and Magnetic Fields: Managing an Uncertain Risk," *Environment* (January/February 1992), states that just the possibility of a health hazard from EMFs is sufficient to justify more research into the problem. The guiding principle, says Hester, is " 'prudent avoidance,' which was originally intended to mean that people should avoid fields 'when this can be done with modest amounts of money and trouble.' " H. Keith Florig, in "Containing the Costs of the EMF Problem," *Science* (July 24, 1992), makes a similar point in his discussion of the expenses that utilities, manufacturers, and others are incurring to reduce EMF exposures in the absence of solid evidence that there is a hazard but in the presence of public concern and lawsuits.

Researchers Hans Wieser, Michael Fuller, and Jon Paul Dobson reported at the May 1993 meeting of the American Geophysical Union that magnetic fields can affect brain activity, suggesting that the body does respond to EMFs from electrical apparatus. On January 27, 1995, *Science* reported that "the U.S. Navy's 90-kilometer-long Extremely Low Frequency (ELF) antenna, set up [in a Michigan forest] in 1986 to communicate with submarines, is invigorating neighboring plant life"—apparently stimulating tree and algal growth in a way that has led some scientists to consider how ELF EMFs might stimulate the growth of cancer cells.

What should society do in the face of weak, uncertain, and even contradictory data? Can we afford to conclude that there is no hazard? Many scientists and politicians argue that even if there is no genuine medical risk from exposure to EMFs, there is a genuine impact in terms of public anxiety. It is therefore appropriate, they say, to fund further research and to take whatever relatively inexpensive steps to minimize exposure are possible. Failure to do so increases public anxiety and distrust of government and science.

It is worth noting that the EMF scare had a precedent in the late 1800s. See Joseph P. Sullivan, "Fearing Electricity: Overhead Wire Panic in New York City," *IEEE Technology and Society Magazine* (Fall 1995).

Students who wish to find more information on the Internet will find this site a useful starting point: http://infoventures.microserve.com/emf/currlit/currlit.html.

PART 5

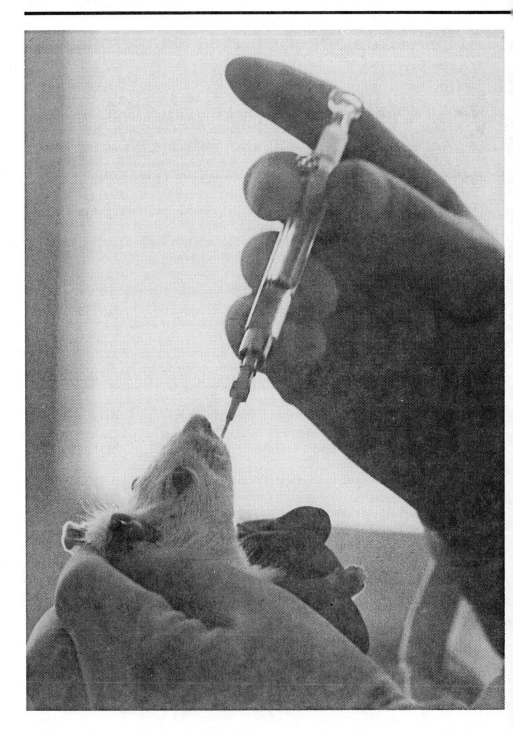

Ethics

Society's standards of right and wrong have been hammered out over thousands of years of trial, error, and (sometimes violent) debate. Accordingly, when science and technology offer society new choices to make and new things to do, debates are renewed over whether or not these choices and actions are ethically acceptable.

Today there is vigorous debate on such topics as the use of fetal tissue in medical research and treatment as well as some of the practices of science itself. This section explores some ethical issues regarding these subjects, starting with a discussion on the use of animals in research and including a debate on human experimentation.

■ Is the Use of Animals in Research Justified?

■ Is It Ethical to Use Humans as "Experimental Animals"?

■ Should Fetal Tissue Be Used to Heal Adults?

ISSUE 15

Is the Use of Animals in Research Justified?

YES: Elizabeth Baldwin, from "The Case for Animal Research in Psychology," *Journal of Social Issues* (1993)

NO: Steven Zak, from "Ethics and Animals," *The Atlantic Monthly* (March 1989)

ISSUE SUMMARY

YES: Elizabeth Baldwin, research ethics officer of the American Psychological Association's Science Directorate, argues that animals do not have the same moral rights as humans do, that their use in scientific research is justified by the resulting benefits to both humans and animals, and that their welfare is protected by law.

NO: Research attorney Steven Zak argues that current animal protection laws do not adequately protect animals used in medical and other research and that, for society to be virtuous, it must recognize the rights of animals not to be sacrificed for human needs.

Modern biologists and physicians know a great deal about how the human body works. Some of that knowledge has been gained by studying human cadavers and tissue samples acquired during surgery and through "experiments of nature" (strokes, for example, have taught a great deal about what the various parts of the brain do; extensive injuries from car accidents and wars have also been edifying). Some knowledge of human biology has also been gained from experiments on humans, such as when brain surgery patients agree to let their surgeons stimulate different parts of their brains electrically while the brains are exposed or when cancer patients agree to try experimental treatments.

The key word here is *agree*. Today it is widely accepted that people have the right to consent or not to consent to whatever is done to them in the name of research or treatment. In fact, society has determined that research done on humans without their free and informed consent is a form of scientific misconduct. However, this standard does not apply to animals, experimentation on which has produced the most knowledge of the human body.

Although animals have been used in research for at least the last 2,000 years, during most of that time, physicians who thought they had a workable treatment for some illness commonly tried it on their patients before they had any idea whether or not it worked or was even safe. Many patients, of course, died during these untested treatments. In the mid-nineteenth century, the French physiologist Claude Bernard argued that it was sensible to try such treatments first on animals to avoid some human suffering and death. No one then questioned whether or not human lives were more valuable than animal lives.

Today millions of animals are used in research. Geneticists generally study fruit flies, roundworms, and zebra fish. Physiologists study mammals, mostly mice and rats but also rabbits, cats, dogs, pigs, sheep, goats, monkeys, and chimpanzees. Experimental animals are often kept in confined quarters, cut open, infected with disease organisms, fed unhealthy diets, and injected with assorted chemicals. Sometimes the animals suffer. Sometimes the animals die. And sometimes they are healed, albeit often of diseases or injuries induced by the researchers in the first place.

Not surprisingly, some observers have reacted with extreme sympathy and have called for better treatment of animals used in research. This "animal welfare" movement has, in turn, spawned the more extreme "animal rights" movement, which asserts that animals—especially mammals—have rights as important and as deserving of regard as those of humans. In its most extreme form, this movement insists that animals are persons in every moral sense. Thus, to kill an animal, whether for research, food, or fur, is the moral equivalent of murder.

This attitude has led to important reforms in the treatment of animals and to the development of several alternatives to using animals (see Alan M. Goldberg and John M. Frazier, "Alternatives to Animals in Toxicity Testing," *Scientific American*, August 1989). However, it has also led to hysterical objections to in-class animal dissections, terrorist attacks on laboratories, the destruction of research records, and the theft of research materials (including animals). In 1989 an undersecretary of the Department of Health and Human Services, in attacking the animal rights movement, said, "We must not permit a handful of extremists to deprive millions of the life-sustaining and life-enhancing fruits of biomedical research."

In the following selection, Elizabeth Baldwin argues in the same vein: animals are of immense value with regard to medical, veterinary, and psychological research, but they do not have the same moral rights as humans. Our obligation, she maintains, is not to treat them as persons but to treat them humanely, and there is a sufficient number of laws and regulations to ensure that this is done.

In opposition, Steven Zak, who has written numerous articles on animals with regard to ethics and the law, argues that morality requires society to recognize the right of animals not to be made to suffer at all for the benefit of humans. Therefore, researchers should always find alternative modes of research.

YES

Elizabeth Baldwin

THE CASE FOR ANIMAL RESEARCH
IN PSYCHOLOGY

Animal liberationists do not separate out the human animal. A rat is a pig is a dog is a boy.

—Ingrid Newkirk, Director, People for the Ethical Treatment of Animals.

The shock value of this quote has made it a favorite of those defending the use of animals in research. It succinctly states the core belief of many animal rights activists who oppose the use of animals in research. Although some activists work for improved laboratory conditions for research animals, recent surveys suggest that most activists would like to eliminate animal research entirely (Plous, 1991). These activists believe animals have rights equal to humans and therefore should not be used as subjects in laboratory research.

The debate over animal research can be confusing unless one understands the very different goals of animal welfare organizations and animal rights groups. People concerned with animal welfare seek to improve laboratory conditions for research animals and to reduce the number of animals needed. These mainstream goals encompass traditional concerns for the humane treatment of animals, and most researchers share these goals. In contrast, the views of animal rights activists are *not* mainstream, since there are few people who would agree with the above quote from Ingrid Newkirk. Indeed, in a national poll conducted by the National Science Foundation, half the respondents answered the following question affirmatively: "Should scientists be allowed to do research that causes pain and injury to animals like dogs and chimpanzees if it produces new information about human health problems?" (National Science Board, 1991). These findings are particularly impressive given the explicit mention of "pain and injury" to popular animals such as dogs and chimpanzees. My own position is that animals do not have rights in the same sense that humans do, but that people have a responsibility to ensure the humane treatment of animals under their care. Animals have played a pivotal role in improving the human condition, and in return, society should strive to treat them well.

From Elizabeth Baldwin, "The Case for Animal Research in Psychology," *Journal of Social Issues*, vol. 49, no. 1 (1993). Copyright © 1993 by The Society for the Psychological Study of Social Issues. Reprinted by permission. References omitted.

BACKGROUND

The modern animal rights movement is intellectual and spiritual heir to the Victorian antivivisection movement in Britain (Sperling, 1988). This 19th-century movement was a powerful force in Britain and arose in part from accelerating changes brought about by science and technology (and the resulting challenges to the prevailing view of humanity's relationship to nature).

The British movement peaked in 1876 with the passage of the Cruelty to Animals Act. This compromise legislation required licenses for conducting animal research, but recognized the societal value of continuing to use animals in research. It was about this time that the scientific community began to organize a defense of animal research. Several challenges to animal research were made in the ensuing 20 years, but in the end, the medical and scientific community were able to successfully protect their interests. The Victorian antivivisection movement, however, did bring about the regulation of research and helped prevent outright abuse (Sperling, 1988).

The beginning of the modern animal rights movement is generally dated to the 1975 publication of *Animal Liberation* by philosopher Peter Singer. Although Singer himself is not an advocate of animal "rights," he provided the groundwork for later arguments that animals have rights—including the right not to be used in research. Most animal rights activists believe animals have a right not to be used for research, food, entertainment, and a variety of other purposes. An inordinate amount of attention is devoted to animal research, however, even though far fewer animals are used for re-search than for other purposes (Nicoll & Russell, 1990).

There has been a phenomenal growth in the animal rights movement since the publication of Singer's book. People for the Ethical Treatment of Animals (PETA), the leading animal rights organization in the United States, has grown from 18 members in 1981 to more than 250,000 members in 1990. (McCabe, 1990). By any standard, the animal rights movement is a force to be reckoned with.

PHILOSOPHICAL ISSUES

There are two basic philosophies that support the animal rights movement, although activists are often unable to articulate them (Sperling, 1988). These two positions are summarized by Herzog (1990) as the *utilitarian* argument and the *rights* argument.

The utilitarian position is that the greatest good is achieved by maximizing pleasure and happiness, and by minimizing suffering and pain. Although traditionally applied only to humans, Singer argues that animals should be included when considering the greatest good. He states, "No matter what the nature of the being, the principle of equality requires that its suffering be counted equally with the like suffering—insofar as rough comparisons can be made—of any other being" (Singer, 1990, p. 8). Utilitarians would thus argue that animals have an interest equal to that of humans in avoiding pain and suffering, and should therefore not be used in experiments that could cause them harm. Two problems with this philosophy are that (1) it is hard to draw a line between creatures that suffer and creatures that do not, and (2) the argument does not address *qualitative* differences in pain and pleasure across species (Herzog, 1990).

The rights position states that animals possess certain rights based on their inherent value. This philosophy, first developed by Tom Regan (1983), argues that animals have a right not to be used by humans in research (and for many other purposes). Major problems with this position arise in deciding just what rights are and in determining who is entitled to hold them (Herzog, 1990).

While the above positions have been developed relatively recently, the alternative view of animals as qualitatively different from humans has a long history in Judeo-Christian thought. Traditionally, humans were believed to have been created in the image of God and to have dominion over animals. Robb (1988) uses this perspective in arguing that humans are unique by virtue of their capacity for moral choice. Because of this capacity, humans can be held responsible for their choices, and can therefore enter into contractual agreements with binding rights and responsibilities for *both* parties. Robb acknowledges that some animals have human capacities in certain areas, but he argues that this does not make them morally equal to humans or give them rights that take precedence over human needs.

The most persuasive argument for using animals in behavioral research, however, is the untold benefit that accrues to both humans and animals. The benefits of behavioral research with animals have been enumerated by such authors as Miller (1985) and King and Yarbrough (1985), and for most people, these benefits are the reason that they support the continued use of animals in research. This argument—which is basically utilitarian—is the one most often cited by the research community in defense of animal research. In contrast to Singer's utilitarianism, however, animals are not given the same degree of consideration as people.

In conclusion, both sides in the animal rights debate have philosophical underpinnings to support their position, but what often emerges in the rhetoric is not reasoned debate but emotion-laden charges and personal attacks. This is not surprising, given the strong passions aroused in the discussion.

FRAMING THE DEBATE

In the 1980s, activists targeted certain researchers or areas of research that they viewed as vulnerable to attack, and researchers were forced to assume a defensive posture. Unfortunately, activists were right about the vulnerability of individual scientists; little or no institutional defense was mounted against these early attacks. The prevailing attitude was to ignore the activists in hopes that they would go away, and thus attract less attention from the public and the press. This passivity left the early targets of animal rights activists in the position of a man asked, "Why do you beat your wife?" No matter how researchers responded, they sounded defensive and self-serving. It took several years for the research community to realize that animal rights activists were not going away, and that the activists' charges needed to be answered in a systematic and serious manner.

This early failure on the part of the research community to communicate its position effectively left the public with little information beyond what was provided by the animal rights activists. Framing the debate is half the battle, and the research community was left playing catch-up and answering the question, "Why do you abuse your research animals?"

The research community also faced the daunting task of explaining the use of animals in research to a public whose understanding of the scientific method was almost nil. The most difficult misconception to correct was the belief that every research project with animals should produce "useful" results (Orem, 1990). Social scientists who have received Senator William Proxmire's "Golden Fleece Award" are well aware of this line of thinking—a line of thinking that displays a complete misunderstanding of how science works, and ignores the vast amount of basic research that typically precedes each "useful" discovery.

It is difficult for scientific rationales to compete with shocking posters, catchy slogans, and soundbites from the animal rights movement. The most effective response from the scientific community has been to point out innumerable health advances made possible by the use of animals as research models. This approach is something that most people can relate to, since everyone has benefited from these advances.

The early defensive posture of scientists also failed to allay public concerns about the ability of researchers to self-regulate their care and use of research animals. Unlike the participation of humans in research (who are usually able to speak in their own defense and give consent), there seemed to be no one in the system able to "speak" for the animals. Or so people were encouraged to believe by animal rights activists. As discussed below, there are elaborate federal regulations on the use of animals in research, as well as state laws and professional guidelines on the care and use of animals in research.

RESTORING TRUST

Scientists, research institutions, and federal research agencies finally came to realize that the charges being leveled by animal rights activists needed to be publicly —and forcefully—rebutted. Dr. Frederick Goodwin, former Administrator of the Alcohol, Drug Abuse, and Mental Health Administration (ADAMHA), was one of the first federal officials to defend animal research publicly, and point out the difference between animal welfare and animal rights (Booth, 1989). Recently, many more federal officials and respected researchers have publicly spoken on the importance of animal research (Mervis, 1990).

Countering Misinformation

Animal rights literature often uses misleading images to depict animal research —images such as animals grimacing as they are shocked with electricity. These descriptions lead readers to believe animals are routinely subjected to high voltage shocks capable of producing convulsions (e.g., Singer, 1990, pp. 42–45). Such propaganda is far from the truth. In most cases, electric shock (when used at all) is relatively mild—similar to what one might feel from the discharge of static electricity on a cold, dry day. Even this relatively mild use of shock is carefully reviewed by Institutional Animal Care and Use Committees before being approved, and researchers must demonstrate that alternate techniques are not feasible. Stronger shock *is* used in animal research, but it is used to study medical problems such as epilepsy (a convulsive disorder). It is also used to test the effectiveness and side effects of drugs developed to control such disorders. It is not within the scope of this article to refute the myriad charges issued against animal research in general, specific projects, and individual researchers. Suffice it to say that such allegations have been persuasively refuted (Coile & Miller, 1984; Feeney, 1987; Johnson, 1990; McCabe, 1986).

Benefits to Animals

Animal rights activists often fail to appreciate the many benefits to animals that have resulted from animal research. Behavioral research has contributed to improvements in the environments of captive animals, including those used in research (Novak & Petto, 1991). The list of benefits also includes a host of veterinary procedures and the development of vaccines for deadly diseases such as rabies, Lyme disease, and feline leukemia. Research in reproductive biology and captive breeding programs are also the only hope for some animals on the brink of extinction (King et al., 1988).

Regulations and Guidelines

It is clear that many people concerned about the use of animals in research are not aware of the elaborate structure that exists to regulate the care and use of animals in research. This system includes federal regulations under the Animal Welfare Act (U.S. Department of Agriculture, 1989, 1990, 1991), Public Health Service (PHS) policy (Office for Protection from Research Risks, 1986), and state laws that govern the availability of pound animals for research.

The Animal Welfare Act, most recently amended in 1985, is enforced by the USDA's Animal and Plant Health Inspection Service (APHIS). The regulations connected with this law include 127 pages of guidelines governing the use of animals in research. It also includes unannounced inspections of animal research facilities by APHIS inspectors who do nothing but inspect research facilities. Their inspections are conducted to ensure compliance with regulations that include everything from cage size, feeding schedules, and lighting to exercise requirements for dogs and the promotion of psychological well-being among nonhuman primates.

In addition to APHIS inspectors who make unannounced inspections of animal research facilities, there are local Institutional Animal Care and Use Committees (IACUCs) that review each proposed research project using animals. Research proposals must include a justification for the species used and the number of animals required, an assurance that a thorough literature review has been conducted (to prevent unnecessary replication of research), and a consideration of alternatives if available. IACUCs are also responsible for inspecting local animal research facilities to check for continued compliance with state protocols.

Each grant proposal received by a PHS agency (National Institutes of Health, and the Centers for Disease Control) that proposes using animals must contain an assurance that it has been reviewed by an IACUC and been approved. IACUCs must have no less than five members and contain at least one veterinarian, one practicing scientist experienced in research involving animals, one member who is primarily concerned in nonscientific matters (e.g., a lawyer or ethicist), and one member who is not affiliated with the institution in any way and is not an immediate family member of anyone affiliated with the institution (Office for Protection from Research Risks, 1986; USDA, 1989).

Beyond federal animal welfare regulations, PHS policy, and the PHS Guidelines (National Research Council, 1985), there are professional guidelines for the care and use of research animals. Examples include the American Psychological Association's (APA) *Ethical Principles of Psychologists* (1990) and *Guidelines for Ethical Conduct in the Care and Use of Animals* (1993), and the Society for Neuroscience's Handbook (Society for Neuroscience, 1991).

The APA also has a Committee on Animal Research and Ethics (CARE) whose charge includes the responsibility to "review the ethics of animal experimentation and recommend guidelines for the ethical conduct of research, and appropriate care of animals in research." CARE wrote the APA's *Guidelines for Ethical Conduct in the Care and Use of Animals,* and periodically reviews it and makes revisions. These guidelines are widely used by psychologists and other scientists, and have been used in teaching research ethics at the undergraduate and graduate level. The APA's Science Directorate provided support for a conference on psychological well-being of nonhuman primates used in research, and published a volume of proceedings from that conference (Novak & Petto, 1991). The APA also helps promote research on animal welfare by membership in and support for such organizations as the American Association for the Accreditation of Laboratory Animal Care (AAALAC).

AAALAC is the only accrediting body recognized by the PHS, and sets the "gold standard" for animal research facilities. To receive AAALAC accreditation, an institution must go beyond what is required by federal animal welfare regulations and PHS policy. AAALAC accreditation is highly regarded, and those institutions that receive it serve as models for the rest of the research community.

Even with all these safeguards in place, some critics question the ability of the research community to self-regulate its use of animals in research. The system can only be considered self-regulating, however, if one assumes that researchers, institutional officials, members of IACUCs (which must include a member not affiliated with the institution), USDA inspectors, animal care and lab technicians, and veterinarians have identical interests. These are the individuals with the most direct access to the animals used in research, and these are the specialists most knowledgeable about the conditions under which animals are used in research.

In several states, animal rights activists have succeeded in gaining access to IACUC meetings where animal research proposals are discussed. On the whole, however, research institutions have fought—and are still fighting—to keep these meetings closed to the general public. There is a very real fear among researchers that information gleaned from such meetings will be used to harass and target individual researchers. Given the escalating nature of illegal break-ins by such organizations as the Animal Liberation Front, this is a legitimate concern. Indeed, on some campuses "reward posters" offer money to individuals who report the abuse of research animals.

Even though IACUC meetings are generally closed to the public, the elaborate system regulating animal research is by no means a closed one. The most recent animal welfare regulations were finalized after five years of proposals recorded in the *Federal Register;* comments from the public, research institutions, professional associations, animal welfare groups, and animal rights groups; the incorporation of these comments; republication of the revised rules; and so forth. Neither researchers nor animal rights groups were entirely pleased with the final document, but everyone had their say. Although certain elements of the regulatory system rely on researchers, it is hard to imagine a workable system that would fail to use their expertise. The unspoken assumption that researchers cannot be trusted to care for their research animals is not supported by the records of APHIS inspections. Good science demands good laboratory animal care, and it is in a researcher's best interest to ensure that laboratory animals are well cared for.

The Benefits of Behavioral Research With Animals

The use of animals in psychological and behavioral research was an early target of animal rights activists. This research was perceived as a more vulnerable target than biomedical research, which had more direct and easily explained links to specific human health benefits. Psychological and behavioral research also lacked the powerful backing of the medical establishment (Archer, 1986).

There is, of course, a long list of benefits derived from psychological research with animals. These include rehabilitation of persons suffering from stroke, head injury, spinal cord injury, and Alzheimer's disease; improved communication with severely retarded children; methods for the early detection of eye disorders in children (allowing preventive treatment to avoid permanent impairment); control of chronic anxiety without the use of drugs; and improved treatments for alcoholism, obesity, substance abuse, hypertension, chronic migraine headaches, lower back pain, and insomnia (Miller, 1985). Behavioral research with nonhuman primates also permits the investigation of complex behaviors such as social organization, aggression, learning and memory, communication, and growth and development (King et al., 1988).

The nature of psychological and behavioral research makes the development and use of alternatives difficult. It is the behavior of the whole organism, and the interaction among various body systems, that is examined. Computer models may be used, but "research with animals will still be needed to provide basic data for writing computer software, as well as to prove the validity and reliability of computer alternatives" (U.S. Congress, Office of Technology Assessment, 1986). The alternative of using nonliving systems may be possible with epidemiologic data bases for some behavioral research, but chemical and physical systems are not useful for modeling complex behaviors. Likewise, in vitro cultures of organs, tissues, and cells do not display the characteristics studied by psychologists.

CONCLUSION

Research psychologists have been asked to eschew emotionalism, and bring logic and reason to the debate over animal research (Bowd, 1990). This is certainly the style most researchers are comfortable with—yet they have also been advised to quit trying to "apply logic and reason in their responses [to animal rights activists]" (Culliton, 1991). Culliton warns that while "animal rights people go for the heart, the biologists go for the head" and are losing the public in the process.

Which path is best? A reasoned approach draws high marks for civility, but will it help scientists in their trench warfare with animal rights activists?

Do animals have rights that preclude their use in laboratory research? I, and the psychologists I help represent, would say no. But researchers do have responsibilities to the animals they use in their research. These responsibilities include ensuring the humane care of their research animals, using the minimum number of animals necessary, and seeing to it that all laboratory assistants are adequately trained and supervised. As stated in the APA's *Ethical Principles*, "Laws and regulations notwithstanding, an animal's immediate protection depends upon the scientist's own conscience" (APA, 1990).

Researchers and others concerned with animal welfare can engage in a useful dialogue as standards of care and use evolve. This dialogue has proven fruitless with animal rights activists, though, since they seem unwilling to compromise or consider other viewpoints. What is the middle ground for a discussion with someone whose goal is the elimination of all research on animals?

The collective decision society has made is that the benefits derived from animal research far outweigh the costs. As public opinion polls indicate, most people are willing to accept these costs but want assurances that animals are humanely cared for. Yes, I'm "speciesist" in the eyes of Ingrid Newkirk—I will never believe my son is a dog is a pig is a rat.

NO

Steven Zak

ETHICS AND ANIMALS

In December of 1986 members of an "animal-liberation" group called True Friends broke into the Sema, Inc., laboratories in Rockville, Maryland, and took four baby chimpanzees from among the facility's 600 primates. The four animals, part of a group of thirty being used in hepatitis research, had been housed individually in "isolettes"—small stainless-steel chambers with sealed glass doors. A videotape produced by True Friends shows other primates that remained behind. Some sit behind glass on wire floors, staring blankly. One rocks endlessly, banging violently against the side of his cage. Another lies dead on his cage's floor.

The "liberation" action attracted widespread media attention to Sema, which is a contractor for the National Institutes of Health [NIH], the federal agency that funds most of the animal research in this country. Subsequently the NIH conducted an investigation into conditions at the lab and concluded that the use of isolettes is justified to prevent the spread of disease among infected animals. For members of True Friends and other animal-rights groups, however, such a scientific justification is irrelevant to what they see as a moral wrong; these activists remain frustrated over conditions at the laboratory. This conflict between the NIH and animal-rights groups mirrors the tension between animal researchers and animal-rights advocates generally. The researchers' position is that their use of animals is necessary to advance human health care and that liberation actions waste precious resources and impede the progress of science and medicine. The animal-rights advocates' position is that animal research is an ethical travesty that justifies extraordinary, and even illegal, measures.

The Sema action is part of a series that numbers some six dozen to date and that began, in 1979, with a raid on the New York University Medical Center, in which members of a group known as the Animal Liberation Front (ALF) took a cat and two guinea pigs. The trend toward civil disobedience is growing. For example, last April members of animal-rights groups demonstrated at research institutions across the country (and in other countries, including Great Britain and Japan), sometimes blocking entrances to them by forming

From Steven Zak, "Ethics and Animals," *The Atlantic Monthly* (March 1989). Copyright © 1989 by Steven Zak. Reprinted by permission.

human chains. In the United States more than 130 activists were arrested, for offenses ranging from blocking a doorway and trespassing to burglary.

To judge by everything from talk-show programs to booming membership enrollment in animal-rights groups (U.S. membership in all groups is estimated at 10 million), the American public is increasingly receptive to the animal-rights position. Even some researchers admit that raids by groups like True Friends and the ALF have exposed egregious conditions in particular labs and have been the catalyst for needed reforms in the law. But many members of animal-rights groups feel that the recent reforms do not go nearly far enough. Through dramatic animal-liberation actions and similar tactics, they hope to force what they fear is a complacent public to confront a difficult philosophical issue: whether animals, who are known to have feelings and psychological lives, ought to be treated as mere instruments of science and other human endeavors....

Animal-rights activists feel acute frustration over a number of issues, including hunting and trapping, the destruction of animals' natural habits, and the raising of animals for food. But for now the ALF considers animal research the most powerful symbol of human dominion over and exploitation of animals, and it devotes most of its energies to that issue. The public has been ambivalent, sometimes cheering the ALF on, at other times denouncing the group as "hooligans." However one chooses to characterize the ALF, it and other groups like it hold an uncompromising "rights view" of ethics toward animals. The rights view distinguishes the animal-protection movement of today from that of the past and is the source of the movement's radicalism.

"THEY ALL HAVE A RIGHT TO LIVE"

Early animal-protection advocates and groups... seldom talked about rights. They condemned cruelty—that is, acts that produce or reveal bad character. In early-nineteenth-century England campaigners against the popular sport of bull-baiting argued that it "fostered every bad and barbarous principle of our nature." Modern activists have abandoned the argument that cruelty is demeaning to human character ("virtue thought") in favor of the idea that the lives of animals have intrinsic value ("rights thought"). Rights thought doesn't necessarily preclude the consideration of virtue, but it mandates that the measure of virtue be the foreseeable consequences to others of one's acts.

"Michele" is thirty-five and works in a bank in the East. She has participated in many of the major ALF actions in the United States. One of the missions involved freeing rats, and she is scornful of the idea that rats aren't worth the effort. "These animals feel pain just like dogs, but abusing them doesn't arouse constituents' ire, so they don't get the same consideration. They all have a right to live their lives. Cuteness should not be a factor."

While most people would agree that animals should not be tortured, there is no consensus about animals' right to live (or, more precisely, their right not to be killed). Even if one can argue, as the British cleric Humphrey Primatt did in 1776, that "pain is pain, whether it be inflicted on man or on beast," it is more difficult to argue that the life of, say, a dog is qualitatively the same as that of a human being. To this, many animal-rights activists would say that every morally relevant characteristic that is lacking in all animals (rationality might be one, according to some ways of defining that term) is also lacking in some "marginal" human beings, such as infants, or the senile, or the severely retarded. Therefore, the activists argue, if marginal human beings have the right to live, it is arbitrary to hold that animals do not. Opponents of this point of view often focus on the differences between animals and "normal" human beings, asserting, for instance, that unlike most human adults, animals do not live by moral rules and therefore are not part of the human "moral community."

The credibility of the animal-rights viewpoint, however, need not stand or fall with the "marginal human beings" argument. Lives don't have to be qualitatively the same to be worthy of equal respect. One's perception that another life has value comes as much from an appreciation of its uniqueness as from the recognition that it has characteristics that are shared by one's own life. (Who would compare the life of a whale to that of a marginal human being?) One can imagine that the lives of various kinds of animals differ radically, even as a result of having dissimilar bodies and environments—that being an octopus feels different from being an orangutan or an oriole. The orangutan cannot be redescribed as the octopus minus, or plus, this or that mental characteristic; conceptually, nothing could be added to or taken from the octopus that would make it the equivalent of the oriole. Likewise, animals are not simply rudimentary human beings, God's false steps, made before He finally got it right with us.

Recognizing differences, however, puts one on tentative moral ground. It is easy to argue that likes ought to be treated alike. Differences bring problems: How do we think about things that are unlike? Against what do we measure and evaluate them? What combinations of likeness and difference lead to what sorts of moral consideration? Such problems may seem unmanageable, and yet in a human context we routinely face ones similar in kind if not quite in degree: our ethics must account for dissimilarities between men and women, citizens and aliens, the autonomous and the helpless, the fully developed and the merely potential, such as children or fetuses. We never solve these problems with finality, but we confront them....

Both advocates and opponents of animal rights also invoke utilitarianism in support of their points of view. Utilitarianism holds that an act or practice is measured by adding up the good and the bad consequences—classically, pleasure and pain—and seeing which come out ahead. There are those who would exclude animals from moral consideration on the grounds that the benefits of exploiting them outweigh the harm. Ironically, though, it was utilitarianism, first formulated by Jeremy Bentham in the eighteenth century, that brought animals squarely into the realm of moral consideration. If an act or practice has good and bad consequences for animals, then these must be entered into the moral arithmetic. And the calculation must be genuinely disinterested. One may not baldly assert that one's own interests count for more. Animal researchers may truly believe that they are impartially weighing all interests when they conclude that human interests overwhelm those of animals. But a skeptical reader will seldom be persuaded that they are in fact doing so....

Even true utilitarianism is incomplete, though, without taking account of rights. For example, suppose a small group of aboriginal tribespeople were captured and bred for experiments that would benefit millions of other people by, say, resulting in more crash-worthy cars. Would the use of such people be morally acceptable? Surely it would not, and that point illustrates an important function of rights thought: to put limits on what can be done to individuals, even for the good of the many. Rights thought dictates that we cannot kill one rights-holder to save another—or even more than one other— whether or not the life of the former is "different" from that of the latter.

Those who seek to justify the exploitation of animals often claim that it comes down to a choice: kill an animal or allow a human being to die. But this claim is misleading, because a choice so posed has already been made. The very act of considering the taking of life X to save life Y reduces X to the status of a mere instrument. Consider the problem in a purely human context. Imagine that if Joe doesn't get a new kidney he will die. Sam, the only known potential donor with a properly matching kidney, himself has only one kidney and has not consented to give it—and his life—up for Joe. Is there really a choice? If the only way to save Joe is to kill Sam, then we would be unable to do so—and no one would say that we chose Sam over Joe. Such a choice would never even be contemplated.

In another kind of situation there *is* a choice. Imagine that Joe and Sam both need a kidney to survive, but we have only one in our kidney bank. It may be that we should give the kidney to Joe, a member of our community, rather than to Sam, who lives in some distant country (though this is far from clear—

maybe flipping a coin would be more fair). Sam (or the loser of the coin flip) could not complain that his rights had been violated, because moral claims to some resource—positive claims—must always be dependent on the availability of that resource. But the right not to be treated as if one were a mere resource or instrument—negative, defensive claims —is most fundamentally what it means to say that one has rights. And this is what members of the ALF have in mind when they declare that animals, like human beings, have rights.

Where, one might wonder, should the line be drawn? Must we treat dragonflies the same as dolphins? Surely not. Distinctions must be made, though to judge definitively which animals must be ruled out as holders of rights may be impossible even in principle. In legal or moral discourse we are virtually never able to draw clear lines. This does not mean that drawing a line anywhere, arbitrarily, is as good as drawing one anywhere else.

The line-drawing metaphor, though, implies classifying entities in a binary way: as either above the line, and so entitled to moral consideration, or not. Binary thinking misses nuances of our moral intuition. Entities without rights may still deserve moral consideration on other grounds: one may think that a dragonfly doesn't quite qualify for rights yet believe that it would be wrong to crush one without good reason. And not all entities with rights need be treated in precisely the same way. This is apparent when one compares animals over whom we have assumed custody with wild animals. The former, I think, have rights to our affirmative aid, while the latter have such rights only in certain circumstances. Similar distinctions can be made among human beings, and also between human beings and particular animals. For example, I recently spent $1,000 on medical care for my dog, and I think he had a right to that care, but I have never given such an amount to a needy person on the street. Rights thought, then, implies neither that moral consideration ought to be extended only to the holders of rights nor that all rights-holders must be treated with a rigid equality. It implies only that rights-holders should never be treated as if they, or their kind, didn't matter.

ANIMALS, REFRIGERATORS, AND CAN OPENERS

The question of man's relationship with animals goes back at least to Aristotle, who granted that animals have certain senses—hunger, thirst, a sense of touch—but who held that they lack rationality and therefore as "the lower sort [they] are by nature slaves, and... should be under the rule of a master." Seven centuries later Saint Augustine added the authority of the Church, arguing that "Christ himself [teaches] that to refrain from the killing of animals... is the height of superstition, for there are no common rights between us and the beasts...." Early in the seventeenth century René Descartes argued that, lacking language, animals cannot have thoughts or souls and thus are machines.

One may be inclined to dismiss such beliefs as archaic oddities, but even today some people act as if animals were unfeeling things. I worked in a research lab for several summers during college, and I remember that it was a natural tendency to lose all empathy with one's animal subjects. My supervisor seemed actually to delight in swinging rats around by their tails and flinging them against a concrete wall as a way of stunning the animals before killing them. Rats and rabbits, to those who injected, weighed, and dissected them, were little different from cultures in a petri dish: they were just things to manipulate and observe. Feelings of what may have been moral revulsion were taken for squeamishness, and for most of my lab mates those feelings subsided with time.

The first animal-welfare law in the United States, passed in New York State in 1828, emphasized the protection of animals useful in agriculture. It also promoted human virtue with a ban on "maliciously and cruelly" beating or torturing horses, sheep, or cattle. Today courts still tend to focus on human character, ruling against human beings only for perpetrating the most shocking and senseless abuse of animals....

Most states leave the regulation of medical research to Washington. In 1966 Congress passed the Laboratory Animal Welfare Act, whose stated purpose was not only to provide humane care for animals but also to protect the owners of dogs and cats from theft by proscribing the use of stolen animals. (Note the vocabulary of property law; animals have long been legally classified as property.) Congress then passed the Animal Welfare Act [AWA] of 1970, which expanded the provisions of the 1966 act to include more species of animals and to regulate more people who handle animals. The AWA was further amended in 1976 and in 1985.

The current version of the AWA mandates that research institutions meet certain minimum requirements for the handling and the housing of animals, and requires the "appropriate" use of pain-killers. But the act does not regulate research or experimentation itself, and allows researchers to withhold anesthetics or tranquilizers "when scientifically necessary." Further, while the act purports to regulate dealers who buy animals at auctions and other markets to sell to laboratories, it does little to protect those animals....

The 1985 amendments to the AWA were an attempt to improve the treatment of animals in laboratories, to improve enforcement, to encourage the consideration of alternative research methods that use fewer or no animals, and to minimize duplication in experiments. One notable change is that for the first time, research institutions using primates must keep them in environments conducive to their psychological well-being; however, some animal-rights activists have expressed skepticism, since the social and psychological needs of primates are complex, and the primary concern of researchers is not the interests of their animal subjects. Last September [1988] a symposium on the psychological well-being of captive primates was held at Harvard University. Some participants contended that we lack data on the needs of the thirty to forty species of primates now used in laboratories. Others suggested that the benefits of companionship and social life are obvious.

The U.S. Department of Agriculture is responsible for promulgating regulations under the AWA and enforcing the law. Under current USDA regulations the cages of primates need only have floor space equal to three times the area occupied by the animal "when standing on four feet"—in the words of the USDA, which has apparently forgotten that primates have hands. The 1985 amendments required the USDA to publish final revised regulations, including regulations on the well-being of primates, by December of 1986. At this writing the department has yet to comply, and some activists charge that the NIH and the Office of Management and Budget have delayed the publication of the new regulations and attempted to undermine them.

One may believe that virtue thought —which underlies current law—and rights thought should protect animals equally. After all, wouldn't a virtuous person or society respect the interests of animals? But virtue thought allows the law to disregard these interests, because virtue can be measured by at least two yardsticks: by the foreseeable effects of an act on the interests of an animal or by the social utility of the act. The latter standard was applied in a 1983 case in Maryland in which a researcher appealed his conviction for cruelty to animals after he had performed experiments that resulted in monkeys' mutilating their hands. Overturning the conviction, the Maryland Court of Appeals wrote that "there are certain normal human activities to which the infliction of pain to an animal is purely incidental"—thus the actor is not a sadist—and that the state legislature had intended for these activities to be exempt from the law protecting animals.

The law, of course, is not monolithic. Some judges have expressed great sympathy for animals. On the whole, though, the law doesn't recognize animal rights. Under the Uniform Commercial Code, for instance, animals—along with refrigerators and can openers—constitute "goods."

ALTERNATIVES TO
US-VERSUS-THEM

Estimates of the number of animals used each year in laboratories in the United States range from 17 million to 100 million: 200,000 dogs, 50,000 cats, 60,000 primates, 1.5 million guinea pigs, hamsters, and rabbits, 200,000 wild animals, thousands of farm animals and birds, and millions of rats and mice. The conditions in general—lack of exercise, isolation from other animals, lengthy confinement in tiny cages—are stressful. Many experiments are painful or produce fear, anxiety, or depression. For instance, in 1987 researchers at the Armed Forces Radiobiology Research Institute reported that nine monkeys were subjected to whole-body irradiation; as a result, within two hours six of the monkeys were vomiting and hypersalivating. In a proposed experiment at the University of Washington pregnant monkeys, kept in isolation, will be infected with the simian AIDS virus; their offspring, infected or not, will be separated from the mothers at birth.

Not all animals in laboratories, of course, are subjects of medical research. In the United States each year some 10 million animals are used in testing products and for other commercial purposes. For instance, the United States Surgical Corporation, in Norwalk, Connecticut, uses hundreds of dogs each year to train salesmen in the use of the company's surgical staple gun. In 1981 and 1982 a group called Friends of Animals brought two lawsuits against United States Surgical to halt these practices. The company successfully argued in court that Friends of Animals lacked "standing" to sue, since no member of the organization had been injured by the practice; after some further legal maneuvering by Friends of Animals both suits were dropped. Last November [1988] a New York City animal-rights advocate was arrested as she planted a bomb outside United States Surgical's headquarters.

In 1987, according to the USDA, 130,373 animals were subjected to pain or distress unrelieved by drugs for "the purpose of research or testing." This figure, which represents nearly seven percent of the 1,969,123 animals reported to the USDA that year as having been "used in experimentation," ignores members of species not protected by the AWA (cold-blooded animals, mice, rats, birds, and farm animals). Moreover, there is reason to believe that the USDA's figures are low. For example, according to the USDA, no primates were subjected to distress in the state of Maryland, the home of Sema, in any year from 1980 to 1987, the last year for which data are available.

Steps seemingly favorable to animals have been taken in recent years. In addition to the passage of the 1985 amendments to the AWA, the Public Health Service [PHS], which includes the NIH, has revised its "Policy on Humane Care and Use of Laboratory Animals," and new legislation has given legal force to much of this policy. Under the revised policy, institutions receiving NIH or other PHS funds for animal research must have an "institutional animal care and use committee" consisting of at least five members, including one nonscientist and one person not affiliated with the institution.

Many activists are pessimistic about these changes, however. They argue that the NIH has suspended funds at noncompliant research institutions only in response to political pressure, and assert that the suspensions are intended as a token gesture, to help the NIH regain lost credibility. They note that Sema, which continues to keep primates in isolation cages (as regulations permit), is an NIH contractor whose principal investigators are NIH employees. As to the makeup of the animal-care committees, animal-rights advocates say that researchers control who is appointed to them. In the words of one activist, "The brethren get to choose."

However one interprets these changes, much remains the same. For example, the AWA authorizes the USDA to confiscate animals from laboratories not in compliance with regulations, but only if the animal "is no longer required... to carry out the research, test or experiment"; the PHS policy mandates pain relief "unless the procedure is justified for scientific reasons." Fundamentally, the underlying attitude that animals may appropriately be used and discarded persists.

If the law is ever to reflect the idea that animals have rights, more-drastic steps—such as extending the protection of the Constitution to animals—must be taken. Constitutional protection for animals is not an outlandish proposition. The late U.S. Supreme Court Justice William O. Douglas wrote once, in a dissenting opinion, that the day should come when "all of the forms of life... will stand before the court—the pileated woodpecker as well as the coyote and bear, the lemmings as well as the trout in the streams."

Suppose, just suppose, that the AWA were replaced by an animal-rights act, which would prohibit the use by human beings of any animals to their detriment. What would be the effect on medical research, education, and product testing? Microorganisms; tissue, organ, and cell cultures; physical and chemical systems that mimic biological functions; computer programs and mathematical models that simulate biological interactions; epidemiologic data bases; and clinical studies have all been used to reduce the number of animals used in experiments, demonstrations, and tests. A 1988 study by the National Research Council, while finding that researchers lack the means to replace all animals in labs, did conclude that current and prospective alternative techniques could reduce the number of animals—particularly mammals—used in research.

Perhaps the report would have been more optimistic if scientists were as zealous about conducting research to find alternatives as they are about animal research. But we should not be misled by discussions of alternatives into thinking that the issue is merely empirical. It is broader than just whether subject A and procedure X can be replaced by surrogates B and Y. We could undergo a shift in world view: instead of imagining that we have a divine mandate to dominate and make use of everything else in the universe, we could have a sense of belonging to the world and of kinship with the other creatures in it. The us-versus-them thinking that weighs animal suffering against human gain could give way to an appreciation that "us" includes "them." That's an alternative too.

Some researchers may insist that scientists should not be constrained in their quest for knowledge, but this is a romantic notion of scientific freedom that never was and should not be. Science is always constrained, by economic and social priorities and by ethics. Sometimes, paradoxically, it is also freed by these constraints, because a barrier in one direction forces it to cut another path, in an area that might have remained unexplored.

Barriers against the exploitation of animals ought to be erected in the law, because law not only enforces morality but defines it. Until the law protects the interests of animals, the animal-rights movement will by definition be radical. And whether or not one approves of breaking the law to remedy its shortcomings, one can expect such activities to continue. "I believe that you should do for others as you would have done for you," one member of the ALF says. "If you were being used in painful experiments, you'd want someone to come to your rescue."

POSTSCRIPT

Is the Use of Animals in Research Justified?

Scientists tend to believe that they are involved in the pursuit of truth. Therefore, all questions are worth asking, and all research methods are worth using, as long as they lead to the answers sought.

Some groups object to the asking of certain questions (such as, "Are there differences in intelligence between races?" or "Is there a genetic basis for violence?"). As for methods, much debate about the lethal experiments that were conducted on nonconsenting human subjects by the Nazis during World War II, as well as the ensuing trials of the Nazi physicians in Nuremburg, Germany, has established a consensus that no scientist can treat people the way the Nazis did. Informed consent is essential, and research on humans must aim to benefit those same humans.

As these ideas have gained currency, some people have tried to extend them to say that, just as scientists cannot do whatever they wish to humans, they cannot do whatever they wish to animals. Harriet Ritvo, in "Toward a More Peaceable Kingdom," *Technology Review* (April 1992), says that the animal rights movement "challenges the ideology of science itself... forcing experimenters to recognize that they are not necessarily carrying out an independent exercise in the pursuit of truth—that their enterprise, in its intellectual as well as its social and financial dimensions, is circumscribed and defined by the culture of which it is an integral part."

For a good overview of the subject, see Marc Leepson, "Animal Rights," *CQ Researcher* (May 24, 1991). Also see Michael P. T. Leahy, *Against Liberation: Putting Animals in Perspective* (Routledge, 1992); F. Barbara Orlans, *In the Name of Science: Issues in Responsible Animal Experimentation* (Oxford University Press, 1993); and Rod Strand and Patti Strand, *The Hijacking of the Humane Movement* (Doral, 1993).

The situation is far more complex than it seems at first glance. Gary E. Varner, in "The Prospects for Consensus and Convergence in the Animal Rights Debate," *Hastings Center Report* (January–February 1994), notes that the animal rights movement is not monolithic but contains a great variety of philosophical stances. He even suggests that there is enough agreement between the philosophical bases of the animal rights movement and those of scientists that considerable potential for convergence of their views exists.

The newsletter of the Doctors in Britain against Animal Experiments can be found on the Internet at: http://www.envirolink.org/arrs/dbae/dbae069.5.html; the same Web page contains a link to the Animal Rights Resource Site (ARRS).

ISSUE 16

Is It Ethical to Use Humans as "Experimental Animals"?

YES: Charles Petit, from "Sunday Interview: A Soldier in the War on AIDS," *San Francisco Chronicle* (January 21, 1996)

NO: Danielle Gordon, from "The Verdict: No Harm, No Foul," *The Bulletin of the Atomic Scientists* (January/February 1996)

ISSUE SUMMARY

YES: Science writer Charles Petit interviews an AIDS patient who underwent a highly experimental treatment and considers those who resist human experimentation to be far too cautious.

NO: Danielle Gordon, assistant editor of *The Bulletin of the Atomic Scientists,* reports the results of a national ethics commission's investigation into experiments that exposed many people to radiation and concludes that experiments on seriously ill patients are ethically troubling.

Biological and medical experimentation on human beings has a bad reputation. This is partly because of what came to light after World War II: Under the Nazi regime, German researchers had, in the name of science, used prisoners to study amputation, healing, infection, and hypothermia. Many of the subjects died during the experiments. The researchers, however, did not ask their subjects for consent, nor did they supply painkillers or try to put the pieces back together afterward. To them, human prisoners were as disposable as lab rats.

The reputation of psychological experimentation also suffered when—in an effort to learn how people could follow authority, even if it meant committing atrocities against another individual (as the Nazis did during the Holocaust, and as Americans did during the Vietnam War)—social psychologist Stanley Milgram devised an experiment in which subjects were told they were the teachers in an experiment on the effects of punishment on memory. The subject's job was to give the learner electric shocks of increasing intensity each time the learner made an error. However, the "learner" was an actor who purposely gave wrong answers, and the shocks were not real, but the subjects did not know that. Although some of the subjects balked partway through the experiment, an appalling number continued to increase the strength of the shocks, even though the "learner" was in obvious agony. Critics of Milgram's research (and research like it) have objected that the essential role that deception plays in such research means that true informed consent is not possible. Critics also object to the psychological harm that such experiments may cause to subjects by showing them things about themselves that they would rather not know (such as a capacity for cruelty).

American medical researchers have also done some apparently very cruel experiments on human subjects. Consider, for instance, the Tuskegee syphilis project. In 1932 researchers began to study 400 Tuskegee, Alabama, black men who were infected with syphilis, as well as 200 uninfected black men as the control group. The purpose of the study was to learn exactly how the disease progressed from infection to the subject's death (whether of syphilis or of other causes, including old age), and, in fact, the project has provided large amounts of information now found in medical textbooks.

However, when antibiotics—which can cure syphilis very quickly—became available in the 1940s, the experimenters denied them to their subjects. Studying syphilis was evidently more important to the researchers than saving the lives of their subjects, and it remained so until the media revealed the project in 1972. Public outcry soon resulted in the project's termination and in the 1974 National Research Act, which calls for Institutional Review Boards to approve all federally funded research on human beings.

The existence of the National Research Act implies that human experimentation can be done under suitable circumstances. Those circumstances require informed consent and concern for the subjects' welfare, among other things. To many ethicists, informed consent requires freedom from duress or pressure; it cannot be obtained from prisoners, the retarded, or terminal patients who, in desperate hope of a cure, may be willing to consent to anything. Those desperate patients, however, may have a very different view. Jeff Getty, the subject of the following interview by Charles Petit, sees himself as a soldier in the war against AIDS and, in submitting to a highly controversial experimental treatment, says, "I wanted a chance to charge out of my foxhole and fight."

The opposing view of human experimentation is very apparent in Danielle Gordon's reaction to the revelation that the U.S. government has sponsored numerous experiments that involved exposing volunteers, institutionalized persons, and terminally ill patients, both with and without consent, to radiation. Gordon criticizes the national ethics commission, which declared that little damage was done, and she argues that the ethical costs of the experiments were high.

YES

Charles Petit

SUNDAY INTERVIEW: A SOLDIER IN THE WAR ON AIDS

On December 14 [1995] Jeff Getty of Oakland made medical history when a purified mixture of baboon bone marrow cells was infused into his bloodstream in an effort to slow or reverse his advanced AIDS. He hopes the cells from the baboon—an animal naturally resistant to HIV—will migrate to his bone marrow and plant the seeds for a strong immune system able to augment his AIDS-ravaged capacity to fight off infection. The procedure is one of the first attempts to install a nonhuman immune system in a person—two others involving less sophisticated methods have failed—and has inspired extensive debate and controversy. Performed at San Francisco General Hospital, the procedure was approved by the Food and Drug Administration only after protracted hearings. Some critics argue that the experiment's architects, Dr. Suzanne Ildstad of the University of Pittsburgh and Dr. Steven Deeks and Dr. Paul Volberding of the University of California at San Francisco, had not done enough basic research with animals and other methods to justify the risks. Possible hazards include dangerous reactions between the baboon cells and Getty's own tissues, or the incubation in his body of baboon viruses that could infect other people. Some fear that new human diseases are inevitable if animal-to-human transplants become common. Backers of the procedure reply that extreme cases justify risky and unproven medical experiments, and that extensive safeguards are in place to prevent the procedure from creating new diseases. Getty left the hospital after three weeks. He suffered no apparent harm and seems to have recovered from radiation and chemotherapy that temporarily stunned his own immune system to increase chances for the baboon cells to take root. His condition will be monitored closely for months. This week a sample of his bone marrow was to be removed and tested to see if the baboon cells are engrafting. Those test results will take several weeks. This interview was conducted on January 10.

Q: How do you feel?
A: I feel better now than I did before the procedure.

From Charles Petit, "Sunday Interview: A Soldier in the War on AIDS," *San Francisco Chronicle* (January 21, 1996). Copyright © 1996 by *San Francisco Chronicle*. Reprinted by permission.

A couple of things have happened that were rather surprising. Since about 1992 I had lost a lot of my sense of smell and taste. We don't know why—possibly because of the radiation or the chemotherapy—but they have returned. I can smell and taste things. And I had some severe asthma since 1992 or so. That has been at least temporarily arrested. I can breathe again.

Given that those two components of my life have been returned and I haven't been feeling sickly and my appetite has been tremendous, I would say life seems to be a little better than before. We have speculated it might be the radiation or the chemotherapy that did this.

I understand I am the first person with late-stage AIDS symptoms to have undergone a pretty effective immune suppression from drugs and radiation and had my immune system come back. This seems to have improved some of my AIDS symptoms, contrary to what several people thought was going to happen. This sort of leads us down another road of research. Everyone involved in this project is kind of pixilated because we are learning so much already. Things we expected were going to happen didn't, and things that weren't expected, did.

Q: This transplant got worldwide attention. What do you have to say to people who wrote you, mostly with good wishes but perhaps some who were not so sympathetic?

A: Well, there were only three (hostile) letters out of hundreds and hundreds of letters of praise and support, mostly from relatives of people who died of AIDS. To those (latter) people, I thank them. I had no idea we were going to touch such a nerve in this country. I was telling a friend today that it seems like a lot of people

were feeling hopelessness and despair. There was a pent-up need for somebody to do something, to do anything. If I can say anything to them, it's that your letters and cards, I read them every day. They really got me through the insanity of the confinement. And to the people who sent me the three ugly hate letters, well, it just reminded me that there is an element of evil out there.

Q: What about the procedure itself? Were you frightened? Was there any sensation?

A: The actual procedure took 37 minutes. I was fully conscious and there were several people staring at me in the room. I was quite frightened inside, although people said I didn't show it. I knew there was a chance I could have been killed right at that moment because of what they call an anaphylactic reaction.

I had a funny taste in my mouth almost immediately. And my head felt as if it was rushing, a strange thing, like when I got bonged on the head when I was a kid. I noticed the faster they let the marrow go in the more I got those sensations, so they slowed that process down. The taste? It tasted like blood.

Q: How did your health and feeling progress during the three weeks you were in the hospital?

A: I started out getting beat up by the radiation and the chemotherapy. My face swelled up like a balloon for several days. Then, I thought I was coming out of it and started eating like a horse, thinking I was on my road to recovery.

What I didn't realize at the time was that the lining of my stomach and my intestines was about to die from the radiation. I experienced that wonderful phenomenon at days five and six after the radiation. I had some really bad days in there. I was throwing up and unable to eat and feeling really unsure about what was going to happen next. Then I was specifically told by Lloyd Damon, a doctor and bone marrow specialist at the University of California, not to worry and that was normal.

Once I knew it was supposed to happen I was fine. It took about another five days before I could get to eating well again. From then on it was just boredom and trying to maintain my privacy.

Q: What other treatments have you undergone?

A: You name it. I have had this disease most of my adult life. I started out really aggressive, doing isoprinosine and ribavirin that I was smuggling in from Mexico in pinatas, till I got caught at it. Then I joined a buyers club and got drugs from there.

I did the egg lipid stuff that everybody was doing in 1989. That was weird, drinking egg lipid. I went from there to experimenting with something called thymic hormones. Then I injected myself with Compound Q in 1989, in the buttocks. You are not supposed to do it that way. It is supposed to be a slow infusion over two hours. Kenny (Getty's partner, Ken Klueh) just shot it right in my butt to see what was going to happen. At the time, we didn't know what to do with it. I suffered severely from that. I got necrosis—two large holes that formed where the skin fell in and the muscle dissolved. I ended up on Channel 7 news. The story was, "Please don't do what Jeff Getty did."

Then, in 1991 I started researching what is called allotransfers, or transferring whole white blood cells from a sibling who is not closely HLA (tissue type) matched. I got the University of California to let me try that at Mount Zion Hospital.

My sister donated. At the time I was suffering acute pseudomonas and cryptococcus (infections). I did that three times over the next year. I cleared cryptococcus and the pseudomonas.

Q: In all your public appearances you seem upbeat. Have you had times when you felt like giving up?

A: I think that we all experience that. I don't stay in those black periods very long. A friend of mine, right before he died in 1986, gave me this flag to fly on my sailboat. It says "Don't Give Up the Ship." And that has really become a theme in my life.

The flag theme comes from the War of 1812 where a guy named (John) Lawrence went out to meet the British, and the British just killed everybody. They didn't take any prisoners. Lawrence's dying words were "Don't give up the ship." Then (Oliver Hazard) Perry went out shortly after that on Lake Erie, and he was outnumbered too. Perry said, "Remember what happened to Lawrence," and whipped out this flag that said "Don't Give Up the Ship." They didn't, and they beat the British.

The take-home lesson from that is the same as AIDS. If you think AIDS takes prisoners, you are fooling yourself. That has been my theme all the way through this thing. As long as I keep fighting, I'll stay alive. So far, it has worked.

Q: How did you learn about the bone marrow transplant?

A: I followed Project Inform's Project Immune Restoration, looking over their shoulder all the time. Then Marty (Project Inform director Martin Delaney) told me the details of it. From that point I started a file, which I often do, to track it, and started gathering as many scientific journal articles as I could around the subject of xenogeneic (cross-species) research.

I built a pretty substantial file. It took me about six months. In the summer of '94 I wrote to Dr. Suzanne Ildstad of the University of Pittsburgh and volunteered myself. I said I was a soldier in the front lines of AIDS, someone willing to die for the cause if necessary, and to describe my credentials as someone willing to take chances, I reiterated my treatment history. I was pretty emotional. I said I was sitting in a foxhole, watching shells landing in my friends' foxholes and watching them die one at a time. I wanted a chance to charge out of my foxhole and fight. I have a rather military approach to this disease.

Q: When did you realize you were really a good candidate?

A: In the fall of '94, I finally got hold of the protocol. I realized I qualified. It was almost amazing. The protocol required that I be cytomegalovirus or CMV positive, and cryptococcus negative. Before I did my sister's blood, I was CMV negative, and cryptococcus positive. That turned that right around. It was fate. They wanted me to be CMV positive because baboons are almost all CMV positive.

Q: Some people call you an AIDS warrior. You call yourself an AIDS activist. What does that mean?

A: I do think I have a take-no-prisoners policy in terms of people who are trying to obstruct AIDS research, particularly in the government, and are trying to delay things because they are afraid they are going to lose their jobs. Instead of talking about it, I get out there and take action. We at ACT UP [AIDS Coalition to Unleash Power] Golden Gate believe that action is how you survive and talk is cheap.

Q: Talk about ACT UP Golden Gate.

A: When I first came there I remember thinking, boy, I don't agree with these guys' politics at all. But the first night I spent in a room with those activists, it was like love at first sight. They were just like me. I had finally found my home. The people I started out with, they have all passed away now, but they were great activists.

Now, I would say, I am extremely active working on several projects at the same time. The purpose, our theme, has been to bring forward promising AIDS treatments as fast as possible to gain access to them any way that we can for people who are dying of AIDS. We are trying to do everything we can to save people's lives. We feel that we have done that. We are prolonging lives.

Q: Some researchers felt more basic work should have been done to justify this experiment on a human. Do you appreciate the reasons for the cautions and concerns that led to the long delay?

A: I studied the research very carefully, and I think that (delay) was nonsense. We believe that most of the people who did not want this research to go forward were covering their ass, especially in the government. If you let something like this go through and something goes terribly wrong, there goes your career, your job. But if you stall it until everybody agrees that it is safe, then you'll never get fired for that. Unfortunately, we die waiting.

What I am saying is that the obstacles and the delays that they put in the way of this kind of research are unreasonable. They do not understand the urgency of this disease. And then they will tell me, "Oh, but Jeff, my very good friends have died of AIDS, I understand your pain." That is a standard line that really upsets us. We can almost predict when they are going to say it. We wait for that line. They should know better than to say that.

Q: Some researchers say use of animal tissue for human transplant carries a risk of creating new human diseases. Does this risk worry you?

A: No, not in any way. This particular animal was extremely clean: I would think that in a lot of ways I would be at more risk taking a transfusion from the blood bank, from something like hepatitis C, or from taking blood from my sisters, than from this animal. The tests on this donor far exceeded anything the U.S. blood supply would get. Then there are the other endogenous, possible, hypothetical, unknown viruses that could appear. Well, I am not going to let the fear of hypothetical risks stop me from going forward.

Q: The animal that provided the marrow was killed. What do you say to animal rights groups that want to make use of animals in medical science more difficult or illegal?

A: I think they are making a really big mistake on this one. They are trying to pit animal rights against AIDS, and they are going to lose. We had to sacrifice this one baboon for this experiment for a couple of reasons. I feel really bad about the fact that the baboon had to be sacrificed, and in the future we very well might not have to (kill the baboon donors) if this is ever repeated.

I would sacrifice my own cat if I thought it would help cure this disease, and I was willing to sacrifice my own life. The baboon, by the way, did have a name. It was Raccoon. I feel worse about the hundreds of friends I have lost to AIDS. I have a phone book in which the words "rest in peace" are written on every page. On every page, someone has died.

Q: It appears that the procedure did you no harm. But if it does not help, will it have been worth it?

A: I already feel I have accomplished my goal, which is to do this thing. I don't expect this to work. This is a real long shot. Just to do this, after they said, "No, you can't," is a victory for people with AIDS everywhere in the world.

Q: Being HIV-positive brings an obligation to practice safe sex. Are there any additional limitations on your behavior due to this transplant?

A: They have asked me not to engage in any contact sex at all in which any fluids are exchanged, such as kissing, until we know I have no baboon viruses, and I have agreed to that. There really are not any other restrictions except not to share toothbrushes, razors, water glasses and things like that. It is the same way you would treat someone with hepatitis.

Q: These are anxious times for you. What do you do for enjoyment?

A: I love to take my boat out sailing on the bay. My boat is Mariah, a 30-foot Pearson sloop. For enjoyment I like to go out with my friends, play music, do art work and some stuff like that.

Q: If this doesn't work, is there anything else you can do besides wait?

A: I am always on the prowl for something new. One thing I always tell people with HIV is that when you make your plans, always have a backup plan. So I am looking into the next thing that is out there. For instance, there is something called a thymus transplant, and we are watching that very closely.

People with any stage AIDS, even late-stage AIDS, should remember that as long as you continue to fight and make plans and take action, you may survive. Some of our friends and I have been, at our lowest points, totally wasted with diseases that we were told would kill us for sure. Well, I am still here.

NO

Danielle Gordon

THE VERDICT: NO HARM, NO FOUL

After 18 months spent examining the records of 4,000 human radiation experiments and hundreds of intentional radiation releases, a 14-member "national ethics commission" found that only a few hundred people should get medical notification, compensation, or even a personal apology from the federal government. The committee concluded that most of the tens of thousands of subjects cannot be identified or came to little physical harm, although the ethical costs of these experiments were high.

Between 1944 and 1974, the federal government authorized and funded experiments to test the effects of radiation on humans. According to the report of the Advisory Committee on Human Radiation Experiments, released in October, the majority of research involved radioisotopes used as tracers to "map" human metabolism, with no harmful effect: "Often nonbeneficial experiments on unconsenting patients constituted only minor wrongs. Often there was little or no risk to patient-subjects and no inconvenience."

But some of the details found in 840,000 pages of documents collected by the committee clash with this overall assessment, according to critics of the report. For example, institutionalized children and adult prisoners were used in experiments, some cancer patients died after being given total body irradiation with no medical benefit, and 410 uranium miners died of lung cancer from a radon hazard that could have been avoided.

The committee was established in January 1994 by Energy Secretary Hazel O'Leary, shortly after the *Albuquerque Tribune* revealed that 18 people had been injected with plutonium in a secret Manhattan Project experiment begun in April 1945. The *Tribune* series won a host of awards including a Pulitzer Prize and captured the public's attention.

President Bill Clinton, members of Congress, and even critics of the committee's report agreed that it provided unprecedented insight into a murky area of American history. But activists are up in arms over the committee's "no harm, no foul" recommendations. They question why so few people will receive any notification or apology, why others will not be given compensation, and why certain subjects of radiation experiments were left out of the committee's consideration.

From Danielle Gordon, "The Verdict: No Harm, No Foul," *The Bulletin of the Atomic Scientists*, vol. 52, no. 1 (January/February 1996). Copyright © 1996 by The Educational Foundation for Nuclear Science, 6042 South Kimbark Avenue, Chicago, IL 60637, USA. A one-year subscription is $36. Reprinted by permission of *The Bulletin of the Atomic Scientists*.

Instead of closing this ugly chapter in America's atomic history, "The committee's report constitutes a continuing conspiracy to conceal the facts," said David Egilman, a clinical assistant professor of medicine at Brown University. According to E. Cooper Brown of the Task Force on Radiation and Human Rights, a coalition of 30 organizations representing citizens exposed to radiation, "We refuse to accept the committee's conclusion that, for those who were put at risk, a warning would be of no benefit. These are the very kinds of determinations and judgments that made the radiation experiments possible in the first place."

AMERICAN ETHIC

The experiments occurred at "one of those times in history in which wrongs were committed by very decent people who were in a position to know that a specific aspect of their interaction with others should be improved," the committee concluded. It praised the goals of the investigators: "The seeming likelihood that atomic bombs would be used again in war... meant the country had to know as much as it could, as quickly as it could."

But the means the radiation investigators used were another story. As far back as the 1940s, officials with the Atomic Energy Commission (AEC), Defense Department, and other agencies involved, should have known better, the report said: "So many of the ideas and values with which we are familiar were apparent then."

Under the Nuremberg Code of Medical Ethics adopted in 1949, researchers were required to get consent and could not conduct experiments in which the harm outweighed the potential benefit

to an individual. The committee found "no evidence that any government statement... contained a provision permitting a waiver of consent requirements for national security reasons."

But researchers were rarely held to, or even informed of, these policies. For example, a stack of copies of the Nuremberg Code was found in Defense Department files, all stamped "top secret." Some doctors did not seek consent from sick patients because they viewed their experiments as justified medical tinkering. Even when there was no prospect of medical benefit, it was common for researchers to conduct experiments without patient consent.

While the committee could not determine if there were "systematic injustices" against certain groups, it found that "ethically troubling [experiments] were conducted on institutionalized children, seriously ill and sometimes comatose patients, African-Americans, and prisoners." Testimony before the committee showed that the poor were seen as appropriate subjects because, as Paul Beeson, a professor at Emory University in the 1940s, said, "We were taking care of them, and felt we had a right to get some return from them, since it wouldn't be in professional fees and since our taxes were paying their hospital bills."

Perhaps most important, the committee found that hiding experiments from subjects was simply the norm. While national security was often used as a justification, secrecy had more to do with "concern for embarrassment to the government, potential legal liability, and concern that public misunderstanding would jeopardize government programs." In some cases, secrecy lasted to the present day. About 250 intentional radiation releases near a Pueblo reservation in New Mexico between 1944 and 1961 were not made public until 1994.

That secrecy had devastating results for science, according to Jackie Kittrell, one of the founders of the American Environmental Health Studies Project and a lawyer representing about 200 women who accuse Vanderbilt University of giving them radioactive iron in what was called a "cocktail." She argued that legal and insurance concerns subverted medical findings: "A veil of secrecy was lowered over the medicine and science of radiobiology. The potential knowledge of that period was warped, subverted, and lost."

WHAT HARM DONE?

The committee found that most of the experiments involved radioactive tracers that caused little harm. In a few nontherapeutic tracer experiments with children, however, "Radioisotope exposures were associated with increases in the potential lifetime risk for developing cancer that would be considered unacceptable today." In some cases, "Patients died soon after receiving external radiation or radioisotope doses in the therapeutic range that were associated with acute radiation effects."

In the 1940s and 1950s, injections of radioactive isotopes, including plutonium and uranium, were given to more than 40 people to learn about the occupational dangers facing nuclear workers. The risks from these experiments were supposed to be low, since most of the people given injections were considered very sick. In fact, some patients had the potential to—and did—live more than 10 years. A few University of Rochester subjects injected with uranium isotopes were suffering from no more than alcoholism or malnutrition.

And the occasional choice of relatively healthy people may not have been accidental: "Although this protocol specified cancer patients as potential subjects, evidently the deliberate choice was made later by the experimenters to select patients without malignant diseases in the hope of ensuring normal metabolism," the committee said. "The uranium injections at Rochester were designed to produce detectable minimal harm—that was the endpoint of the experiment."

The government also sponsored 30 years of total body irradiation experiments. In the early years, total body irradiation was thought to be a legitimate treatment for cancer. But "dual-use" experiments continued even after evidence was found that other treatments were more effective—and less risky. "There was no indication that the army reviewers considered whether any therapeutic benefits to the patients outweighed the risks that the TBI treatments might pose," the committee said of one series of treatments. Total body irradiation "may have contributed to the deaths of at least eight and as many as 20 patients," according to contemporaneous reports.

Prisoners and institutionalized children were targeted in some radiation experiments. The committee found that 11 of 21 research projects they reviewed "exposed children to much higher risk than is acceptable today," partly because of an inadequate understanding of radiation. One of these experiments involved small amounts of radioactive substances with no medical benefit given to institutionalized mentally retarded children at the Fernald State School in Massachusetts. Between the late 1940s and 1961, researchers manipulated these children into participating in experiments by offering special treats like extra milk, occasional outings, and membership in a "Science Club."

In addition to medical experiments, government contractors released radiation into the environment on hundreds of occasions between 1944 and 1968, mostly around the nuclear weapons complexes where residents already were subject to numerous unintentional releases. The committee found that the scientists responsible knew intentional releases carried risks....

MOSTLY HARMLESS

"Damage is measured in the pain felt by people who believe that they or their loved ones were treated with disrespect for their dignity," according to the committee.

But this kind of damage alone does not warrant medical follow-up or financial compensation under the committee's recommendations to Congress. None of these recommendations, however, bar individuals from seeking compensation from private institutions or state government—if they learn of their exposure.

The committee concluded that to be eligible for medical notification from the government, a person must have an increased lifetime risk of dying from radiation-induced cancer of more than one in 1,000 (compared to the normal lifetime risk of 220 per 1,000).

One group exceeded this level of risk. Between half a million and 2.3 million schoolchildren throughout the country, according to the Centers for Disease Control and Prevention, were part of nasal radium experiments or received these treatments between 1945 and 1965 for ear and adenoid infections. The committee estimated they would have a 4.35 per 1,000 lifetime risk of incurring deadly tumors to the central nervous system—a 62 percent increase over the normal risk. Using these numbers, Stewart Farber, a consulting scientist and organizer of the Radium Experiment Assessment Project, concluded that between 2,368 and 10,241 people would die of cancer from this exposure.

But these subjects should not be notified because, according to the committee, they would not benefit medically from early detection and treatment of their cancers: "At greatest risk are the brain, and head, and neck tissues, for which there is neither an acceptable nor recommended screening procedure." Thus, the committee concluded there was "no subject of biomedical experiments for whom there is a need to provide active notification and medical follow-up for the purpose of protecting their health."

Subjects of other experiments will at least hear from the government—if their names are found. For the subjects of intentional releases and the uranium workers, the committee recommended changes in existing environmental exposure compensation laws to include additional subjects and diseases.

A select few should get personal, individual apologies and financial compensation, regardless of whether they suffered physical harm. This group includes the families of 18 people who received plutonium injections in the experiments described by the *Albuquerque Tribune;* one woman—known only as CAL-Z—who received a zirconium injection in 1948; and several who received total body irradiation during World War II. These people were singled out because the committee found conclusive evidence that the government kept information secret from them for the express purpose of avoiding embarrassment and liability. Only the

identities of those who received plutonium are known.

Other individuals would be eligible
for apologies and financial compensation
—medical expenses and related harms
—if they met two requirements: if
they suffered physical harm, and if
the experiments were misrepresented as
conventional treatments or had no direct
medical benefit. Some of the people
that may meet these requirements, but
will have to prove it in court, are the
subjects of total body irradiation, iodine
131 and uranium injections, and a group
of prisoners who received testicular
irradiation.

The committee was divided on what
to do about other experiments with no
medical benefit and no physical harm.
Early drafts of the report included recommendations that individual apologies
be offered as "a symbol of the country's
expression of regret to all others who
were similarly situated but who may not
now be identifiable." But three committee
members did not support this recommendation.

In the end, the committee agreed to recommend apologies in cases where people were unjustly selected as subjects or
there was clear and conclusive evidence
they did not give consent. Under these
requirements, only the Fernald children,
prisoners, and some people who received
radioactive injections will receive individual apologies.

The committee added that there are
probably many other groups that deserve
apologies, but "experiment-specific fac-
tual support is not currently available."
Instead, they will have to settle for President Clinton's October 3 speech, which
included a general apology to all subjects
and to the American public.

NOT FAR ENOUGH

Even before the committee's recommendations were released, critics attacked its
decision to base compensation on the
consequences of experiments rather than
ethical transgressions. Under the committee's notion of harm, "If the government shoots someone and misses, they
are under no obligation to apologize for
the shooting. The bullet must have hit
and seriously injured or killed someone
in order to elicit an apology," Egilman of
Brown University said. Plaintiff lawyer
Leonard Schroeter called the recommendations a sellout that will result in the
"betrayal of hundreds of thousands of
victims of radiation experiments," and
decrease "confidence in an already belea-
guered government."

In addition to dismissing many human rights claims, the committee did not
consider precedents for compensation for
non-physical harm or a legal theory for
compensation based on the "rental" of
an experimental subject's body, Anthony
Roisman of the Human Experiment Litigation Project said. The committee report "essentially holds no one responsible or accountable for their actions," said
Brown of the Task Force on Radiation and
Human Rights.

"The government still is making decisions from its pocketbook, and is scared
to look too deeply," lawyer Kittrell said.
But Washington attorney Kenneth Fein-
berg, a member of the committee, de-
fended the decision to limit compensation in a *Washington Post* op-ed piece.
"These recommendations deserve consideration both by the public and policy
makers all too eager to find wrongdo-
ing and write a blank check to the victims.... The mere possibility of compen-

sation breeds a proliferation of grievances —real and imagined."

Roisman argued that by limiting the possibility of compensation, the committee is "dispensing justice by political committee." The federal government is protected from lawsuits by sovereign immunity. "Whether by congressional act or executive order, justice requires that this shield be set aside, for it is only through the court-sanctioned discovery process that individual experiment victims and their families will finally gain access to the full truth," Brown said.

Sen. John Glenn, an Ohio Democrat, was more concerned with the lack of medical monitoring offered to subjects. "It seems to me that the government has a moral and ethical responsibility to provide health tests and monitoring to those people involved in these experiments— even if the risk of cancer is infinitesimally small," he said.

Brown University's Egilman also disagreed with the committee's decision to assess harm by looking at deaths rather than illness, and to notify only those people with a more than one in 1,000 increased risk of dying: "Given the committee's guidelines, a government experiment on 50,000 people attending a football game which is expected to cause 50 deaths is an acceptable form of covert experimentation." He compared this to Environmental Protection Agency standards for regulating hazards with risks of one in 100,000. "The committee's report will set risk assessment and regulatory efforts back several decades," he said.

Egilman added that by not providing notification and medical follow-up, the government has shifted the burden of proof to subjects, while refusing them necessary epidemiological studies. "The Nuremberg Code states 'the duty and responsibility for ascertaining the quality of consent rests upon each individual who initiates, directs, or engages in the experiment,'" he pointed out.

Other critics questioned whether the scientific knowledge to make decisions about risk is even available. Lawyer Kittrell argued that the committee recognized that government fear of litigation "led to the scientific and medical process not having integrity. But then it buys into the results of this distorted process without doing the necessary follow-up."

The issue of medical notification was particularly contentious for the subjects of nasal irradiation. Lorraine Marin, a board member of the North American Brain Tumor Coalition and a radiation oncologist, said although there are no cheap or simple screening tests for brain, head, and neck cancers, "there is a medical benefit to people knowing if they were subject to nasal radiation. They could alert their doctors and get more complete checkups." She added: "Ideally the government should sponsor an epidemiological study."

Geoffrey Sea, director of the Atomic Reclamation and Conversion Project, added that the increased risk to these children is actually much higher than the committee's estimate of 62 percent. "This estimate is just for brain cancer. The committee ignored the risks of thyroid, nasopharyngeal, and other cancers," he said....

THE RIGHT COMMITTEE?

For some critics, the shortcomings in these recommendations reflect the biases of the committee. Their backgrounds "interfered with their ability to objectively analyze the historical evidence," Egilman of Brown University said. Sea of the Atomic Reclamation and Conversion Project pointed out that there were no subjects of experiments on the committee, although the inclusion of a representative from the most affected community is a requirement for many presidential committees. The committee also had only one biostatistician and no epidemiologist: "It was heavily weighted toward radiation biologists, oncologists, and lawyers. It was weak in terms of public health," said David Rush, head of the epidemiology program at Tufts University.

"I have a suspicion that at root, there was too much deference to the experiment industry by this committee," Roisman of the Human Experiment Litigation Project said. Four of the committee's 14 members were from institutions where human radiation experiments were, and may still be, carried out. For example, committee chair Ruth Faden is director of the Bioethics Institute at Johns Hopkins University. In the 1940s, Johns Hopkins trained "the Army and Navy doctors who performed the initial experiment and popularized the radium nasal irradiation procedure," Farber wrote in a letter to Faden.

In addition, committee member Henry Royal co-authored two studies on the health effects of Chernobyl with Eugene Saenger, the chief researcher behind the total body irradiation experiments at the University of Cincinnati. Royal acknowledged this connection, but explained in a letter to Faden that they did not work together on the project and had only limited social interaction. The committee did not ask Royal to recuse himself from reviewing the Cincinnati experiments.

Committee Executive Director Guttman called the charges against these members scandalous. "The fact of the matter is that all experts in this field have some affiliation with some institute being investigated." Noting that the committee devoted a great deal of its time, and much criticism, to the research being done today with human subjects, he said, "If there was a conflict for these people, they wouldn't have criticized current research at their own institutes." ...

THE RIGHT THING

President Clinton accepted the committee's report in a White House ceremony on October 3. In his remarks he said—five times—that America must "do the right thing" for the subjects of radiation experiments. "Our greatness is measured not only in how we so frequently do right, but also how we act when we know we've done the wrong thing; how we confront our mistakes, make our apologies, and take action."

The committee no longer has the authority to decide what should be done for these people. Eighteen months and 925 pages later, its offices are closed and phones disconnected. And the subjects of human radiation experiments now look to Congress, which is expected to take up some of the committee's recommendations this year, to do the right thing.

POSTSCRIPT

Is It Ethical to Use Humans as "Experimental Animals"?

The February 8, 1996, *San Francisco Chronicle* reported that although Jeff Getty is feeling better, "sophisticated tests were unable to detect any clear signs of the baboon bone marrow infused into his system on December 14. Presumably the foreign cells were destroyed by Getty's own defenses or died without multiplying in his own bone marrow." On the other hand, he *is* feeling better. Perhaps the pretransplant radiation treatment "somehow knocked down his HIV infection." "It's intriguing that there may be unexpected benefits from the process. He's given us a number of interesting avenues to explore," said one of his physicians.

Was the experiment worth doing? Both Getty and his physicians think so, but there are ethicists who find the use of seriously ill patients very troubling, especially when the patients cannot be expected to benefit (Getty's improvement was *not* expected). Indeed, the welfare of the patient is considered paramount in modern medical research, which tests drugs and surgical procedures for efficacy and safety generally by giving them to one group of patients while denying them to another (the control group). Today, when an experimental treatment shows strong signs of being more effective than a control treatment, it is immediately offered to the control group. If the treatment shows signs of causing more harm than no treatment at all, the experiment is halted.

Some critics of human experimentation focus on the reason why the experiments are done. For instance, Arjun Makhijani, in "Energy Enters Guilty Plea," *The Bulletin of the Atomic Scientists* (March–April 1994), argues that the government-sponsored human radiation experiments were so closely linked to military purposes, even when their avowed purposes were something else, they were ethically suspect at best.

Others focus on the risks to patients from such things as animal-borne viruses. In March 1996 the Nuffield Council on Bioethics in London, England, released the report *Animal-to-Human Transplants: The Ethics of Transplantation*, which urges that transplants of animal tissues to humans not be approved until the risks of infection are better understood. The council also has moral reservations about using primates (such as baboons) as tissue sources.

Measures such as the National Research Act have not stopped human experimentation, but they have made such work more difficult. It is therefore worth noting that there are alternative ways of studying processes that hold the potential to damage human health. One is "experiments of nature," in which the subjects of study are victims of human accident and neglect, as well as war.

An unfortunate example came to light at the end of the cold war and the collapse of the Iron Curtain, when it was revealed to the world that the Soviet Union and East Germany ignored precautions against exposing uranium miners and processors to radioactive material but kept careful records of worker exposures and any health effects. Now available to researchers is an archive of data on some 450,000 workers, which German science writer Patricia Kahn has called "the world's biggest data collection on low-level radiation and health—and potentially one of the most valuable for studying the associated cancer risks" (see "A Grisly Archive of Key Cancer Data," *Science,* January 22, 1993). Other data collections covering Soviet nuclear accidents are also now becoming available. As researchers analyze these data, they will surely learn a great deal that they could not learn in other ways (the necessary experiments would never be permitted by institutional review boards).

For more details on the Nazi experiments, see A. Mitscherlich and F. Mielke, *Doctors of Infamy* (Henry Schuman, 1949) and Arthur L. Caplan, ed., *When Medicine Went Mad: Bioethics and the Holocaust* (Humana Press, 1992). The U.S. radiation experiments are also discussed by Charles C. Mann in "Radiation: Balancing the Record," *Science* (January 28, 1994). For an analysis of Stanley Milgram's obedience experiments, see his *Obedience to Authority: An Experimental View* (Harper & Row, 1974). And for more on the ethics of experimentation on human beings, see Caplan's "When Evil Intrudes," *Hastings Center Report* (November–December 1992) and Bernard Barber's "The Ethics of Experimentation With Human Subjects," *Scientific American* (February 1976).

More information on the human radiation experiments can be found on the Internet at: http://www.ohre.doe.gov.

ISSUE 17

Should Fetal Tissue Be Used to Heal Adults?

YES: Council on Scientific Affairs and Council on Ethical and Judicial Affairs, from "Medical Applications of Fetal Tissue Transplantation," *Journal of the American Medical Association* (January 26, 1990)

NO: James Tunstead Burtchaell, from "University Policy on Experimental Use of Aborted Fetal Tissue," *IRB: A Review of Human Subjects Research* (July/August 1988)

ISSUE SUMMARY

YES: The American Medical Association's Council on Scientific Affairs and Council on Ethical and Judicial Affairs argue that using fetal tissue to treat adult illnesses is ethical, provided appropriate precautions are taken, and that related research should be funded by the federal government.

NO: Theologian James Tunstead Burtchaell asserts that research with aborted fetal tissue is unethical because informed consent cannot be obtained from a fetus and because the researcher cannot be morally separated from the abortion itself.

Physicians have long wished to be able to replace their patients' missing or defective parts, just as an auto mechanic can replace a brake pad, a spark plug, or a carburetor. The earliest attempts to replace a person's "parts" included performing transfusions with sheep's blood, which seemed like a good idea at the time (after all, blood is blood, isn't it?) but failed dismally (the patients died). In time, researchers learned that biological parts have subtleties that machine parts do not—they are labeled by their chemistry as belonging to one individual of one species, and the body rejects those parts that have the wrong labels. Individuals who share the same genes (such as identical twins) also share the same labels, so the first successful human organ transplants were between identical twins. Later, researchers discovered drugs that suppress the immune system and prevent the rejection of parts with different labels. Today, many body parts are transplanted almost routinely.

Yet not all body parts are equivalent. A heart is a heart; it pumps blood. A piece of brain tissue, however, is not like heart tissue; it must be able to grow and establish connections with other parts of the brain in order to function. And adult brain tissue does not do this well. Fetal tissue does because it is still relatively unformed and is not yet locked into a single function within the body. The cells of fetal tissue are still able to multiply, assume special functions (differentiate), and stimulate the growth of neighboring cells. In a transplant, they are also less likely to provoke the recipient's immune system to reject them.

Fetal brain tissue, bone marrow, pancreatic tissue, and liver tissue all have similar advantages. Some physician researchers have considered transplanting these tissues into patients who could not otherwise be helped, such as the 500,000 Americans with Parkinson's disease, a progressive disease that causes deterioration of the brain and that is marked by progressively worsening tremors and other movement difficulties. Drugs are of limited value for this disorder and have serious side effects. However, researchers have theorized that if the damaged portion of the brain could somehow be replaced or if the brain's production of the chemical dopamine (which functions as a neurotransmitter in the brain) could be supplemented by the active fetal tissue, patients could at least be helped.

Whether or not fetal transplants will work is almost beside the point because as soon as the *possibility* of using fetal tissue in this way arose, many people asked, "Where does the fetal tissue come from?" Since the answer was necessarily "abortions," many people reacted strongly against the transplants. They felt that if fetal tissue proved useful for saving people's lives, then abortion might become widespread: women who would otherwise not choose to have abortions might change their minds because of the potential benefits; doctors might encourage women to abort their fetuses for the sake of other patients; and women might get pregnant deliberately in order to provide fetal tissue to treat a friend's or loved one's illness or even to sell.

In the mid-1970s, soon after abortion was legalized in the United States, the National Institutes of Health (NIH) established a moratorium on (a suspension of) federal funding of research using human fetuses, either alive or dead. Legislation soon changed the moratorium to a ban, with the only exception being research intended to aid the fetus. In 1988 an NIH panel declared that the government should fund research on fetal tissue transplantation, and in 1992 Congress voted to end the ban. However, then-president George Bush vetoed the legislation because he felt that it might encourage abortion.

Despite the ban on federal funding of fetal tissue transplantation research, the work has continued with private funding in the United States and with public funding in other countries. In the selections that follow, the American Medical Association's Council on Scientific Affairs and Council on Ethical and Judicial Affairs summarize much of the work that had been done by 1990, stress its potential value, and argue that using fetal tissue to treat adult illnesses is ethical with appropriate precautions. James Tunstead Burtchaell objects to fetal transplantation research on the grounds that informed consent cannot be adequately obtained, and he argues that the association of the researcher with the destruction of the fetus raises further moral questions.

YES

Council on Scientific Affairs and Council on Ethical and Judicial Affairs

MEDICAL APPLICATIONS OF FETAL TISSUE TRANSPLANTATION

The prospect of therapeutically effective fetal tissue transplants for disorders such as diabetes and Parkinson's disease has raised new questions in the ethical discussion on fetal research. These questions are distinct from those addressed in the 1970s that focused on invasive procedures performed by some researchers on living, viable fetuses. They are also separate from the questions that were raised by the development of new techniques for prenatal diagnosis, such as fetoscopy and chorionic villus sampling. Although the use of transplanted tissue from a fetus after spontaneous or induced abortion appears to be analogous to the use of cadaver tissue and organs, the moral issue for many is the possibility that the decision to have an abortion will become coupled with the decision to donate fetal tissue for transplantation procedures.

The utilization of human fetal tissue for transplantations is, for the most part, based on research data derived from experimental animal models. At this time, the number of such transplantations performed has been relatively small, but the various applications are promising avenues of clinical investigation for certain disorders. The purpose of this report is to (1) review the data on fetal tissue transplantation in animals and in specific clinical disorders, (2) review the legal and ethical issues involved in fetal tissue transplantation, and (3) provide ethical guidelines for the use of fetal tissue for transplantation.

FETAL TISSUE TRANSPLANTATION

Human fetal tissue research has led to the development of a number of important research and medical advances. Embryonic human tissues have been the source of scientifically valuable cell lines in culture that have been important research models for studying cell-to-cell interactions and gene expression.

From Council on Scientific Affairs and Council on Ethical and Judicial Affairs, "Medical Applications of Fetal Tissue Transplantation," *Journal of the American Medical Association*, vol. 263, no. 4 (January 26, 1990), pp. 565–569. Copyright © 1990 by The American Medical Association. Reprinted by permission. References omitted.

The research and development of the polio vaccine was accomplished with the use of human fetal kidney cells. Currently, human fetal cells are being used to study the mechanism of viral infections and to diagnose viral infections and inherited diseases.

Fetal cells have four basic properties that make them clinically useful for grafting or transplantation applications: (1) the ability to grow and proliferate, (2) the ability to undergo cell and tissue differentiation (intrinsic plasticity), (3) the ability to produce growth factors, and (4) reduced antigenicity compared with adult tissue (although this property does not always apply).

The plasticity of transplanted fetal tissue has been demonstrated in numerous animal studies. Embryonic wing tissue from a chicken retains the functional capacity to differentiate into a leg when transplanted into the appropriate limb bud region of the developing chick. In animal experiments in which the recipient is a fully differentiated adult, intracerebral implants of fetal neurons can establish extensive synaptic connection and under certain conditions can become partially integrated into the circuitry of adjacent neural tissue. The ability of fetal cells to grow and proliferate in vivo [in the living body] following transplantation increases the success rate of functional engraftment....

Fetal cells have the additional ability to produce trophic substances that not only can increase their own ability to survive and grow but also can promote regeneration of nearby damaged tissue. Angiogenic factors from fetal tissue can promote blood vessel formation, and nerve growth factors released by fetal neuroblasts can assist in neural tissue regeneration.

A theoretically important factor in successful fetal tissue engraftment is the ability of the transplanted cells to escape the immune surveillance of the host, but this is not true for all fetal tissues....

Human fetal tissue transplantations have been attempted in a number of human disorders, including Parkinson's disease, diabetes, severe combined immunodeficiency, DiGeorge's syndrome, aplastic anemia, leukemia, thalassemia, Fabry's disease, and Gaucher's disease. With the immunodeficiency disorders, restoration of immune function and long-term patient survival have been achieved. The following sections review the major research areas for the clinical application of human fetal transplants.

Immunodeficiency Disorders

... Since graft-vs-host disease (GvHD) is a major barrier to the transplantation of allogeneic hematopoietic [blood-forming] cells and since immunocompetent T cells present in transplanted bone marrow are associated with GvHD, the fetal liver has been considered a possible alternative source of hematopoietic tissue. Animal experiments have shown that transplanted fetal liver cells are capable of restoring hematopoiesis and immunity in lethally irradiated rodents. Even when the fetal tissue donor and recipient are mismatched for histocompatibility [HLA] antigens, the resulting GvHD was mild and delayed compared with what occurred following bone marrow transplantations (BMTs)....

Clinically, fetal liver transplantations have been attempted in patients with SCID [severe combined immunodeficiency]. This relatively heterogeneous condition often leads to death from opportunistic infections before the age of 1 year. Bone marrow transplantation has resulted in long-term survival in patients with SCID; the success rate is as high as 80% when the HLA type of the donor is identical to that of the recipient. . . .

Fetal liver transplantation represents a third approach to immune reconstitution in SCID, but it currently is of less clinical significance. . . . Sustained engraftment of lymphoid progenitor cells from fetal liver has been achieved in a number of patients. Complete immunologic reconstitution, including normal T-cell function, has been demonstrated despite HLA mismatch between donor and recipient cells. Fetal liver grafts may be optimal when used in conjunction with fetal thymus tissue from the same donor, but this has not been established conclusively. Clinical experience indicates that the optimal age of the fetal liver for transplantation is 8 to 13 weeks; the risk of GvHD is higher in livers older than 20 weeks. The relative efficacy of fetal liver compared with HLA haploidentical T-cell–depleted BMT has not been studied. . . .

Hematologic Disorders

More than 100 patients with aplastic anemia have undergone treatment with fetal liver transplants. However, because these patients still have functioning immune systems that react against HLA-mismatched fetal liver tissues, transplantation cannot be successful in most instances; engraftment has been low (3%), as documented by cytogenetic analysis. Therefore, the true efficacy of fetal liver transplantation for aplastic anemia cannot be evaluated until transplantations have been attempted following immunosuppressive therapy.

Fetal liver transplantations have been attempted in 39 patients with acute myelogenous leukemia. In treating acute myelogenous leukemia, human fetal liver transplantations could result in successful engraftment, with reconstitution of hematopoietic function and/or expedited recovery of the patient's own hematologic system. However, transplant failure is common. Antigenic barriers appear to be too great for successful engraftment without prior immunosuppression with drugs and radiation. As with aplastic anemia, human fetal liver transplantation for acute myelogenous leukemia has not been conducted under immunosuppressive conditions that would permit evaluation of engraftment success. Part of the problem in determining the efficacy of fetal liver cells in accelerating hematopoietic tissue recovery is the dependency of this procedure on the initial effectiveness of chemotherapy against acute myelogenous leukemia. Because of the variable response to chemotherapy, further evaluation of any additional improvement resulting from the fetal liver infusion will require controlled clinical trials.

Diabetes

The potential to cure experimentally induced diabetes mellitus in animals through the syngeneic [genetically identical] transplantation of fetal pancreatic tissue has been documented. That human fetal pancreatic tissue transplantations could cure patients has been proposed as a result of these preclinical studies. However, the application of fetal cell transplantations to diabetes is complicated by inadequate engraftment success in immunosuppressed recipients as well as insufficient quantities of viable fetal tissue and storage arrangements for such tissue.

Transplantation of cultured fetal pancreas cells has been tried in more than 100 insulin-dependent patients. So far there have been no successful grafts as judged by complete long-term withdrawal of insulin therapy, but there has been one report of survival of transplanted fetal pancreas tissue for 13 weeks. Reduced insulin requirements ... also have been reported, but the effects have been transient. Although the current attempts have been relatively unsuccessful, the human fetal pancreas does exhibit the necessary plasticity and proliferative properties outlined earlier. ...

With ... encouraging results in animal studies together with advances in the cryopreservation of the fetal pancreas tissue, research on fetal cell transplantation for diabetes is worth pursuing. ...

Other Metabolic and Genetic Disorders
Fetal liver transplantations have been tried in a small number of patients with thalassemia, Fabry's disease, and Gaucher's disease. Treatment by this approach is preliminary, but some beneficial clinical results have been reported. Fetal tissue transplantation experiments for these and other inherited disorders have been suggested as forerunners to the use of genetically engineered cells.

Parkinson's Disease
Fetal nerve-cell grafts have been carried out successfully in animal models of neurodegenerative disease. The technique of neural grafting was initially used in neurobiology to study nerve-cell development and regeneration, primarily in invertebrate models. The consistent transplant-induced improvements in motor, sensory, cognitive, and endocrine functions in animal models prompted the rationale that similar transplantations of human fetal neurons could improve the clinical symptoms of neurologic disorders such as Parkinson's disease. New approaches to the treatment of this disorder are critical, since the response to currently available drug therapy is reduced as the disease state progresses. ...

[Work on primates] suggests that fetal neural grafts will be an effective treatment of Parkinson's disease in human patients. Fetal implants for Parkinson's disease have been performed in the People's Republic of China, Mexico, Sweden, Canada, Great Britain, Cuba, and the United States. Little information is available on the outcome of the Chinese and Cuban transplantations. In the Mexican trial, the two patients receiving human fetal nerve cell transplants appeared to improve progressively following surgery; however, no reliable signs of symptom alleviation could be demonstrated. Similarly, the degree of long-term improvement in motor function in the American, Canadian, English, and Swedish transplant patients has not yet been ascertained.

The inconclusive results of the clinical trials together with the complexities of human fetal neural grafting suggest that caution must be exercised in promoting these types of transplantations.

FUTURE DIRECTIONS

[Some] alternatives to the use of human fetal tissue are available [or are being researched, including] ... genetically engineer[ed] cell lines capable of both proliferating and producing a specific neurotransmitter.

Many of these manipulative procedures, particularly the development of genetically engineered cells, will not be accomplished in the near future. In the meantime, human fetal tissue transplantation research may eventually lead to some beneficial therapeutic approaches to patients with Parkinson's disease and those suffering from other disorders. For example, the continued efforts to purify specific fetal cell populations may improve the application of fetal cell transplantation for immunodeficient disorders and diabetes. The results of future transplantation studies will be needed to further assess this procedure.

LEGAL AND ETHICAL IMPLICATIONS

The transplantation of human fetal neural or pancreatic tissue and, to a lesser extent, fetal lymphoid cells is subject to federal regulations protecting human subjects (ie, recipients of the procedure). Approval of the transplantation protocol requires review and approval by an institutional review board to ensure that the risks to the patient are minimized. The acquisition of tissue from an aborted fetus is not governed by federal regulations. Instead, federal regulations leave the disposition of fetal remains to state and local regulation....

The acquisition and use of tissue obtained from dead fetuses is governed by the Uniform Anatomical Gift Act, which has been adopted by all states and the District of Columbia. The Uniform Anatomical Gift Act provides the primary legal standard for fetal tissue use, permitting fetal tissue to be donated for research purposes with the consent of either parent and if there is no objection from the other parent.

Several states have restrictive statutes governing the donation of fetal tissue for research. Massachusetts and Michigan have laws that prohibit abortion if it is conditional on the use of the fetal tissue for research. Arizona law specifically prohibits the postmortem use of fetal remains for "any medical experimentation" if the tissue is derived from an induced

abortion. Other states (eg, Ohio, Oklahoma, and Indiana) have statutes that restrict research on abortion fetal remains.

The demand for fetal tissue transplantation for neural or pancreatic cell engraftments may be expected to increase if further clinical studies conclusively show that these procedures provide long-term reversal of neural or endocrine deficits. The ethical issues that fetal cell transplantation has raised are distinct from ethical points addressed during the previous discussions of fetal tissue research.

Prominent among the currently identified ethical concerns is the potential for fetal transplantations to influence a woman's decision to have an abortion. These concerns are based at least in part on the possibility that some women may wish to become pregnant for the sole purpose of aborting the fetus and either donating the tissue to a relative or selling the tissue for financial gain. Others suggest that a woman who is ambivalent about a decision to have an abortion might be swayed by arguments about the good that could be achieved if she opts to terminate the pregnancy. These concerns demand the prohibition of (1) the donation of fetal tissue to designated recipients, (2) the sale of such tissue, and (3) the request for consent to use the tissue for transplantation before a final decision regarding abortion has been made.

The abortion process may also be influenced inappropriately by the physician. Consequently, measures must be taken to ensure that decisions to donate fetal tissue for transplantation do not affect either the techniques used to induce the abortion or the timing of the procedure itself with respect to the gestational age of the fetus. Also, to avoid conflicts of interest, physicians and other health care personnel involved in performing abortions should not receive any direct benefit from the use of tissues derived from the aborted fetus for research or transplantation. The retrieval and preservation of usable tissue cannot become the primary focus of abortion. Therefore, members of the transplantation team should not influence or participate in the abortion process.

There is potential commercial gain for those involved in the retrieval, storage, testing, preparation, and delivery of fetal tissues. Providing fetal tissue by nonprofit mechanisms designed to cover costs only would reduce the possibility of direct or indirect influence on a woman to acquire her consent for donation of the aborted fetal remains.

In summary, the use of fetal tissues for transplantation purposes is ethically permissible when (1) the guidelines of the Council on Ethical and Judicial Affairs on clinical investigation and organ transplantation are followed as they pertain to the recipient of the fetal tissue transplant, (2) fetal tissue is not provided in exchange for financial renumeration above what is necessary to cover reasonable expenses, (3) the recipient of the tissue is not designated by the donor, (4) a final decision regarding abortion is made before discussion of the transplantation use of fetal tissue is initiated, (5) decisions regarding the technique used to induce abortion as well as the timing of the abortion in relation to the gestational age of the fetus are based on concern for the safety of the pregnant woman, (6) health care personnel involved in the termination of a particular pregnancy do not participate in or receive any benefit from the transplantation of tissue from the abortus of the same pregnancy, and (7) informed consent on behalf of both donor and the recipient is obtained in accordance with applicable law.

CONCLUSION

At this time, fetal neural grafting is a promising area of clinical investigation that should receive federal funding. The current transplantation experiments may be viewed as the initial step in determining the effectiveness of this approach for the treatment of Parkinson's disease, other neurodegenerative conditions, and diabetes. Parkinson's disease remains the most attractive disorder for this procedure because of the relatively localized region of deficit compared with the more widespread degeneration observed in such neurologic disorders as Alzheimer's disease.

The donation of fetal tissue for transplantation from spontaneous or induced abortions is governed legally by the Uniform Anatomical Gift Act. A number of states prohibit experiments on fetal remains from elected abortions, but such statutes may not apply if fetal cell transplantation becomes routine (ie, nonresearch in nature). The principal ethical concern in the use of human fetal tissue transplants is the degree to which the decision to have an abortion can be separated from the decision to donate the postmortem tissue. Safeguards to reduce any motivation, reason, or incentive by the woman to have an abortion can be developed to allow the benefits of this procedure to be made available to those who are in need of improved therapies.

NO
James Tunstead Burtchaell

UNIVERSITY POLICY ON EXPERIMENTAL USE OF ABORTED FETAL TISSUE

In December 1987 the University of Notre Dame's IRB [internal review board] concluded several years' deliberation and decided that research should not be permitted on fetal materials derived from elective abortion. This article sets forth most of the course of reasoning that led to the decision.

Human tissue has become an effective medium for medical therapy. Examples are the transfusion of blood and its derivatives; the transplanting of organs such as kidneys, eye parts, hearts and lungs; and immunization by pathogens, antigens, or antibodies. New therapies are now being proposed through the implantation of fetal tissues, which appear to have especially potent regenerative effects upon neural and endocrine systems. The therapeutic use of tissue from human bodies aroused a series of ethical concerns. May one put parts of someone's body to alien use? Need consent be obtained and, if so, from whom and under what conditions? May human tissue be bought or sold? The recent proposal to use fetal tissue—typically obtained from aborted subjects—puts a new spin on those questions.

The issue raised here, however, concerns the use of human fetal tissue for experimentation, not for therapy.

There are distinct advantages in the laboratory use of fetal remains. This is notably so, for instance, in studying neural tissue. In comparison with tissues obtained from mature bodies, those of the unborn or very young adapt more readily to *in vitro* environments, proliferate more abundantly, are less differentiated and therefore more versatile for experimental uses. In a word, they perform much more naturally and normally and responsively *in vitro*.

Are there countervailing moral realities that would dissuade or interdict the use of human fetal tissue for experiment? One considers with repugnance the prospect of women hired to conceive and nurture offspring intended for abortion and marketing as a prime supply of tissue for research and therapy. But the basic moral issue is, in its substance, not all that new. One must decide at the outset not to exploit any human individuals to obtain prospective benefits for others. The scientific result from such exploitation might be good

From James Tunstead Burtchaell, "University Policy on Experimental Use of Aborted Fetal Tissue," *IRB: A Review of Human Subjects Research* (July/August 1988). Copyright © 1988 by The Hastings Center. Reprinted by permission.

but the undertaking could not be. That principle has always been at the heart of the need to protect the human subjects of research.

INFORMED CONSENT

The first consideration is that of informed consent. Who can grant consent for experimental use of electively aborted fetal remains? One might propose that the mother can do so, because the tissue is from her body. The flaw in this claim is that the tissue is from within her body but it is the body of another, with distinct genotype, blood, gender, etc. Thus she cannot assign rights to its use in her own name. She would have to be acting as the parent/protector of her offspring.

In that role she could give consent, as mother, at the time she signs the consent form for the surgery. But there is a growing conviction that when a parent resolves to destroy her unborn fetus she has abdicated her office and duty as the guardian of her offspring, and thereby forfeits her tutelary powers. She abandons her parental capacity to authorize research on that offspring and on his or her remains.

An alternative might be that the right to dispose of the remains devolves upon the abortionist, as the physician in possession. But there is no ground for claiming that medical professionals incur rights over the bodies or the corpses of their patients. Still less is that so when death has resulted from nontherapeutic intervention by the practitioner, most especially when the victim has not consented to that activity.

The prerogative of the father to release the remains of his aborted offspring for medical research is rarely considered, yet in comparable instances of significant parental guardianship neither parent is considered to act rightfully when he or she avoids consultation or consensus with the other parent. Fathers are by design almost never involved in consent procedures prior to abortion. The absence of their consent, unless the right to give it could credibly be assumed to have been waived, would further encumber any others' claim to dispose of the remains.

When the natural protectors of the immature have either deserted or abused or absented themselves from their wards, guardianship usually devolves upon the State as *parens patriae*. But if the State agrees—as some have suggested—to consign to research the remains of only those fetuses who have perished under the ultimate abuse, that inevitably places the State in a position of patronage toward their destruction. The State would, like the aborting mother, also be implicitly derelict in its protective powers.

Thus no guardian emerges whose consent would rightfully suffice to release the remains of the deceased fetus for research.

Yet how prohibitive is that? Physicians and surgeons since Vesalius have sought cadavers to study anatomy. Their first obstacle was the conviction that the human body, live or dead, was inviolable. Their way round that resistance was to appeal to free consent (of the decedent or a guardian). But since, until recently, their usual supply had to be the corpses of derelicts, what really counted was the absence of anyone to object, more than the presence of anyone to consent. Thus consent has been interpreted as removing an obstacle, not as a positive and necessary warrant. But there may be more at stake here than this suggests.

Ours is an ancient obligation to treat human remains—body and property—

with deference. The body may be mere corpse and the estate mere chattels, but our treatment of them—insofar as they are identifiable with the person who left them behind—takes on the color of our relationship to that person. How we treat human remains is both a function and a cause of our bond with human persons. No one who remembers Mussolini's body hanging by the heels from a Milan lamppost could doubt it. The partisans were dishonoring his person, and enacting defiance against any future tyrant. Creon's insistence that Polyneice's corpse lie exposed, and Antigone's determination to bury her brother at peril of her own life, are both quite personal actions: toward the dead youth, and toward all whose spirits crave rest. John Kennedy's funeral and the disposal of Adolph Eichmann's remains both illustrate how our treatment of bodies is, in a powerful way, our definitive treatment of those they embodied.

If we honor a person while she is living we have no choice but to honor her body after death. To confiscate it discredits all ostensible dignity we accorded that person *in vivo* and orients us to treat still other persons with contempt. If my property is the extension of my person, then my body is my surrogate. Especially if one has had an ambiguous association with someone's death, to appropriate the dead person's remains for one's own purposes dissolves all ambiguity. When we requisition someone's body we are treating that person—not just that person's corpse—as of negligible dignity, or none.

There is nothing inherently unethical in experimentation upon the remains of humans who are victims of homicide, provided that consent is given, as is normally required, by the surviving guardian or next-of-kin. But the very agents of someone's death would surely be disqualified to act on the behalf or in the stead of the victim—disqualified as a man who has killed his wife is morally disqualified from acting as her executor. And in the case of a human abortus, it is the very guardians of the unborn who have collaborated in his or her destruction.

MORAL COMPLICITY

There is an additional ethical question, quite beyond the absence of rightful consent. The researcher would become a party, after the fact, to the destruction of the unborn.

The notion of complicity in mischief has been blurred and perhaps trivialized by its reduction in the popular mind to a legality. It is a much larger reality than that. It is the awesome moral fact that often we fancy ourselves as bystanders to injustice and injury—distressed and regretful bystanders, to be sure—when actually we are confederates in the very affliction we ostensibly deplore.

One can discern four types of moral complicity in evil: active collaboration in the deed; indirect association that implies approval; failure to prevent the evil when possible; and shielding the perpetrator from penalty.

The classic cooperator in evil is the driver of the getaway car. Without ever entering the bank, he or she is an active and causative member of the team. Every member of that team is the coauthor, *in solido*, of all the harm any one of them inflicts.

One way of disavowing the moral burden of complicity is the claim that "If I hadn't done it, they would simply have gotten someone else to do it." If we don't sell arms to General Stroessner to subdue the Paraguayans he will buy them from the Belgians or the Czechs. Medical personnel are asked to perform civil executions because with or without their participation the prisoners would meet the same doom. This proves to be only a rationalization, however, for the arms merchants soon lose an ethical restraint in purveying their merchandise of death, and the medics who kill are deformed in a way their recusant colleagues are not. There is, after all, a stark moral difference between beholding outrage and staffing it. It is not an indifferent matter whether I or another is the cooperator, since the cooperator is the one stunted personally and morally by his involvement.

There is a second mode of moral complicity, by association, when one is not actually joining in the work itself but somehow enters into a supportive alliance. The difference here between a neutral (or even an opponent) and an ally derives from the way in which one does or does not hold oneself apart from the enterprise and its purposes.

One may be an adverse observer, as when one consorts with an organized crime ring as a journalist or a researcher or a covert agent of law enforcement. This by itself would not necessarily make the observer a party to immoral activity. In a different mode, one might be associated with immoral activity in order to serve its victims, as when a chaplain or a physician agrees to serve the inmates of a genocidal concentration camp. Even in this close association, one can refrain from being party to the operation, for instance, by specifically refusing to be a staff member. The International Red Cross, in its services to war prisoners, must cooperate with belligerents but hold itself aloof from any partnership that would convert it into a partisan or a confederate.

As one enters into closer association, however, one eventually becomes party to the activity. Suppose that a sociologist struck an agreement with a child pornography operation in order to study the effects of such employment on the children. Or suppose an economist secured admission to the workings of a red-lining real estate operation in order to study the racial discrimination at work there. These researchers would undertake their studies, not with the informed consent of persons at risk, but with the informed consent of the victimizers. This would have the effect of drawing them into a sort of acquiescent partnership.

It is the sort of association which implies and engenders approbation that creates moral complicity. This situation is detectable when the associate's ability to condemn the activity atrophies.

There is no measurable way to determine such complicity. One must use sense and judgment, and one's assessments will be arguable. But they will be real. Imagine a pharmaceutical experiment carried out on an unsuspecting group of women in a Third World country: an experiment which leads to the death of several dozen subjects. If tissue from their cadavers were available from the experimenters for further research, it would seem that those who used the specimens could not avoid being complicit, albeit after the fact, with those who had destroyed those women. If the primary research, however, had led to the production of a new and powerfully therapeutic medication, a physician who prescribed that drug, even though sadly aware of its malicious origins, could reasonably be considered not to have entered into confederacy with the offense.

This is a distinction arrived at by analogy, not by measurement. The moral realities it detects are no less objective.

A third sort of complicity arises from culpable negligence. When parents are derelict in supervising their children they become responsible for their children's vandalism. When an employer turns a blind eye upon careless safety compliance by workers, she is morally complicit in the injuries that result. Anyone with supervisory responsibility who defaults in that duty becomes morally engaged precisely by that inactivity. One is morally complicit, not only by involvement in another's actions but also by shirking an obligatory involvement.

To go still further, it is possible to be morally complicit in another's wrongful behavior by actions that purport to curb the ill effects of the behavior but actually legitimate it or even stimulate its continuance. The single-minded policy of many public agencies in this country to curb adolescent pregnancy simply by proffering contraceptives and abortions to teenagers has had a misplaced effect. By addressing only the consequences (pregnancy) and not the activity (inappropriate sex), the program tacitly approves of what its sponsors deplore, and in the eyes of the sexually active teenagers it seems not only to acquiesce in their promiscuity but even to facilitate it. Thus the puzzling research finding that the incidence of teenage sexual activity and pregnancy and abortion has resolutely increased in direct proportion to the benevolent availability of contraceptives. Any venture that prescinds from the ethical aspect of someone's behavior, to alleviate only its consequences, may become naively complicit in it.

One can discern, then, four modes of moral complicity: direct and active participation, association that fails to disentangle itself, dereliction of the duty to supervise, and protective assistance. The common reality which is steadily present throughout these different ways of sharing moral intentionality is approbation. However one aligns oneself with another's act, by collaboration or working alongside or looking the other way or shielding from after-effects; whether by being active or by being passive; whether it furthers another's undertaking or merely endorses it: the complicity puts one person in the same moral stance that another person has assumed by direct action.

Naturally, all of these forms of association with harm vary in degree. There is a difference between the driver of the getaway car and the mother who prepares breakfast on the day of the crime with the faint intuition that mischief is afoot. It must be a human estimate how close and operative complicity actually is.

There is difficulty for some in identifying complicity after the fact. One cannot cause a deed that is already done. But this is to misconstrue the two elements in complicity. I am an accomplice in evil, first, insofar as I produce the harmful or immoral event, and second, insofar as my association with the evil causes me to be corrupted alongside the principal agent. Actually the chief effect of evil behavior is not the harm it inflicts on another but the moral disintegration and compromise it incurs in myself. This latter, more intrinsic element of complicity is present even when actual causative harm is not.

Experimentation upon fetal tissue derived from elective abortion places the scientist in moral complicity with the abortionist. The mode would be the second described above. The researcher is a confederate by resorting to the abortionist as a ready supplier of tissue from unborn humans who have been purposely destroyed.

Scholars anxious to perform research on such subjects often plead that their involvement offers them no financial advantage, plays no causative role in the harmful activity because it would have occurred with or without their presence, and at least allows them to extract some beneficial result from an otherwise regrettable enterprise. The gist of this plea is that conspiracy in harm requires causative responsibility. But this argument from moral nonchalance, as we have stated, does not disengage one from complicity. A partnership whereby one achieves direct benefit from another person's injurious behavior, after the fact, can place the former in silent but unmistakable alliance with what the latter is doing.

When this argument is employed to justify medical experimentation on the remains of those who have suffered injury or death at the hands of others, there is a special irony. For the obligation in the Helsinki Declaration to obtain informed consent from the subjects of research was one of the chief outcomes of the Medical Trials for war crimes after World War II. The physicians who experimented upon the Nazi victims argued that they played absolutely no part in the decisions to imprison, torment, and exterminate those subjects. That would have happened with or without their participation. The response of the witnessing world was that their professional presence offered endorsement and legitimacy to the victimizers, and established them as accomplices in the exploitation of the helpless. No benefit, it was asserted, could morally be derived for medical therapy if it were extorted from the innocent and helpless anguish of the afflicted. The doctors had entered fully into collusion with the SS by accepting their victims as experimental subjects. One need not cause a wrongful act to be party to it; it is enough to have abetted it.

There are then two sturdy ethical objections to experimentation upon the remains of fetuses aborted electively: absence of informed consent by anyone who could rightfully act on behalf of the unborn; and complicity in the elective destruction of the unborn by the researchers themselves.

ALTERNATIVE SOURCES FOR RESEARCH MATERIAL: CELL LINES

There are other possible sources of fetal materials for research. There is no moral objection to using the remains of unborn or newborn children who have perished from spontaneous abortion or trauma. The same would be true when surgery to save a pregnant mother's life has unavoidably aborted or destroyed her child. The parents would retain the right to release the body of the child for study. The drawbacks here are scientific, not ethical. Spontaneous abortion is often associated with genetic abnormalities that would compromise the physical remains as material for research, as would also be the case with many neonatal deaths.

A second drawback arises from the difficulty in approaching emotionally traumatized parents to ask them to release portions of the bodies of their stillborn or deceased newborn children for research. While these are real obstacles, however, they make the acquisition of fetal or newborn tissue difficult, not impossible. There are enough fetal deaths with no genetic abnormality to yield considerable research material if there is a concerted effort to solicit it. And the emotional difficulty of asking parental consent in the wake of a wrenching loss is no more difficult than that faced by surgical teams doing heart transplants, who typically obtain the organs from young motorcyclists just killed in road accidents.

There is another possible source: cell lines cultured from fetal tissue. Some kinds of human tissue can be cultured *in vitro* and induced to reproduce and metabolize and proliferate. Though there is great variation among the kinds of tissue and their respective susceptibilities to cultivation, when it is possible it can produce stable, controlled and plentiful tissue that can last through as many as 50 cycles of replication. In a few cases a tissue culture will undergo "transformation" and become a quasi-permanent "cell line."

The proposal has been made to secure a modest amount of primary tissue from electively aborted abortuses (usually in their second-trimester) and culture that tissue to produce stable cell lines available for research. Is this any different ethically from using fresh aborted remains?

MORAL DISTANCE

There is a significant difference, one might suggest. A moral distance intervenes between the abortion that yielded the original tissue and the cultured cells that are many generations descended from that original flesh. But this is an assumption we must examine.

Let a parallel illustration serve to illustrate. If I defraud your mother of her life's savings and then launder the money by converting the dollars into pesos, there is no acceptable moral claim that those pesos need not be returned since they are

not what was stolen. There is a moral identity between the money before and after the exchange. And if I use those pesos to buy a house for my own mother who is unaware of its source, the house would still revert by ethical right to your mother. My mother would incur the duty to restore it to your mother when she learned the truth. And if she refused, she would then become my partner in the fraud. No claim of moral distance through transaction would protect her.

But the legal and moral rule of prescription holds that wrongfully obtained property, if held long enough, should eventually be considered a rightful possession by the one who holds it. Thus a piece of land which B obtained from A by fraud a century or so earlier should now be left in quiet title to the innocent heirs of B and not subject to claim by the aggrieved descendants of A. In criminal law the statute of limitations serves a similar purpose: the people agree not to prosecute anyone for a crime committed so long ago that its reality has really faded from present human relations.

It would appear that the reality of moral distance which would enable an injustice or an injury to fade away is merely a matter of time. This purifying moral distance, however, is not absolute. It has exceptions. Prescription is usually not recognized, even after centuries have passed, if the beneficiaries were aware that their possession was wrongfully obtained, or if the aggrieved parties have in the intervening period been pressing their claim for justice. And certain crimes of greater enormity are exempted from most statutes of limitations. In fact the willingness to allow moral claims of justice to expire seems based entirely on society's need, for the common peace, to have limits put on the investigation and possible upheaval of present circumstances.

Stipulate that a laboratory—one of the National Institutes of Health, for instance —were to culture and make available on a nonprofit basis certain cell lines derived years previously from aborted tissue. The technicians at the NIH had no participation in the events that yielded the primary tissue. Even less would the experimenter/user be associated with those events. Could it not be said that the tissue has been purged of the stigma of complicity in the original destruction? Can bygones be ethical bygones in this case?

The question is whether the generation of cells cultured *in vitro* creates a significant enough moral distance to neutralize the original lack of informed consent and complicity in abortion. There are grounds to propose that it might not.

Moral association in the activities of others allows of a more and a less, and therefore it can be attenuated to the point of insignificance. For instance, would it amount to a protest against war to picket or boycott a corporation because it manufactured cluster bombs with a fragmentation effect calculated to destroy civilian populations? If we grant that it would, then compare that to an identical demonstration against a corporation which produces soap, on the grounds that the nation's troops at war bathed with that soap. Surely the latter demonstration would carry with it very little moral credibility by comparison with the former.

If it were known that an abundant supply of cadavers of persons in relative youth and sound health were available internationally for medical research, that would surely present to medical schools a better learning medium than the cadavers of aged people or derelicts that they receive now through donation arrangements. But suppose that those bodies were all black, and all from South Africa. Then would medical school deans think it ethically neutral to avail themselves of this supply source?

Perhaps the most widely known human tissue supply in modern research is the "HeLa" cell-line derived from the body of Henrietta Lacks (generally known pseudonymously as Helen Lane), an American woman who died of cancer in 1951. That tissue has been cultured and manipulated in virtually all major teaching laboratories in this country. But suppose that it were the "EsDa" cell-line instead, derived from the body of a Polish woman named Esther Dawidowicz who died of typhus in 1944... in Auschwitz. It is very doubtful that scientists would have considered themselves as free to retain and use that material, for a nonchalance about it would make a moral statement: a statement of neutrality about the Holocaust.

There are indeed limits to the persistence of moral taint. It can attenuate. But when, in human experience, its source is particularly odious, a casual willingness to ignore it would still constitute complicity even when separated by the passage of time. If an attentive world failed to see the moral taint of the Bitberg war cemetery bleached out after four quiet decades, or that of President Kurt Waldheim's wartime involvements neutralized after four decades of energetic public service to the world, can we believe that the casual experimental usage of abortion-derived tissue could fail to embody a moral indifference toward an intentional victimization whose death toll in this country alone now stands at nearly four times that of the genocide which provoked the first explicit moral norms about research on human subjects? It would be a nonchalance imbued with moral apathy.

In any case, the claim that moral distance has obliterated or attenuated all significant association of researchers with the original destruction may at least be argued when the offense has been publicly repudiated and terminated. The claim is hardly credible if the exploitation is still ongoing and enjoys a measure of public indifference which scientific collaboration could only legitimate.

It would seem that the moral reality of abortion resonates about as clearly and distinctly along the cell-line as it does in primary tissue taken directly from abortuses. Indeed, the readiness of researchers to accept such material must exercise a considerable moral influence in awarding to the abortion industry the quiet and complicit acquiescence of the scientific profession.

This article concludes with the proposition that, in terms of both primary tissue and of cultured cells and cell lines, it is difficult but not impossible to obtain human fetal materials, fresh or cultured, that derive from unintentional death instead of intentional destruction, and that are made available by informed consent. This alternative renders moot the question of whether one need or ought, out of the urgent potentialities of research, resort to using aborted tissue. But even were that option to be considered, it ought be rejected as unethical, for lack of informed consent and because it would place the researchers in complicity with the abortion.

POSTSCRIPT

Should Fetal Tissue Be Used to Heal Adults?

Warren Kearney, Dorothy E. Vawter, and Karen G. Gervais, in "Fetal Tissue Research and the Misread Compromise," *Hastings Center Report* (September–October 1991), discuss the bill to restore federal funding for human fetal tissue research and conclude that even though it would require women who donate fetal tissue to certify that they are not having their abortions with the intent to donate, that requirement could not possibly be more than a symbolic gesture. That symbol was too tenuous for conservative Republicans, and the bill was vetoed. The ban on federal funding for fetal tissue research remained in place until 1993, when President Bill Clinton ended it. The Clinton administration also abolished a fetal tissue bank that was established by President George Bush in May 1992. See C. B. Cohen and A. R. Jonsen, "The Future of the Fetal Tissue Bank," *Science* (December 10, 1993).

In January 1994 the NIH awarded a research grant to Curt Freed of the University of Colorado Health Sciences Center to study the use of fetal tissue in treating Parkinson's disease. According to Jon Cohen, in "New Fight Over Fetal Tissue Grafts," *Science* (February 4, 1994), Freed's $4.5 million study of 40 patients would be "the largest, most ambitious study of implants to date." However, some researchers in the field are objecting that the study is too narrow in concept and that it involves some questionable procedures.

In April 1994 researchers working on a procedure that would benefit a much larger population of people reported that they had successfully implanted fetal heart cells into a mouse's heart. They hope to be able to develop this procedure to the point where the added cells can strengthen the mouse's heartbeat and then to use fetal heart cells to repair the damage done to humans by heart attacks. If they are successful, human fetal tissue will become a lifesaver for millions of people, and objections to research and treatment will likely be difficult to sustain.

For other views on this issue, see Emanuel D. Thorne, "Tissue Transplants: The Dilemma of the Body's Growing Value," *The Public Interest* (Winter 1990); Andrew Simons, "Brave New Harvest," *Christianity Today* (November 19, 1990); Stephen G. Post, "Fetal Tissue Transplant: The Right to Question Progress," *America* (January 12, 1991); and John Fletcher, "Human Fetal and Embryo Research: Lysenkoism in Reverse—How and Why?" in Robert H. Blank and Andrea L. Bonnicksen, eds., *Emerging Issues in Biomedical Policy*, vol. 2 (Columbia University Press, 1993).

The Internet site http://www.mcs.com/dougp/stopftr.html contains material that is critical of fetal tissue research.

CONTRIBUTORS
TO THIS VOLUME

EDITOR

THOMAS A. EASTON is professor of life sciences at Thomas College in Waterville, Maine, where he has been teaching since 1983. He received a B.A. in biology from Colby College in 1966 and a Ph.D. in theoretical biology from the University of Chicago in 1971. He has also taught at Unity College, Husson College, and the University of Maine. He is a prolific writer, and his articles on scientific and futuristic issues have appeared in the scholarly journals *Experimental Neurology* and *American Scientist* as well as in such popular magazines as *Astronomy, Consumer Reports,* and *Robotics Age.* His other publications include *Focus on Human Biology,* 2d ed. (HarperCollins, 1995), coauthored with Carl E. Rischer, and *Careers in Science,* 3rd ed. (National Textbook, 1996). Dr. Easton is also a well-known writer and critic of science fiction.

STAFF

David Dean   List Manager
David Brackley   Developmental Editor
Tammy Ward   Administrative Assistant
Brenda S. Filley   Production Manager
Libra Ann Cusack   Typesetting Supervisor
Juliana Arbo   Typesetter
Diane Barker   Proofreader
Lara Johnson   Graphics
Richard Tietjen   Systems Manager

AUTHORS

SY ALPERT is a fellow of and an executive scientist at the Electric Power Research Institute in Palo Alto, California, which was founded in 1972 to conduct a broad economically and environmentally acceptable program of research and development in technologies for producing and utilizing electric power. An expert in energy technology, he has directed the development of new energy systems, and he has experience in developing new technology for the chemical and petroleum industries. He is currently performing exploratory research in biological systems and mitigation strategies for global climate change.

ELIZABETH BALDWIN is a research ethics officer for the American Psychological Association's Science Directorate. Her work involves a broad range of research ethics issues, including those relating to the use of animals in research. Prior to her position at the American Psychological Association, she worked at the Congressional Research Service in the Division of Science Policy. She holds a B.A. in biology, an M.S. in entomology, and an M.A. in science, technology, and public policy.

DOUG BEASON is director of research at the U.S. Air Force Academy in Colorado Springs, Colorado. He was a member of the Synthesis Group for the Bush administration's White House Science Office, which was formulated to find the best way to travel to Mars, and he has also served on the White House staff for the Clinton administration.

WILFRED BECKERMAN is a fellow of Balliol College at Oxford University in Oxford, England, where he has been teaching since 1975. He has also been a professor of economy at the University of London and the chair of the Department of Political Economy at the University College in London. He is coauthor, with Stephen Clark, of *Poverty and Social Security in Britain Since 1961* (Oxford University Press, 1982). He received a Ph.D. from Trinity College at Cambridge University in 1950.

PAUL BRODEUR is an author and a staff writer for *The New Yorker* magazine. He has published books on asbestos, ozone depletion, and the electromagnetic field–cancer link, including *Currents of Death: Power Lines, Computer Terminals, and the Attempt to Cover Up Their Threat to Your Health* (Simon & Schuster, 1989) and *The Great Powerline Coverup: How the Utilities and the Government Are Trying to Hide the Cancer Hazard Posed by Electromagnetic Fields* (Little, Brown, 1993). He has won the National Magazine Award, a Sidney Hillman Foundation Award, and an American Association for the Advancement of Science Award, and the United Nations Environment Program has named him to its Global 500 Roll of Honor.

JAMES TUNSTEAD BURTCHAELL was a professor of theology at the University of Notre Dame in Notre Dame, Indiana, where he served as the chair of the University Committee for the Protection of Human Subjects in Research. He is currently a priest at Our Lady of Princeton Church in Princeton, New Jersey. His publications include *Rachel Weeping, and Other Essays on Abortion* (Andrews & McMeel, 1982) and *The Giving and Taking of Life: Essays Ethical* (University of Notre Dame Press, 1989). In 1988 he was a member of the National Institutes of Health's Human Fetal Tissue Transplantation Research Panel.

DANIEL CALLAHAN, a philosopher, is cofounder and president of the Hastings Center in Briarcliff Manor, New York, where he is also director of International Programs. He received a Ph.D. in philosophy from Harvard University, and he is the author or editor of over 31 publications, including *Ethics in Hard Times* (Plenum Press, 1981), coauthored with Arthur L. Caplan; *Setting Limits: Medical Goals in an Aging Society* (Simon & Schuster, 1987); and *The Troubled Dream of Life: In Search of Peaceful Death* (Simon & Schuster, 1993).

WENDY CLELAND-HAMNETT is acting deputy assistant administrator for policy, planning, and evaluation at the U.S. Environmental Protection Agency in Washington, D.C.

MARY H. COOPER is a staff writer for the Congressional Quarterly's *CQ Researcher*, a weekly magazine providing in-depth analysis of current issues. She is the author of *The Business of Drugs* (Congressional Quarterly, 1988).

LAURA CORNWELL is a policy analyst for the Regulatory Innovations Staff of the U.S. Environmental Protection Agency in Washington, D.C. She is also a graduate research assistant in the International Institute for Ecological Economics at the University of Maryland in College Park, Maryland.

ROBERT COSTANZA is director of the International Institute for Ecological Economics at the University of Maryland in College Park, Maryland, and a professor at the University of Maryland's Center for Environmental and Estuarine Studies in Solomons, Maryland. He is cofounder and president of the International Society for Ecological Economics, and his research focuses on the interface between ecological and economic systems.

COUNCIL ON ETHICAL AND JUDICIAL AFFAIRS, established in 1990 by the American Medical Association, includes as members Russell H. Patterson, Jr. (chairman), John A. Barrasso, Oscar W. Clarke, Nancy W. Dickey, John Glasson, Douglas D. Lind (resident representative), Richard J. MacMurray (vice chairman), Michael A. Puzak, Robert Wolski (medical student representative), and David Orentlicher (secretary).

COUNCIL ON SCIENTIFIC AFFAIRS, established in 1990 by the American Medical Association, includes as members William C. Scott (chairman), Scott L. Bernstein (medical student representative), Yank D. Coble, Jr., A. Bradley Eisenbrey (resident representative), E. Harvey Estes, Jr., Mitchell S. Karlan, William R. Kennedy, Patricia J. Numann, Joseph H. Skom, Richard M. Steinhilber, Jack P. Strong, Henry N. Wagner, William R. Hendee (secretary), and William T. McGivney (assistant secretary).

DANIEL C. DENNETT is Distinguished Arts and Sciences Professor and director of the Center for Cognitive Studies at Tufts University. He is the author of *Brainstorms: Philosophical Essays on Mind and Psychology* (MIT Press, 1980), *Elbow Room: The Varieties of Will Worth Wanting* (MIT Press, 1984), and *Consciousness Explained* (Little, Brown, 1991).

FRANK DRAKE is a professor of astronomy and astrophysics at the University of California, Santa Cruz, where he has also served as dean of natural sciences. He is president of the SETI Institute and former president of the Astronomical Society of the Pacific, which is one of the world's leading astronomical organizations.

ELLIOT W. EISNER is a professor of education and art at Stanford University in Stanford, California. He is the author of *Cognition and Curriculum Reconsidered* (Teachers College Press, 1994).

CHRISTOPHER FLAVIN is vice president for research at the Worldwatch Institute, a private nonprofit research organization devoted to the analysis of global environmental issues. His research and writing focus on solutions to global environmental problems, particularly sustainable development and strategies to slow climate change, and he has written extensively on the implications of new energy technologies and new approaches to energy policy. He is coauthor, with Nicholas Lenssen, of *Power Surge: Guide to the Coming Energy Revolution* (W. W. Norton, 1994).

ROSS GELBSPAN was an editor and reporter at the *Philadelphia Bulletin,* the *Washington Post,* and the *Boston Globe* over a 30-year period. In 1984 he was a corecipient of the Pulitzer Prize for public-service reporting.

STEPHEN L. GILLETT earned his doctorate in geology from the State University of New York at Stony Brook. He is currently a research associate at the Mackay School of Mines and a member of the Department of Geographical Sciences at the University of Nevada in Reno, Nevada. He is the author of *World-Building* (Writer's Digest Books, 1996).

DANIELLE GORDON is assistant editor of the *Bulletin of the Atomic Scientists.*

DAVID H. GUSTON is an assistant professor of public policy at the Eagleton Institute of Policies at Rutgers–The State University of New Jersey. In 1990–1991 he served on the staff of the Panel on Scientific Responsibility and the Conduct of Research at the National Academy of Sciences. He is the coeditor, with Kenneth Keniston, of *The Fragile Contract: University Science and the Federal Government* (MIT Press, 1994).

JAMES P. HOGAN is a writer of science fiction novels. Before moving from the United Kingdom to the United States in 1977, he was a systems-design engineer.

JAMES HUGHES, a sociologist, is assistant director of research in the MacLean Center for Clinical Medical Ethics, Department of Medicine, at the University of Chicago and the editor of *Doctor-Patient Studies.* His special interests include health care reform and the social construction of personhood at the intersection of medical and environmental ethics. He received his doctorate in sociology from the University of Chicago in 1994.

KENNETH KENISTON is Andrew W. Mellon professor of human development in the Program in Science, Technology, and Society at the Massachusetts Institute of Technology. He is coeditor, with David H. Guston, of *The Fragile Contract: University Science and the Federal Government* (MIT Press, 1994).

ANDREW KIMBRELL is policy director of the Foundation on Economic Trends in Washington, D.C., which was founded in 1977 to disseminate information through lectures and the distribution of educational materials on issues such as the environment, religion, genetics, and engineering in order to effect social change.

JESSE MALKIN writes about economic issues for *Investor's Business Daily.* He is a Rhodes scholar, and he holds B.A. degrees from Oxford University and Oberlin College.

JOHN S. MAYO is president emeritus of Lucent Technologies Bell Laboratories, formerly AT&T Bell Laboratories.

JOHN MERCHANT is president of RPU Technology in Needham, Massachusetts. He is a former senior staff engineer at Loral Infrared and Imaging Systems in Lexington, Massachusetts.

HANS MORAVEC is a principal research scientist in the Robotics Institute at Carnegie Mellon University in Pittsburgh, Pennsylvania, and director of the university's Mobile Robot Laboratory. He received a Ph.D. from Stanford University in 1980 for his design of a TV-equipped, computer-controlled robot that could negotiate cluttered obstacle courses. His publications include *Mind Children: The Future of Robot and Human Intelligence* (Harvard University Press, 1988).

NATIONAL ACADEMY OF SCIENCES is a private, nonprofit, self-perpetuating society of distinguished scholars engaged in scientific and engineering research. The academy is dedicated to the furtherance of science and technology and to their use for the general welfare. Upon the authority of the charter granted to it by the Congress in 1863, the academy has a mandate that requires it to advise the federal government on scientific and technical matters. Dr. Bruce Alberts is president of the National Academy of Sciences.

NATIONAL RESEARCH COUNCIL is the principal operating agency of the National Academy of Sciences and the National Academy of Engineering, which are private organizations created by a congressional charter to advise the federal government on any scientific or engineering discipline. Part of its function is to stimulate research in the mathematical, physical, and biological sciences in order to increase knowledge in those disciplines and to find ways to use this knowledge for the public welfare. It is not a membership organization and it has no research laboratories. Rather than conducting its own research, it generally evaluates and compiles research done by others.

JON PALFREMAN is an award-winning senior producer for *Frontline* at WGBH, Boston's public television station, where he specializes in issues at the intersection of medicine and politics.

CHARLES PETIT is a science writer with the *San Francisco Chronicle*.

MILTON F. SEARL, now retired, was an energy supply economist for the Electric Power Research Institute (EPRI) in Palo Alto, California, which was founded in 1972 to conduct a broad economically and environmentally acceptable program of research and development in technologies for producing and utilizing electric power. A pioneer of research in the relationship between the use of electricity and real gross national product, he has been a consultant to the president emeritus of the EPRI since 1989.

JOHN R. SEARLE is a professor of philosophy at the University of California, Berkeley.

JAMES H. SNIDER is a university fellow of political science at Northwestern University in Illinois. He is coauthor of *Future Shop: How New Technologies Will*

Change the Way We Shop and What We Buy (St. Martin's Press, 1992).

DAVA SOBEL is a science and medicine writer for several newspapers and magazines, including *Harvard Magazine, Omni, Good Housekeeping,* and the *New York Times Book Review.* She is a former science reporter for the *New York Times,* and she is the author of *The Incredible Planets: New Views of the Solar Family* (Reader's Digest Association, 1992) and *Longitude* (Walker, 1995).

CHAUNCEY STARR is a professor emeritus and the former founding president and vice chairman of the Electric Power Research Institute in Palo Alto, California, which was founded in 1972 to conduct a broad economically and environmentally acceptable program of research and development in technologies for producing and utilizing electric power. He was a pioneer in the development of nuclear propulsion for rockets, in the miniaturization of nuclear reactors for space,

and in the development of atomic power electricity plants. In November 1990 he was awarded the National Medal of Technology from President George Bush for his contribution to engineering and the electrical industry.

RICHARD G. TESKE is a professor of astronomy at the University of Michigan in Ann Arbor, Michigan, who specializes in the study of supernova remnants. He is also former director of the Michigan–Dartmouth–MIT Observatory in Arizona.

STEVEN ZAK is an attorney in Los Angeles, California. He received a B.A. in psychology from Michigan State University in 1971, an M.S. from the Wayne State University School of Medicine in 1975, and a J.D. from the University of Southern California Law School in 1984. He has written about animals with regard to ethics and the law for numerous publications, including the *Los Angeles Times,* the *New York Times,* and the *Chicago Tribune.*

INDEX